The Earth and its place in the Universe

3

Photo on title page   The Earth from space, photographed from about 3.6×10^4 km above the Earth's surface by Apollo 17 astronauts on the last Apollo lunar landing mission in 1972. The view extends from the Mediterranean Sea over Africa and the Arabian peninsula, to the Antarctic south polar ice-cap. Heavy cloud covers much of the Southern Hemisphere.

The Open University, Walton Hall, Milton Keynes MK7 6AA

First published 1998

Written, edited, designed and typeset by the Open University.

Printed and bound in the United Kingdom by Jarrold Book Printing, Norfolk, England.

ISBN 0 7492 8189 8

This text forms part of an Open University course, S103 *Discovering Science*. The complete list of texts that make up this course can be found on the back cover. Details of this and other Open University courses can be obtained from the Course Reservations and Sales Office, PO Box 724, The Open University, Milton Keynes MK7 6ZS, United Kingdom: tel. (0044) 1908 653231.

For availability of this or other course components, contact Open University Worldwide Ltd, The Berrill Building, Walton Hall, Milton Keynes MK7 6AA, United Kingdom: tel. (00 44) 1908 858585, fax (00 44) 1908 858787, e-mail ouwenq@open.ac.uk. Alternatively, much useful course information can be obtained from the Open University's website http://www.open.ac.uk

s103block3i1.1

Contents

1 Introduction

The Earth seems vast on a human scale, but compared with the Universe, it is extremely small. Yet the whole Universe is the realm of science, from the huge distances faced by astronomers studying remote celestial bodies to the tiny sizes of the atoms in the ink and paper of this page. Being of intermediate size, we are well placed to look up to the skies and to look 'down' into the structure and make-up of matter. And we have already found in Block 2 that something as everyday as the Earth's surface temperature is a result of interactions between the very large (the Sun) and the very small (the molecules of greenhouse gases in the atmosphere). But to understand these interactions and discover which are important and why, we had to understand each component part of the system. This course has therefore been designed so that Blocks 3 to 7 reveal our surroundings on different scales from the astronomical to the atomic, starting with the Universe and progressing down in size. Since most of our experience is of the Earth — our home in space — this block takes apart the Universe to reveal the place of the Earth within it and then identifies the component parts of the Earth itself. We will thus encounter such diverse objects as distant galaxies and the Earth's core. But this voyage of discovery is not some stock-taking exercise on the Universe for we shall also be seeking explanations for the phenomena we encounter.

As a first step in 'taking the world apart', Sections 2 and 3 explore the place of the Earth in the Solar System, and the place of the Solar System among the stars. In the course of this exploration you will see that the various celestial bodies are all in motion. Section 4 introduces Newton's laws of motion, the fundamental physical principles which enable us to make sense of movement, not only in the Solar System and beyond, but in more familiar terrestrial contexts. In Section 5 we return to the Solar System, but this time to look at the individual bodies more closely, homing in on the Earth, which we shall explore thoroughly in the remainder of the block.

The Earth is a particularly active planet, and its component parts of atmosphere, ocean and the solid, rocky part of the Earth, introduced in Section 6, interact in many interesting ways. Earthquakes, volcanoes and the formation of rocks are dealt with in Sections 7 to 9 and our picture of the Earth is completed in Section 10 with a look at the hidden structure of our planet's interior. To make sense of the observations of the Earth's active solid surface, the theory of plate tectonics is introduced and explored in Sections 11 to 16. We find that this wonderfully simple theory, in which the Earth's surface is described by a mosaic of slowly jostling plates, accounts for much of the observed pattern of activity. Furthermore the Earth's solid surface is continually being formed and reformed by a rock cycle (Section 17) which involves interactions between the Earth's interior, surface, oceans and atmosphere. Faced with this planetary turmoil, how does life, one of the Earth's most characteristic features, cope? Section 18 reveals that life interacts with the other parts of the Earth in often surprising ways and that life influences the Earth as much as Earth influences life.

Your study of this block will introduce you to some of the key scientific ideas concerning the Earth and the Universe and, particularly through the activities, it will also help you develop a range of skills used in doing science. These include making your own observations and interpretations of natural phenomena from video, information held on CD-ROM, and rock specimens. Diagrams, maps, graphs and tables are used extensively in this block to convey and summarize information about the Earth, the Universe and the way they work, and you will develop skills both in reading information from these sources and in producing them for yourself.

Activity 1.1   Planning and organizing your work for Block 3

Before you begin your work on this block, take a few minutes to consider how you intend to tackle it, and draw up a work plan for Block 3. ◀

2 The view from the Earth

Our exploration of the Universe starts with the view we get of the sky from the surface of the Earth. On a clear, dark, and moonless night the sky is brilliant with stars, whereas during the day it is the Sun that dominates. What is the relationship between the Sun and the stars? Are they fundamentally different sorts of body? At what distances do they lie from the Earth? These are the sorts of question that are answered in this section.

2.1 The Sun

In Block 2 you saw that solar radiation sustains the Earth's surface temperature, and the Sun is therefore essential for the existence of life on this planet. Were the Sun to be switched off, the Earth's surface temperature would plunge to 0 °C within a very few weeks, on its way to far lower temperatures. Eventually the oceans would freeze, and then the atmosphere would condense and freeze too.

The Sun is a copious source of radiation because its surface is very hot. At 5 500 °C, the Sun's surface is at a much higher temperature than the surface of the Earth, which averages only 15 °C.

○ How does the wavelength range of solar radiation compare with that of the radiation emitted by the Earth's surface? (You may need to refer back to Block 2, Section 5.2.2.)

○ Solar radiation is concentrated at visible wavelengths, and at the adjacent ultraviolet and infrared wavelengths, whereas radiation emitted by the Earth's surface is concentrated at longwave infrared wavelengths.

○ How would the power emitted by the Sun's surface compare with that emitted by the Earth's surface, *if the two bodies had the same surface area*?

○ Because its temperature is much higher, the power emitted by the Sun would be much greater than that emitted by the Earth's surface (Block 2, Section 5.2.2).

This question raises the issue of the comparative sizes of the Earth and the Sun. As well as being hotter than the Earth, the Sun is also much bigger. This makes it an even more copious source of radiation than if it were merely hotter but the same size as the Earth. In other words, the high luminosity of the Sun (Block 2, Section 5.1) is a result of its large size *and* of its high surface temperature.

But how do we specify the size of celestial objects like the Earth and the Sun? The specification of size depends on the *shape* of the object. The Earth and the Sun are spheres, that is, they are ball-shaped, and indeed if we were to shrink them to the size of a snooker ball they would each be almost as smooth! The spherical shape of the Earth is not immediately apparent, because we are so close to its surface. In the case of the Sun, a typical image through a telescope (as shown in Figure 2.1) looks like a disc, though this is no more than the illusion we get when, for example, we view a uniformly illuminated ball at arm's length. (*Note that you can easily damage your eyes by looking at the Sun even with the unaided eye, so please avoid looking at the Sun, and don't even glance at it through binoculars or a telescope, or you will suffer severe and irreversible eye damage.*)

Figure 2.1 A photograph of the Sun. The dark spots, called sunspots, are regions where the temperatures are lower than the 5 500 °C of the rest of the surface, ranging down to about 4 000 °C.

The size of a sphere is specified by its radius or by its diameter, as explained in Box 2.1, *Circles, discs and spheres*. Measurements made from the surface of the Earth have shown that the radius of the Earth is 6.37×10^6 m and that the Sun's radius (the solar radius) is 109 times greater.

Box 2.1   Circles, discs and spheres

The radius of a sphere is a quantity closely related to the radius of a circle.

Circles and discs

A circle is shown in Figure 2.2a. The distance from the curve to the centre is called the **radius** of the circle, and it has the same value for all points around the curve, as you can readily check. The distance across the circle is twice the radius, and this is called the **diameter** of the circle. *The size of a circle is specified by its radius or by its diameter.*

⬤ What are the radius and the diameter of the circle in Figure 2.2a, in millimetres?

◯ Measured with a ruler, the radius is 13 mm, and the diameter is 26 mm.

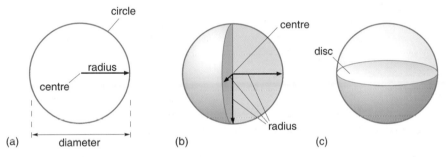

Figure 2.2   (a) A circle. (b) A sphere with a segment cut away to show the radius. (c) A sphere cut in half.

A flat surface with a circular perimeter is called a **disc**. Strictly, a disc is a featureless surface, though the term is often used for surfaces with a circular boundary that are not featureless, such as the surface of a coin, and the term is also used for circular objects which have some thickness, such as a whole coin. A compact disc (CD) is another familiar example of a disc in this broader sense.

Spheres

A **sphere** is the three-dimensional version of a circle in that all points on the surface of a sphere are the same distance from the centre of the sphere, as illustrated in Figure 2.2b. This distance is also called the radius, in this case the radius of the sphere. The diameter of a sphere is twice its radius. *The size of a sphere is specified by its radius or by its diameter.*

⬤ What are the radius and diameter of the sphere in Figure 2.2b, in millimetres?

◯ The radius is 13 mm, and the diameter is 26 mm.

If we cut a sphere in half, then the flat surface is a disc with the same radius as the sphere (Figure 2.2c). This is also the shape we think we see when we look at a sphere and fail to notice that the surface curves away from us.

Figure 2.3 shows the Earth and part of the Sun drawn to the same scale. A pair of everyday objects with approximately the same ratio of radii (pronounced 'ray-dee-eye') is a soccer ball (for the Sun) and the head of a mapping pin a bit more than 1 mm radius (for the Earth). The Sun is therefore very much bigger than the Earth. It looks small in the sky only because of its huge distance from us, about 24 000 times the Earth's radius — far further than shown in Figure 2.3.

Figure 2.3 The Earth and part of the Sun drawn to scale. The Earth's radius is 6.37×10^6 m, and the Sun's radius is 6.96×10^8 m. Note that the distance between the Sun and the Earth is not drawn to scale; it would be 24 m if drawn to the same scale as the Earth and Sun. The average distance between the Earth and the Sun is 1.50×10^{11} m.

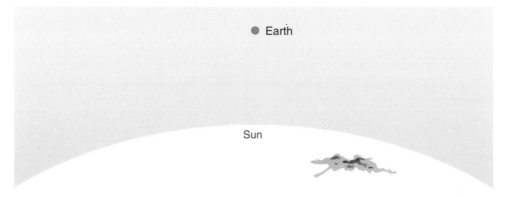

Earth

Sun

Question 2.1   What would happen to the Sun's luminosity if (a) its surface temperature fell, or (b) its radius increased? ◀

2.2   The Moon and the planets

After the Sun, the Moon is the most obvious object in the sky. It looks about the same size as the Sun, but in fact the Moon's radius is about 400 times smaller. The two bodies *appear* to be the same size because the Moon is about 400 times closer than the Sun, just as a coin held at arm's length appears to be the same size as a much larger disc further off. The Moon shines by reflecting the light of the Sun, and not by emitting visible radiation — its surface is much too cool for that (Block 2, Activity 5.3).

There are many other objects in the sky that also shine by reflecting the light of the Sun. The most obvious of these are the planets Venus, Mars, Jupiter, and Saturn, and all except Saturn can seem brighter than the brightest stars. With powerful binoculars, these four planets are visible as discs, though the largest, Jupiter, has a radius of only about one-tenth of the solar radius.

Of these four planets, Saturn is the most distant from the Earth. There are four other major planets, three of which are further away than Saturn, but even the most distant planet (Pluto) is never more than about 50 times further from the Earth than the distance from the Earth to the Sun. The planets move in paths around the Sun and shine by reflecting sunlight; these two properties define what we mean by a planet. The Earth also moves around the Sun, and shines by reflecting sunlight. Therefore, the Earth too is a planet. Most of the planets have satellites in orbit around them; the Earth has one satellite, which is the Moon. The Sun and the retinue of objects in orbit around it constitute the Solar System, and we shall return to this system in Section 3.

2.3 The stars

When you look up on a clear moonless night from a dark site, you can see about 1 000 stars, and with binoculars you can see a lot more. You cannot tell how far away the different stars are; they could all be at the same vast distance, brilliant points on a heavenly backdrop. However, measurements show that this is not so, and that the stars lie at a great range of distances beyond the Solar System. The nearest star beyond the Sun, called Proxima Centauri, is 266 000 times further away from the Earth than the Earth is from the Sun, and the most distant stars visible with the unaided eye are about 2 000 times further than Proxima Centauri! It's a pity we can't perceive with our eyes this great cosmic perspective.

Question 2.2   In measuring the distances to the stars, will there be a significant difference if we measure them from the Sun rather than from the Earth? ◀

We turn now to the physical nature of the stars. What do astronomers know about them? A variety of measurements show that the stars are nearly spherical and have radii ranging from about 1% of the solar radius to about 1 000 times the solar radius.

◗ Why then, to the unaided eye, do the stars look like points in the sky, rather than like discs?

○ This is because of their great distances from the Earth.

Only for a few particularly large and relatively close stars have astronomers obtained images of the discs, and even then only with the most powerful telescopes.

Measurements of stellar spectra (Block 2, Section 5) have revealed that the stars shine for the same reason that the Sun shines — they have hot surfaces, with temperatures of different stars ranging from about 2 000 °C to about 40 000 °C. Therefore, some stars are hotter than the Sun, and some are cooler. Hot, large stars are far more luminous than the Sun, and appear to us to be fainter only because they are so much further away. This is just the same effect as a candle flame seeming a lot brighter when it is a metre from you than a bonfire a kilometre away.

The range of stellar surface temperatures is apparent to the unaided eye through the colour tints of the stars.

◗ How does the wavelength range of the emitted radiation vary with temperature?

○ The higher the temperature, the shorter the wavelength (Block 2, Section 5.2.2).

This shift to shorter wavelengths changes the tint, blue light having shorter wavelengths than red light (Block 2, Figure 5.1). The hottest stars are a bluish white, and the coolest stars are an orange white. The Sun, at the modest temperature of 5 500 °C, has a yellowish white tint. The tints are fairly delicate. Nevertheless, if you compare the brightest stars on a clear, dark night, you should be able to see that some have an orange tint, some have a yellowish tint, and some have a bluish tint. The effect is enhanced with binoculars, particularly if you defocus them slightly. Figure 2.4 shows a photograph of a group of stars where the colour tints are readily visible.

Question 2.3   If two stars are at the same distance from the Earth, and they have the same surface temperature, what stellar property can make one star appear brighter than the other? Will the two stars have the same colour tint? ◀

Figure 2.4   The bright stars in the constellation Orion, showing different colour tints that result from the different surface temperatures. A constellation is a pattern of stars in the sky. The individual stars lie at different distances from the Solar System. The images of the brightest stars are bloated in order to bring out their colours.

We have accumulated some intriguing information about the stars that allows us to compare them with the Sun:

- Like the Sun, stars are nearly spherical, and the range of stellar radii includes the Sun's radius.
- Like the Sun, they shine because they have hot surfaces, and the range of stellar temperatures includes the Sun's surface temperature.

○ What does this information suggest about the Sun?

○ It suggests that the Sun is a star, of rather modest size and temperature.

Size and surface temperature would be sufficient for most astronomers to classify the Sun as a star. This classification is borne out by a number of other observations, though these won't concern us in this course.

Why is there such a variety of stars? There are two main reasons. First, stars have life cycles. They are born, they live, they grow old, they die. Some of the variety in the stars is because we are seeing stars at different times in their lives. Second, stars are born with different masses, and with slightly different compositions.

2.4 The Milky Way

When you look up on a clear moonless night from a dark site you will not only see 1 000 or so stars, but also, during much of the year, what looks like a ragged white cloud arching across the sky from one horizon to another, as in Figure 2.5a. To many people of ancient civilizations it looked like a stain of milk on the black backdrop of the heavens; even today we call it the **Milky Way**. Unfortunately, there is now so much light pollution at night that from most places this magnificent spectacle is obscured. But from a dark site its true nature is revealed even with modest binoculars: the Milky Way consists of a great number of stars. This is also apparent in Figure 2.5b. Seen without binoculars the individual stars are so faint and so packed together in the sky that they appear to merge into a faint band of light.

Within the Milky Way, clusters of a few hundred stars are common. Elsewhere, in the huge spaces between the stars — interstellar space — there are glowing clouds of gas, and what appear to be star-free voids, which turn out to be dark dust clouds obscuring the stars beyond them. This interstellar matter is very sparse — interstellar space is almost a vacuum — but it is extensive enough in some places to show up easily.

The Milky Way appears to encircle the Earth, but how does this faint band of stars, star clusters, and interstellar matter relate to the stars, star clusters, and interstellar matter that we see all over the rest of the sky? The time has come for a journey into space.

Figure 2.5 (a) The Milky Way as it can appear to the unaided eye, stretching from one horizon to the other. The circular edge is the Earth's horizon in this very wide-angle photograph. (b) A photograph of part of the Milky Way. Note the numerous stars, the glowing patches of gas in the space between the stars, and dark clouds obscuring the stars beyond them. The images of the brightest stars are bloated in order to bring out their colours.

(a)

(b)

2.5 Summary of Section 2

The sizes of near-spherical objects like the Earth, Sun, and the other stars and planets can be specified in terms of the radii of the spheres to which they approximate.

The Sun is much larger than the Earth and has a far hotter surface. Consequently it emits far more radiation than the Earth, and much of this radiation is at visible wavelengths. The Sun is a star, and compared with other stars it has a modest surface temperature and a modest radius.

The Moon and the planets (which include the Earth) are much smaller than the Sun, and shine at visible wavelengths by reflecting sunlight.

The stars are very much further away from the Earth than is the Sun and the other planets.

The Milky Way arches across the sky and appears to encircle the Earth. With binoculars or a telescope it is seen to consist of billions of stars, some in clusters, plus glowing clouds of gas and dark obscuring dust.

Exploring the Universe

3

In this section we will explore the Earth's place in the Solar System, and the Solar System's place in the Universe. We start this exploration by making a journey from the Earth to way beyond the Sun, to a vantage point from where the layout of the part of the Universe in which we live is revealed. The distances involved are vast, so much so that for now this has to be an imaginary journey: it will be a long time indeed before such a journey becomes possible. By contrast, in science fiction, the characters travel with great facility between the stars, at enormous speeds. Let's boldly go some way to where the science fiction writers have gone before, and travel as fast as we can. Just how fast this could be, and how long we would have to travel, are topics for Section 3.3. We will not travel towards the Milky Way, but in a direction such that the Milky Way encircles our direction of travel as we leave the Earth, as indicated in Figure 3.1.

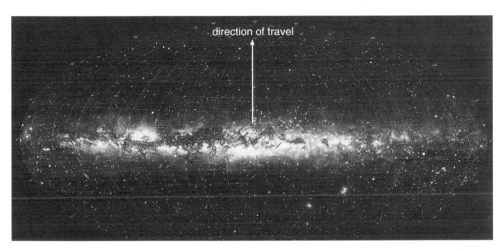

direction of travel

Figure 3.1 The journey into space starts from the Earth in a direction encircled by the Milky Way. (The grid and boundary have been used in this photograph to frame the Milky Way and put coordinates on it. These are not needed for our purposes.)

3.1 The Solar System

Imagine that we accelerate away from the Earth, and soon reach our cruising speed. The distance from the Earth now increases rapidly, until, at the huge distance of 10^{13} m (nearly 70 times the distance of the Earth from the Sun), we have a good view of the Solar System. If the paths of the planets around the Sun were somehow marked, then from our vantage point we would see them as in Figure 3.2 (*overleaf*). These paths are called **orbits**, a general term for the path of any celestial body around another.

Because of our direction of travel in Figure 3.1, we are seeing the orbits obliquely in Figure 3.2. If we were to view each orbit face-on, i.e. from a direction perpendicular to the orbit, we would see that each one is not very different from a circle. From a direction perpendicular to the Earth's orbit, the view of the planetary orbits would be as shown in Figure 3.3a (*p.17*). The orbits of the four inner planets (which include the Earth) have been drawn to a larger scale. Even at this larger scale the Sun is a bit too small, and the planets are much too small, to be shown. The Moon is in orbit around the Earth, but its orbit is also just a bit too small to show at this scale .

Figure 3.2 The view towards the Earth from a vantage point 10^{13} m along the direction of travel in Figure 3.1. The central square box is $10^{12} \times 10^{12}$ m.

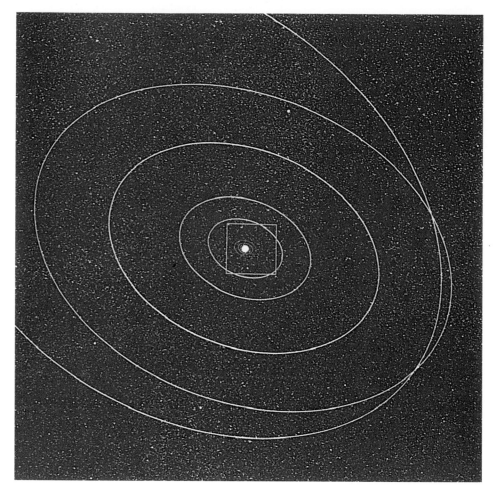

From a direction edgewise to the Earth's orbit, the view would be as shown in Figure 3.3b. You can see that, with the exception of the outermost planet Pluto, the orbits lie almost on an imaginary flat surface, i.e. in the same plane.

The direction of motion around each orbit is the same in all cases. The **orbital period** is the time it takes one celestial body to complete an orbit around another, and so a planetary orbital period is the time it takes the planet to complete one orbit of the Sun. This orbital period increases with the size of the orbit, partly because the larger the orbit the further the planet has to travel around it, and partly because the larger the orbit the more slowly the planet moves. For the Earth, as a matter of definition, the orbital period is one year. The orbital periods of the planets range from 0.241 years (88 days) for Mercury, to 248 years for Pluto.

○ What is the ratio of the orbital period of Pluto to that of Mercury? (Refer back to Block 1, Box 2.4, if you are unsure about ratios.)

○ The ratio is 248 : 0.241. This is equivalent to 1 030 : 1. (Note that the ratio has been rewritten so that the smaller quantity is equal to 1, a common practice.)

Note that the answer has been given to three significant figures, in accord with the guidelines given in Book 2, Box 2.1, *Uncertainties and significant figures*.

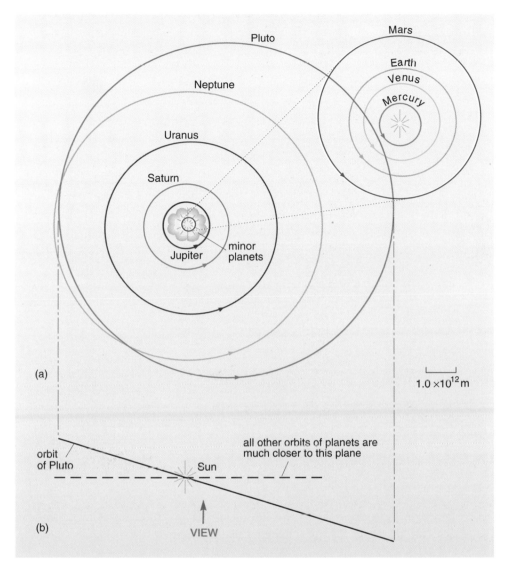

Figure 3.3 The orbits of the planets to scale: (a) from a viewpoint perpendicular to the Earth's orbit; (b) from edgewise to the Earth's orbit. The average distance of the Earth from the Sun is 1.50×10^{11} m (150 million kilometres).

In the Solar System, as well as the Sun and the nine planets in Figure 3.3, there are **natural satellites** in orbit around most of the planets (such as the Moon around the Earth), a swarm of minor planets (also known as asteroids) orbiting the Sun and lying mainly between Mars and Jupiter, and tenuous interplanetary dust and gas. The nine planets in Figure 3.3 are called the **major planets**, to distinguish them from the minor planets.

We now resume our imaginary journey from the point we left it in Figure 3.2, and travel on in the same direction along which we started (Figure 3.1). We pause again when we have travelled 1 000 times further, and have reached 10^{16} m from the Earth (and almost exactly the same distance from the Sun). Had we travelled towards the nearest star (Proxima Centauri) we would now only be a quarter of the way there. From this range (Figure 3.4, *overleaf*) the Sun is like the other stars in the sky in that no disc is discernible to the unaided eye, though it is still the brightest star.

Figure 3.4 A view looking towards the Sun, from a distance of 10^{16} m, from a vantage point along the direction of travel in Figure 3.1. The planetary orbits are too small on this scale to show. The central square box is $10^{15} \times 10^{15}$ m .

○ Why does the Sun in Figure 3.4 seem brighter than stars that are hotter or larger?

○ It is still much nearer than any other star.

The distance of 10^{16} m from the Sun is significant, because though we are far from the planets, we have only just left the Solar System. Its boundary is marked by the orbits of its outermost members. These are the **comets**, small bodies, a few kilometres across, that range far and wide across the Solar System, though most of them spend most of their time near the Solar System's extremities. Though there are about 10^{11}–10^{12} comets, they are so tiny and so faint that none is visible in Figure 3.4.

The orbits of the comets, the planets, and all the other bodies in the Solar System, raise the question of what prevents these bodies from shooting off into space. What enables the Sun to hold onto its family? The answer is the gravitational attraction of the Sun, as you will see in Section 4.4. Gravitational attraction is a universal phenomenon, by which any object attracts any other object. A familiar example of gravitational attraction is that of the Earth on you, which stops you floating off into space. The boundary of the Solar System is an imaginary surface centred on the Sun, within which the gravitational attraction of the Sun is greater than that of any other star. In Figure 3.4 we are just outside this surface, and have entered interstellar space.

3.2 The Galaxy

We resume our journey, and travel into the depths of interstellar space.

At 10^{18} m the Sun is lost among millions of stars, many of them shining far brighter than the Sun. We travel on, and complete our journey at 10^{21} m. Around us, the stars are far more thinly dispersed than they were at the start of our journey. Looking back towards the Earth (Figure 3.5a), the stars seem to have blended together to give us a view quite different from any we have had before. The remainder of Section 3.2 is devoted to a description and interpretation of what we can see.

(a)

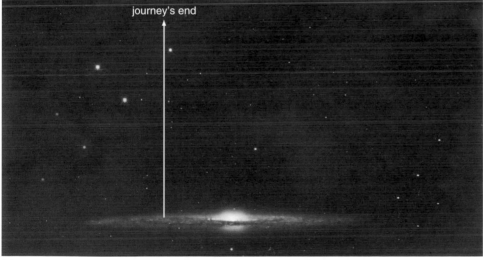

(b)

Figure 3.5 Two schematic views of the Galaxy. (a) A view looking towards the Sun, from a distance of 10^{21} m, from a vantage point along the direction of travel in Figure 3.1. The Sun (and the Earth) are located at the point marked **S**. (b) The edge view of the structure in (a). The disc (with spiral arms) is about 1.2×10^{21} m diameter.

Question 3.1   (a) Calculate the factor by which the distance to the Sun from the viewpoint in Figure 3.5a, exceeds the distance to the Sun from the viewpoint in Figure 3.4, expressing your answer in powers of ten notation. (Box 6.2 in Block 2 shows you how to perform calculations involving powers of ten. Note that the factor by which one quantity exceeds another is obtained by dividing the larger quantity by the smaller.)

(b) Comment on the statement 'If we had continued our journey from 10^{21} m to 10^{22} m, we would not have gone much further, because 22 is not much bigger than 21.' ◀

3.2.1 The layout of the Galaxy

The view in Figure 3.5a has been inferred from Earth-based observations, such as the sort of image in Figure 2.5a, and from measurements of the distances to the stars and to interstellar clouds of gas and dust. The view from any viewpoint can be inferred in this way, and Figure 3.5b shows the edge view of the structure in Figure 3.5a.

Figure 3.5 shows a huge assemblage of about 10^{11} stars, plus interstellar matter. This assemblage is called the **Galaxy**. You can see that most of the stars are concentrated into a thin disc, and this is the case for the interstellar gas and dust too. This Galactic disc (as it is called) is about 1.2×10^{21} m in diameter, and about 2×10^{19} m thick, a ratio of diameter to thickness of about $60:1$. For comparison, for a compact disc (CD) the corresponding ratio is about $100:1$. Therefore, a rough model of the galaxy would be obtained by placing two CDs together, though it must be stressed that, unlike those of a CD, the surfaces of the Galactic disc are very 'fuzzy', the average distance between the stars increasing gradually as we travel out of the disc. The thickness of the disc is therefore a somewhat arbitrary value.

Figure 3.5 also shows the location of the Sun, and you can see that it is within the Galactic disc. We can now explain the Milky Way: it is the view we have from the Earth of the more distant parts of the Galactic disc. We see the disc as a great band of stars and interstellar matter encircling the Earth. The stars are so numerous and so distant that to the unaided eye they seem to blend together. The stars and interstellar matter that appear to lie outside the Milky Way are mostly within the disc too — they happen to be close to us and so can appear in all directions, as illustrated in Figure 3.6.

Figure 3.6 A schematic edge view of the Galactic disc in the Sun's neighbourhood. Nearby stars in the Galactic disc can lie in any direction. The more distant stars are concentrated in directions that make small angles with respect to the plane of the Galactic disc.

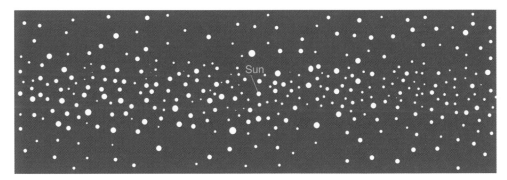

Sun

Figure 2.5a shows that the Milky Way is thicker in some directions than in others. This is our view of the extremities of the bulge at the centre of the Galactic disc, apparent in Figure 3.5, and called the nuclear bulge. ('Nuclear' here has nothing to do with nuclear energy but arises from the bulge being at the heart, or nucleus, of the Galaxy.) As well as being thicker than the disc, the concentration of stars and interstellar matter is generally greater in the nuclear bulge than elsewhere, and at its centre there is something pouring out copious amounts of energy, perhaps involving a black hole — an object into which matter and light disappear, giving out energy as they do so. Our view of the Galactic centre is blocked at visible wavelengths by interstellar dust, and so it is to other wavelengths that we look to explore this mysterious region, notably to radiowaves.

○ How do radiowaves differ from visible radiation?

○ Radiowaves have longer wavelengths (Block 2, Figure 5.1).

Radiowaves emitted by stars and interstellar matter in the region of the Galactic centre are not blocked by interstellar dust. Radiotelescopes on Earth receive the radiowaves, and produce detailed images, and other information. However, the source of energy at the Galactic centre is still something of a mystery.

Outside the nuclear bulge, the most obvious feature in the face view in Figure 3.5a is the spiral pattern called, unsurprisingly, the spiral arms of the Galaxy. This might seem to indicate a strong clustering of stars into these arms, but this is not so! Stars and interstellar matter in general are not much more concentrated in the arms than elsewhere in the disc. Instead, the arms contain a greater abundance of *bright* stars and a larger proportion of interstellar gas that is glowing brightly.

○ Where is the Sun located with respect to a spiral arm?

○ From Figure 3.5a you can see that the Sun is near the edge of a spiral arm, about half of the way from the Galactic centre to the edge of the disc.

From the Earth it is not easy to pick out the spiral arms, but detailed mapping of the stars and interstellar matter reveals their existence. Further discussion of the spiral arms is in Section 3.2.2.

The Galactic disc is enclosed by a volume with a poorly known radius, but certainly exceeding the radius of the disc. This is called the Galactic halo and it is illustrated in Figure 3.7. It contains far fewer stars that the disc, and its interstellar gas and dust is more thinly dispersed. However, its huge volume means that it contains a significant proportion of the total mass of the Galaxy. A large fraction of the stars in the halo are contained in globe-like clusters, called globular clusters (Figure 3.8), each containing up to about a million stars, though even in the relatively packed centres of globular clusters the stars are still separated by *huge* distances compared to their diameters. The clusters in the Galactic disc that were mentioned in Section 2.4 are much less densely packed and are more irregular in shape — these are called open clusters.

In addition to stars and sparse interstellar gas and dust, the halo also contains other matter, a lot of it. Evidence for its existence is outlined in Section 3.2.2.

That completes our account of the layout of the Galaxy. Table 3.1 (*overleaf*) summarizes some sizes and distances in the Galaxy, and Activity 3.1 should enable you to get a better 'feel' for these.

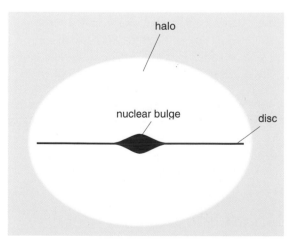

Figure 3.7 The halo that encloses the disc of the Galaxy. Its diameter is poorly known.

Figure 3.8 A globular cluster called M13. This is about 10^{18} m in diameter, which is about 10^3 times smaller than the diameter of the Galactic disc.

Table 3.1 Sizes and distances in the Galaxy.

Size or distance	Value/m
radius of the Earth	6.37×10^6
radius of the Sun	6.96×10^8
average distance of the Earth from the Sun	1.50×10^{11}
distance from the Sun to the nearest star (Proxima Centauri)	3.99×10^{16}
thickness of the disc of the Galaxy (approximate, outside the bulge)	2×10^{19}
diameter of the disc of the Galaxy (approximate)	1.2×10^{21}

Activity 3.1 A scale model of the Galaxy

In Block 2, Box 9.1, you met a scale model of the Earth — a geographical globe. The task here is to use the information in Table 3.1 to plan scale models of the Galaxy. ◀

3.2.2 Motions in the Galaxy

The stars and interstellar matter in the Galaxy are not stationary but are in motion. In the disc of the Galaxy the predominant motion is a circular swirl around the Galactic centre. This motion is in the plane of the disc, as shown (approximately) in Figure 3.9. Thus most of the stars and interstellar matter are in approximately circular orbits around the Galactic centre. From Figure 3.9 you can see that the further a body is from the Galactic centre, the smaller the fraction of its orbit that it covers in a given time. After 60 million years (60 Ma) the Sun (B) has moved a quarter of the way around its orbit, but a star at the edge of the disc (A) has moved around much less than a quarter of its orbit.

Figure 3.9 Motion in the plane of the Galactic disc. A, B, C denote stars at different distances from the Galactic centre, at four times in their orbits. The time interval between successive depictions is 20 million years (20 Ma).

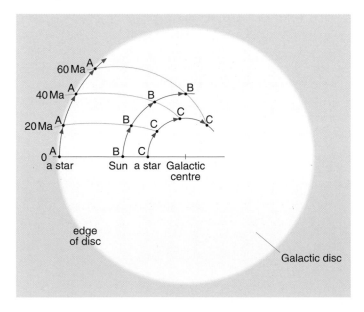

○ What is the orbital period of the Sun around the Galactic centre?

○ It moves a quarter of the way around its orbit in 60 Ma, and therefore the orbital period is 240 Ma.

As well as the Sun, nearly all the matter in the disc at the same distance as the Sun from the Galactic centre takes about 240 Ma to complete one orbit. Closer to the centre the orbital period is less, and further from the centre it is greater.

○ If the Galaxy rotated like a rigid disc (such as a wheel, or a compact disc) then how would the orbital period vary with distance from the centre?

○ The orbital period would be the same at all distances: the time taken to rotate once around the centre is the same for a point near the centre of a wheel (or a CD) as for a point near the periphery.

Question 3.2   Use Figure 3.9 to make *rough* estimates of the orbital periods around the Galactic centre of:

(a) a star (like C) at about two-thirds of the distance of the Sun from the Galactic centre;

(b) a star (like A) at the outer edge of the Galactic disc.

You can assume that the orbits are circular and that the stars go around their orbits at constant speed. ◀

The stars travel in circular orbits around the Galactic centre because of gravitational attraction. Remember that gravity is a universal phenomenon. Therefore, in the Galaxy any star or piece of interstellar matter is attracted to all the other stars and interstellar matter. Quite how this explains the circular orbits around the Galactic centre will become apparent in Section 4.4. For now the important point is that gravity does explain motion in the Galaxy.

Gravity explains motions outside the disc as well as within it. Outside the Galactic disc the motion is less orderly. The individual stars and globular clusters orbit the Galactic centre, but they swarm around in all directions, those in inclined orbits plunging through the disc as they do so. They also retreat to the farthest-flung parts of the halo, and when stellar motions in those distant regions are examined something very curious emerges. The amount of matter far out in the halo can be inferred from the effect its gravitational attraction has on the motion of these distant objects. It is clear that there is more matter out there than can be seen as stars and interstellar gas and dust. The matter detected *only* by its gravitational effect is called dark matter and there could be at least ten times as much dark matter in the Galaxy as non-dark matter, much of it in the halo. The nature of this dark matter is unknown and it is a hot area of research.

Activity 3.2   Spiral galaxies

This activity requires you to work with a video sequence in which the motions in the Galactic disc are displayed more fully, including a motion not discussed above — the motion of the spiral arms. ◀

Star birth

You saw in the video 'Spiral galaxies' that stars pass through the spiral arms. This also applies to interstellar gas. When the gas enters an arm it becomes slightly compressed by its surroundings. The cooler, denser regions of the gas were on the verge of contracting, and this slight compression triggers the contraction. The contracting gas forms open clusters of stars. Left-over gas in the vicinity of star formation is bathed in radiation from the new stars, particularly from the most

Figure 3.10 A young cluster of stars, with glowing interstellar gas and dark dust. The distance across this image is about 1.6×10^{17} m.

luminous of these stars, and this causes the gas to glow, as in Figure 3.10. A few million years later, when the new stars and interstellar matter emerge from the leading edge of the spiral arm, the gas around many young stars has dissipated, and the most luminous of the young stars are so short-lived that they have vanished. Thus the spiral arms are lit up rather in the manner of a set of flash bulbs that go off inside the arms. It is this that delineates the arms, and not the slightly greater concentration there of stars and interstellar matter. Stars do form outside spiral arms, but less frequently.

Outside the arms the less luminous stars live on, and the open clusters in which they were born gradually break up to yield isolated stars, or stars in small clusters of two or three. Later, these stars will enter a spiral arm again, as the Sun has done many times.

3.3 The journey time

To calculate how long the imaginary journey in Sections 3.1 and 3.2 would have taken us, we must assume a speed of travel. Speed is the distance travelled divided by the time interval taken. The word equation for this is:

$$\text{speed} = \frac{\text{distance travelled}}{\text{time interval}} \tag{3.1}$$

To calculate the time taken to travel a certain distance at a given speed we have to rearrange Equation 3.1 so that it has the form 'time interval = …'. This procedure is described in Box 3.1, *Rearranging equations*. The outcome is:

$$\text{time interval} = \frac{\text{distance travelled}}{\text{speed}} \tag{3.2}$$

If distance is measured in the SI unit metres, and time in the SI unit seconds, then the speed is in the SI unit metres per second, or m s^{-1}. The greatest speed at which spacecraft can presently leave the Earth is about $3 \times 10^4 \text{ m s}^{-1}$ (30 km per second). A feasible goal for the late 21st or 22nd centuries is that spacecraft will be able to travel 1 000 times faster than this, at $3 \times 10^7 \text{ m s}^{-1}$. At this speed a spacecraft would circumnavigate the Earth in 1.3 seconds, and would be able to reach the Sun in 5 000 seconds (83 minutes).

Question 3.3 If we had travelled at $3 \times 10^7 \text{ m s}^{-1}$, how many years would it have taken us to reach the end of our journey in Figure 3.5, exactly 10^{21} m from the Earth? (There are 3.16×10^7 seconds in a year.) ◄

The answer to Question 3.3 shows that, even at the huge speed of $3 \times 10^7 \text{ m s}^{-1}$, the view in Figure 3.5a would be attained only after about 40 000 human generations. It is a journey humans will probably never make, unless, somehow, we can travel at far, far greater speeds. Alas! there seems to be a cosmic speed limit.

The greatest speed possible according to our present understanding is the speed at which electromagnetic waves travel through a vacuum, usually called the **speed of light**. (In science fiction this is often called 'warp factor 1', a rather low speed in science fiction terms.) The speed of light is $3.00 \times 10^8 \text{ m s}^{-1}$ (to three significant figures).

◯ What percentage of the speed of light is our anticipated speed of $3 \times 10^7 \text{ m s}^{-1}$?

◯ The percentage is $\left(\dfrac{3 \times 10^7 \text{ m s}^{-1}}{3.00 \times 10^8 \text{ m s}^{-1}} \right) \times 100\%$, which is 10%.

Our anticipated speed is thus a substantial fraction of the cosmic speed limit. But if we can reach 10% of the speed of light, why not 100%? It turns out that the greater the speed, the greater the amount of energy needed to increase the speed by a given amount. A spacecraft speed of 10% of the speed of light is ambitious, so the prospects for travel at much more than 10% of the speed of light in the foreseeable future are poor.

Box 3.1 *Rearranging equations*

Consider the word equation

$$\text{speed} = \frac{\text{distance travelled}}{\text{time interval}} \tag{3.1}$$

This represents an equality of quantities: the distance travelled divided by the time interval is *equal* to the speed. This equation also gives us the means of calculating the speed from the distance travelled and the time interval: the value of the distance travelled is divided by the value of the time interval. We say that 'speed' is the *subject* of this equation because we can calculate a value for it by substituting values for the quantities on the right-hand side of the equation. But suppose that we knew the speed and the time interval and that we wanted to calculate the distance travelled. To do so we need an equation like:

distance travelled = ?

The question mark involves only the speed and the time interval. Likewise, if we want to calculate the time interval from the speed and the distance travelled we need an equation like:

time interval = ?

where the question mark involves only the speed and the distance travelled. These new equations are re-arrangements of Equation 3.1, in which we have changed the subject of the equation. In Equation 3.1 the subject is the speed, whereas in the first of the new equations it is the distance travelled, and in the second, the time interval.

Before the rearrangement of Equation 3.1 is tackled, consider something less abstract, namely the arithmetical equation

$$6 = \frac{18}{3}$$

Like Equation 3.1 this also represents an equality of quantities: 18 divided by 3 is equal to 6. The equality is retained provided that we do *exactly* the same thing to both sides of the equation.

Example 1

We can multiply both sides of the equation by 3:

$$3 \times 6 = 3 \times \frac{18}{3}$$

You can readily verify that 3×6 is equal to $3 \times \frac{18}{3}$, namely 18 in both cases.

Note that we can simplify the right-hand side of the equation, by dividing the 3 on the top by the 3 on the bottom. This division gives us 1. The equation then reads:

$$3 \times 6 = 1 \times 18$$

and the equality still holds. Any quantity multiplied by 1 leaves the quantity unchanged. Therefore:

$$3 \times 6 = 18$$

This equation also works if we write it as:

$$18 = 3 \times 6$$

Example 2

Now try a different operation.

● If each side of the last equation is divided by 6, show that the equality is still retained.

○ The result is $\frac{18}{6} = \frac{3 \times 6}{6}$ which is 3 in both cases.

The right-hand side can be rearranged so that the equation becomes:

$$\frac{18}{6} = 3 \times \frac{6}{6}$$

which can be simplified to:

$$\frac{18}{6} = 3 \times 1$$

and further simplified to:

$$\frac{18}{6} = 3$$

In all these forms you can show that the equality holds.

> Whatever we do, as long as we do the same thing to both sides of the equation, the equality is retained.

Returning to Equation 3.1, suppose that we want to make the distance travelled the subject of the equation. We thus need to get rid of the time interval on the right, to leave the distance travelled isolated. The way to remove the time interval on the right is to multiply both sides of the equation by the time interval. (In Example 1 you saw that when both sides were multiplied by 3 the equality was retained.) We get:

$$\text{time interval} \times \text{speed}$$
$$= \text{time interval} \times \frac{\text{distance travelled}}{\text{time interval}}$$

On the right-hand side we can divide the time interval on the top by the time interval on the bottom. These are exactly the same quantity and therefore the division cancels to 1. We thus have:

$$\text{time interval} \times \text{speed} = 1 \times \text{distance travelled}$$

Multiplying by 1 leaves a quantity unchanged, so:

$$\text{time interval} \times \text{speed} = \text{distance travelled}$$

We can read this equation either from left to right, or from right to left. If we read it from right to left it says that the distance travelled equals the time interval multiplied by the speed. We can write this as the word equation:

$$\text{distance travelled} = \text{time interval} \times \text{speed} \qquad (3.3a)$$

This is the rearrangement of Equation 3.1 in which the distance travelled is the subject of the equation. This rearrangement is equally serviceable in the form:

$$\text{distance travelled} = \text{speed} \times \text{time interval} \qquad (3.3b)$$

All we have done here is reverse the order on the right-hand side. It does not matter in which order we multiply quantities: 2×3 is the same as 3×2.

Equation 3.3 (a or b) is half way to the rearrangement of Equation 3.1 in which the time interval is the subject of the equation. To complete this second rearrangement each side of the equation can be

divided by speed, rather as in arithmetical Example 2 when both sides were divided by 6. The four steps are as follows (all of which are in the arithmetical example):

$$\frac{\text{distance travelled}}{\text{speed}} = \frac{\text{time interval} \times \text{speed}}{\text{speed}}$$

$$\frac{\text{distance travelled}}{\text{speed}} = \text{time interval} \times \frac{\text{speed}}{\text{speed}}$$

$$\frac{\text{distance travelled}}{\text{speed}} = \text{time interval} \times 1$$

$$\frac{\text{distance travelled}}{\text{speed}} = \text{time interval}$$

Again we can write this last equation the other way:

$$\text{time interval} = \frac{\text{distance travelled}}{\text{speed}} \qquad (3.2)$$

This is the rearrangement in which the time interval is the subject of the equation.

In this box we have shown you how to rearrange equations in which one quantity equals a second quantity divided by a third, or in which one quantity equals a second quantity multiplied by a third. The rearrangement of other types of equations will be explained in later blocks. Rearrangement of equations is part of the subject of *algebra*.

Question 3.4   As you may recall from Blocks 1 and 2, the density of a substance is given by:

$$\text{density} = \frac{\text{mass}}{\text{volume}}$$

(a) Rearrange this equation to make mass the subject.

(b) Now rearrange the equation you obtained in part (a) to make volume the subject. ◀

Question 3.5   The area of a rectangle is given by:

$$\text{area} = \text{length} \times \text{width}$$

If we know the area and the length of the rectangle, then we can calculate its width from a rearrangement of the equation into the form:

$$\text{width} = ?$$

Work out the equation in full. ◀

Rearranging equations can be demanding. There will be more cases and more practice later in the course.

3.4 Galaxies galore!

The Galaxy is clearly a huge, complicated structure. But is it the entire Universe? Is there nothing but a boundless void beyond it, or is the Galaxy itself just one entity among many?

This question was not answered until the 1920s, just about within living memory. Up to that time there was a vigorous debate among astronomers about the nature of some of the so-called nebulae (pronounced 'neb-ewe-lee') that had been observed for generations. A nebula is a celestial object that under low magnification looks like a continuous patch of light: 'nebula' is the Latin word for 'mist'. By 1920 many such nebulae were known and the brightest 100 or so had been catalogued much earlier, in the 1780s, by the French astronomer Charles Messier. Messier's objects are numbered M1 to M110 and are often referred to by these numbers even if they are included in other catalogues or have proper names. Figure 3.11 (*overleaf*) shows some typical examples of his assorted menagerie of nebulae.

Under high magnification, such as in Figure 3.11, some nebulae were long ago seen to be collections of stars — open and globular clusters of which Figures 3.11a and b are examples. Other nebulae remained mist-like, and analysis of the light from them showed that they consist of hot gas. These hot gas clouds vary considerably from one to another in appearance, and in other properties: Figure 3.11c is just one example. Yet other nebulae could not be seen as separate stars at even the highest magnification usable in the 1920s, though analysis of the light they emit showed that they must contain large numbers of stars, plus interstellar gas: Figures 3.11d and 3.11e show two examples of these. They belong to another class of objects that vary considerably in appearance, and also vary in other ways, such as the average properties of the stars that they contain, and the proportion and properties of interstellar matter.

But are the nebulae within the Galaxy or beyond it? The crucial evidence required to answer this question is the distance of the nebulae from us, and the size of the Galaxy. If the nebulae are at distances beyond the boundary of the Galaxy then they must be external; otherwise, they must be within the Galaxy. The US astronomer Edwin Powell Hubble (1889–1953) made a particularly important contribution to the distance measurements, and we will describe how he did this in Block 11. The crucial measurements were made in the 1920s, and they showed that though some nebulae lie within the Galaxy, some are external to it. The Galaxy was thus shown *not* to comprise the whole Universe.

Of the different types of object in Figure 3.11, star clusters and gas clouds (Figure 3.11a–c) are found within the Galaxy. The types of nebulae found to lie external to the Galaxy are those of which Figures 3.11d and 3.11e are examples, i.e. those that consist of large numbers of stars, plus interstellar matter. These external structures are themselves now called **galaxies**, not nebulae. Note the use of the lower case 'g' to distinguish these other galaxies from our own galaxy, the Galaxy. This convention extends to 'galactic' versus 'Galactic', for example as in 'galactic centre' and 'Galactic centre'. Figure 3.11d shows an example of a spiral galaxy, so called because of its spiral arms. Figure 3.11e shows an example of an elliptical galaxy, a different class of galaxy that is devoid of spiral arms but has a regular shape. Some elliptical galaxies are roughly spherical; some are tangerine-shaped; some are rather like rugby balls. Within these different shaped boundaries there are stars everywhere, though with some concentration towards the centre. The other major class of galaxy is the irregular galaxy, which, as its name suggests, is characterized by a ragged shape.

(a)

(c)

(b)

(d)

(e)

Figure 3.11 Some nebulae from the Messier catalogue:
(a) the open cluster M67; (b) the globular cluster M13;
(c) the Crab Nebula, M1; (d) the spiral galaxy M83;
(e) the elliptical galaxy M49. The approximate distances
across the frames are (a) 3×10^{17} m; (b) 1×10^{18} m;
(c) 6×10^{16} m; (d) 10^{21} m; (e) 2×10^{21} m.

○ What class of galaxy does the Galaxy belong to?

○ It has spiral arms (Figure 3.5a), so it is a spiral galaxy.

The realization that the Galaxy is a spiral galaxy has enabled astronomers to use observations of other spiral galaxies to elucidate the nature of our own.

Question 3.6   Suppose that the Solar System were relocated near to the centre of an elliptical galaxy that was nearly spherical.

(a) In two or three sentences, describe the main differences between the appearance of the night sky in this new location, and the night sky from our present location.

(b) Noting that an elliptical galaxy has no spiral arms, state, with a brief justification, whether there will be any open clusters in the sky. (You can assume that star formation has the same requirements in all types of galaxies.) ◄

Billions of galaxies are now known, some much less massive and smaller than our own Galaxy, others more massive and larger. There are several galaxies within 10^{22} m of the Galactic centre, which is a distance only ten times larger than the 10^{21} m diameter of the Galactic disc. The furthest galaxies that have been observed lie about 10^{26} m away from us — 10^5 times the Galactic diameter, and this is about as far as we can see at present.

Galaxies, like stars, are grouped in clusters. The galaxies are in motion within the clusters, and the clusters move as a whole with respect to each other. This large-scale architecture of the Universe, and its large-scale motions, will be explored in Block 11. The next task in this block is to introduce Newton's laws of motion and his law of gravity, and then use these laws to explain some of the motions that you have already met.

3.5   Summary of Section 3

The orbits of the planets in the Solar System are roughly circular and, with the exception of Pluto, the orbits lie in nearly the same plane. All the planets go around their orbits in the same direction. The comets have a great variety of orbits, and most of them spend most of their time near the outer edge of the Solar System.

The Milky Way is our view of the more distant parts of the Galactic disc from our location within the disc. The disc contains most of the 10^{11} stars and most of the visible interstellar matter that constitutes the Galaxy. The disc displays spiral arms that rotate as a rigid pattern, in contrast to the orbits of the stars and other matter around the Galactic centre, which have orbital periods that generally increase with distance from the centre. The arms are delineated by a larger number of bright young stars, and by a higher proportion of glowing interstellar gas than in the disc between the arms. Gas entering the arms is compressed and contracts to form star clusters.

In the central region of the disc is the nuclear bulge, at the centre of which there might be a black hole.

The disc is surrounded by a halo where visible interstellar matter is more thinly dispersed than in the disc, and where there are fewer stars, many of them in globular clusters. There is, however, a huge mass of dark matter in the halo.

Sizes and distances in the Galaxy are summarized in Table 3.1.

Beyond the Galaxy there is a huge number of various sorts of other galaxies. Some of them are spiral galaxies like the Galaxy, but others have no spiral arms. Observations of other spiral galaxies has helped astronomers to elucidate the nature of our own galaxy.

Speed is the distance travelled divided by the time interval taken:

$$\text{speed} = \frac{\text{distance travelled}}{\text{time interval}}$$

This equation can be rearranged to give equations for the distance travelled, or for the time interval.

Newton's laws

4

Newton's laws are of universal and profound importance, and give excellent explanations of many types of motion over a very wide range of circumstances. These laws not only enable us to make sense of motion on a cosmic scale, but enable us to make sense of motion right down to an atomic scale, including our everyday world in between. They are the first examples of fundamental scientific laws that you will meet in this course. They were enunciated in 1687 by the British scientist and mathematician Isaac Newton (1642–1727). After your introduction to these laws, we will use them to explain the orbital motion of the planets around the Sun, and the orbital motion of stars and interstellar matter around the Galactic centre. In Section 15.3, large-scale motions of the Earth's surface will be related to Newton's laws.

4.1 Newton's first law of motion

What do you think is the 'natural' state of motion of an object? In other words, how does it move (if at all) when there is no external influence on it? You might well have answered that the object stays where it is — it remains at rest. All around us we seem to have examples of the need to disturb something to make it move. For example, a glass on a table just sits there unless it is disturbed in some way, perhaps by being pushed, or lifted. If you push the glass it comes to rest soon after you stop pushing it. If you throw a ball it ultimately comes to rest. It would seem that being at rest is the undisturbed state of motion, and indeed this was the view of many of the philosophers of antiquity, notably the Greek philosopher Aristotle (384–322 BC). It might therefore come as a surprise to learn that this is *not* the viewpoint that underlies Newton's laws of motion.

To come to the Newtonian viewpoint, suppose you now place the glass on a very smooth table. You could then give it a push, and after you had finished pushing it, it would continue moving, only gradually slowing down, and possibly falling off the end of the table with unfortunate consequences.

○ Would the glass move across the table in a straight line, or along a curved path?

○ The glass would move along a straight line.

A puck on an ice rink behaves in a similar way — it slides along in a straight line and only slowly comes to rest. The difference between the ice rink, or the very smooth table, and an ordinary table is that with the ordinary table there is considerable friction between the surface and the glass. Friction opposes motion. Try continuously pushing a glass across a rough table and then across a smooth table and you can *feel* the greater opposition to motion in the former case.

Let's now do a thought experiment and imagine some *super*-smooth horizontal surface that has no friction at all. In this case, once you set the glass moving, it will not slow down but will continue moving at constant speed in a straight line. The only way to slow it down, or speed it up, or change its direction of motion whilst it is on this surface, is to disturb it, by pushing it again, in front, or from behind, or to one side. Thus the undisturbed motion in this case is constant speed in a straight line. Friction is a disturbance, which is why objects moving on real surfaces eventually come to rest unless there is something pushing them along. Note that when friction eventually brings the glass to rest the frictional disturbance then vanishes. The glass is again undisturbed, so being at rest is merely a special case of undisturbed motion, and not the only case as was believed by Aristotle.

In all situations we can conclude that undisturbed motion is either being at rest, or moving in a straight line at a constant speed. The proper scientific name for the sort of disturbances that we have been considering here is **force**: a push is a force, friction is a force, and there are many other kinds, some of which we shall be considering later. A disturbance that destroys the undisturbed state of motion of an object is an **unbalanced force**.

We can now state **Newton's first law of motion**:

> An object remains at rest or moves in a straight line at constant speed unless it is acted on by an unbalanced force.

We need to explore this first law, to clarify what we mean by 'motion in a straight line at constant speed', and to explain what is meant by 'an unbalanced force'.

4.1.1 Exploring the first law of motion

Motion in a straight line at constant speed

Imagine going for a drive, during which, at different times, you travel over the four stretches of road shown in Figure 4.1.

○ Which of these pieces of road are straight, in that they curve neither left or right, nor up or down?

○ The roads in Figures 4.1a and b.

In Figure 4.1a the road is not only straight but horizontal — there is no gradient down or up. The road in Figure 4.1b is also straight, but now there is a steady gradient — a hill of uniform slope to climb or descend. The road in Figure 4.1c is clearly not straight but follows a bend, whereas the one in Figure 4.1d curves up and then down as we cross the bridge.

Consider now the meaning of 'constant speed'.

○ Write down a word equation for speed.

○ $$\text{speed} = \frac{\text{distance travelled}}{\text{time interval}}$$

You met this equation in Section 3.3 — Equation 3.1. For the speed to be constant the distance travelled in a fixed time interval must be constant. For example, if the time interval is 10 seconds, the distance travelled must be the same during every interval of 10 seconds. Moreover the distance travelled must be the same during every interval regardless of how short we make that time interval, otherwise we could travel during one interval of, say, six seconds at the same speed at every instant, and in the next six seconds we could travel very slowly for the first three seconds and then make up for this by travelling very quickly for the remaining three. Figure 4.2 shows snapshots of a car moving at a constant speed along the straight roads in Figures 4.1a and b. These snapshots are taken at intervals of 2 seconds, and you can see that the distances covered are the same during each interval.

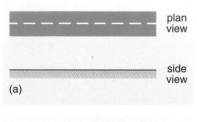

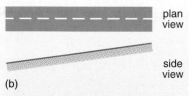

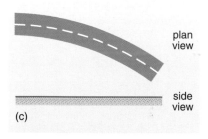

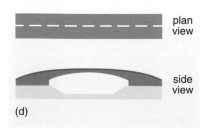

Figure 4.1 Four pieces of road: (a) straight and horizontal; (b) straight but climbing a uniform hill; (c) a horizontal curve; (d) a curve over a bridge. A plan view is the view from above.

● What is the speed of the car in each case?

○ In Figure 4.2a the car covers 28 metres in 2 seconds, so, from Equation 3.1:

$$\text{speed} = \frac{28 \text{ metres}}{2 \text{ seconds}} = 14 \text{ m s}^{-1}$$

In Figure 4.2b the car covers 20 metres in 2 seconds, so, from Equation 3.1:

$$\text{speed} = \frac{20 \text{ metres}}{2 \text{ seconds}} = 10 \text{ m s}^{-1}$$

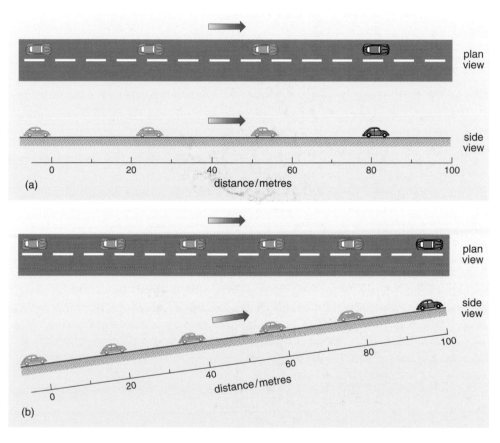

Figure 4.2   Snapshots every 2 seconds of a car moving at constant speed: (a) along a straight and horizontal road; (b) up a straight, uniform hill.

Now consider the car moving along the straight roads in Figures 4.1a and 4.1b, but with snapshots as in Figure 4.3 (*overleaf*). Clearly the distances travelled change from one 2-second interval to another, and so the speed is varying: in these cases the motion is in a straight line, but it is *not* at constant speed. Thus, from Newton's first law of motion we can deduce that an unbalanced force must be acting on the car: if an object is *not* at rest and *not* moving in a straight line at constant speed then it is being acted on by an unbalanced force.

Figure 4.3 Snapshots every 2 seconds of a car moving at a varying speed: (a) along a straight and horizontal road; (b) up a straight hill of uniform slope.

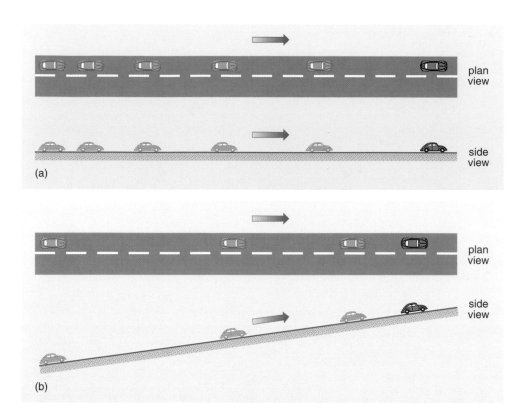

Balanced and unbalanced forces

The notion of an unbalanced force arises from the possibility that an object can be acted on by more than one force at a time. In Figure 4.4a the glass at rest on the table is actually being acted on by two forces. One is the downward force of gravity due to the gravitational attraction of the Earth on the glass, and the other is the upward push of the table surface on the glass. The upward push arises from the compression of the surface of the table when the glass is placed on it. The downward pull of gravity on the glass forces it against the table surface, and as a result the atoms in the surface layers of the table are pushed slightly closer together. This is rather like compressing a spring, and like a spring the atoms push back, and we get the upward push force on the glass.

The forces on the glass are, however, balanced, in that the upward force has a strength equal to the downward force, and so the glass remains at rest. Now let's imagine that the surface of the table is frictionless and that the glass is sliding along it *after* having been pushed to get it going. The only forces on the glass are again the downward force of gravity and the upward push of the table: these are still balanced and so the glass moves in a straight line at constant speed (Figure 4.4b). When the table is not frictionless, then we must keep pushing the glass to keep it moving at constant speed in a straight line. In this case there are four forces acting on the glass, as in Figure 4.4c, but again they are balanced: the downward force of gravity and the upward push of the table still balance, and so now do the push force and the force of friction. Of course, to get the glass going the push force had to exceed the force of friction initially. If the push force is removed, the force of friction will bring the glass to rest.

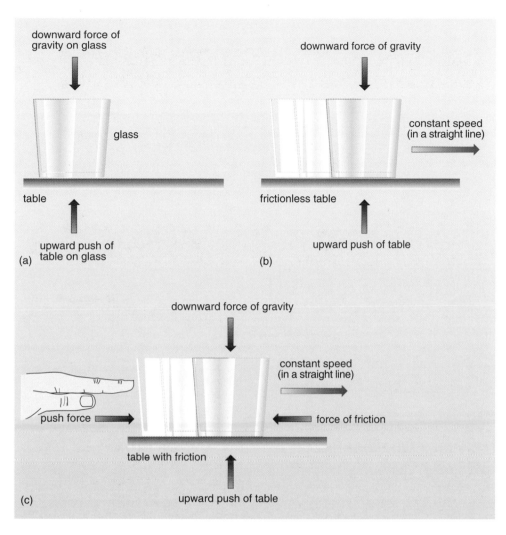

Figure 4.4 A glass on a table: (a) at rest; (b) moving with constant speed in a straight line along a frictionless table; (c) being pushed in a straight line at constant speed along a table with friction.

Consider now a car being driven along a straight horizontal road at constant speed. An important difference from the case of the glass is that the push force originates outside the glass, whereas for the car it originates inside, from the engine. The push force originates within the moving object in many other cases, such as in a person walking along, or cycling, or rowing a boat, or travelling in a self-propelled wheelchair. Internal origination is possible, it's familiar, but how does it happen? The essential point emerges from a further example. Imagine that you are lying face down on a floor, and that you push along the surface of the floor with the palms of your hands so that you slide along the floor. To cause you to slide, the floor must be pushing on your hands. This arises because in your pushing along the floor you distort the floor slightly along its surface, and as a result the floor exerts a push force on your hands. Wheels are more complicated, but the essential point is that in trying to rotate a wheel, whether on a car, bike, or wheelchair, the road is made to exert a push force on the object. The forces on a car being driven along a straight horizontal road are thus as shown in Figure 4.5 (*overleaf*). At constant speed in a straight line, the strength of the push force equals the strength of the frictional force.

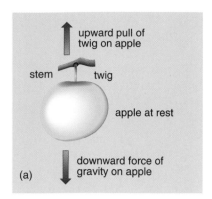

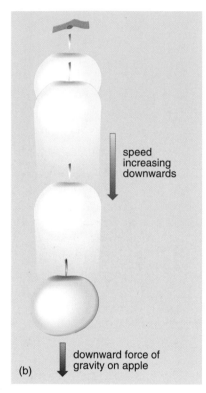

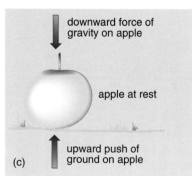

Figure 4.6 An apple: (a) at rest under balanced forces; (b) increasing its speed due to the unbalanced force of gravity; (c) again at rest under balanced forces.

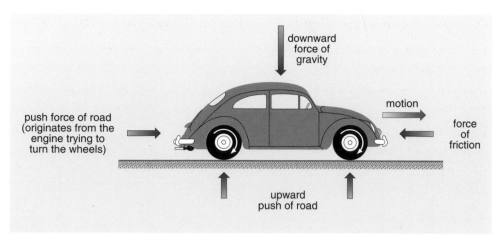

Figure 4.5 A car driven along a straight horizontal road at constant speed in a straight line.

If, in either of the cases shown in Figure 4.4c and Figure 4.5, the push force is increased, then the force in the direction of motion is no longer balanced: there is 'too much push' and so the glass or car gains speed.

◉ What happens if the push force is reduced?

○ The glass or car will lose speed.

The glass or car will also lose speed if the frictional force increases. For the car, the frictional force in Figure 4.5 is the sum of a number of frictional forces. We can increase this sum by applying the brakes, and the car slows down.

Another example of balanced forces is shown in Figure 4.6a. The gravitational attraction of the Earth on the apple tries to pull it downwards, but the apple remains at rest because the upwards pull of the twig on the stem is equal to the gravitational force. However, if the stem breaks from the twig then the only force acting on the apple is gravity, and there is no force to balance it. Consequently the apple increases its speed towards the centre of the Earth (Figure 4.6b). It hits the surface of the Earth, and comes to rest (after bouncing a bit) when the upward push force of the surface of the Earth balances the downward force of gravity (Figure 4.6c).

Note that in Figures 4.6a and 4.6b we show the force of gravity below the apple, whereas in Figure 4.4 it is above the glass, and in Figure 4.6c it is above the apple. There is no significance to this: it is just a matter of convenience in fitting all the arrows on the diagram. The important point is that the direction and size of each force acting on each object are represented clearly.

Question 4.1 An oil tanker is moving through the sea in a straight line at a constant speed. There is no wind and there are no ocean currents.

(a) What forces are acting on the tanker, and how does Newton's first law of motion indicate that they are balanced?

(b) A head wind springs up. Why does the tanker slow down? How can the original speed be restored? ◀

Question 4.2 Imagine a village tug-of-war contest between red and blue teams.

(a) Early on in the proceedings the two teams are equally matched and so there is no movement of the rope at all.

(b) Having been more moderate over lunch, the blue team begins to pull the red team along at an increasing speed in a straight line.

(c) The red team steady themselves but only to the point where they are being pulled at constant speed in a straight line.

Describe each of the stages (a)–(c) in this contest in terms of the forces exerted by the teams on the rope, and whether the forces are balanced. ◀

4.1.2 The case of a change of direction

From Newton's first law of motion, we have seen that if an object is *not* at rest and *not* moving in a straight line at constant speed then it is being acted on by an unbalanced force. So far we have examined cases where there is evidence of an unbalanced force because, though the object was moving in a straight line, it was *not* doing so at constant speed. Thus, the glass, car, apple, tanker, and tug-of-war rope all increased or decreased their speed in a straight line when there was an unbalanced force.

What about the case when a car is moving at constant speed but *not* in a straight line? Figure 4.7 shows a set of snapshots at 2-second intervals.

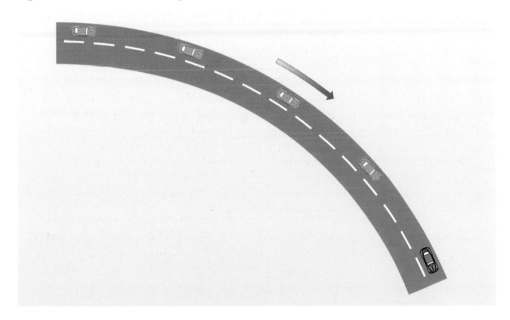

Figure 4.7 A car going around a bend at constant speed. The snapshots are at 2-second intervals.

● Is the car in Figure 4.7 taking the bend at constant speed?

○ Yes — the distance covered is the same for each 2-second interval.

So the car is moving at constant speed, but *not* in a straight line. Therefore, according to Newton's first law of motion, there must be an unbalanced force acting on the car. To see what this force is, imagine that you are with a friend who is pushing a loaded supermarket trolley along at constant speed in a straight line. You come to a corner, and because you both know the difficulty of steering a supermarket trolley from behind, your friend makes no attempt to steer it, but continues to push it at constant

Figure 4.8 A sideways force causes a change in direction of a supermarket trolley.

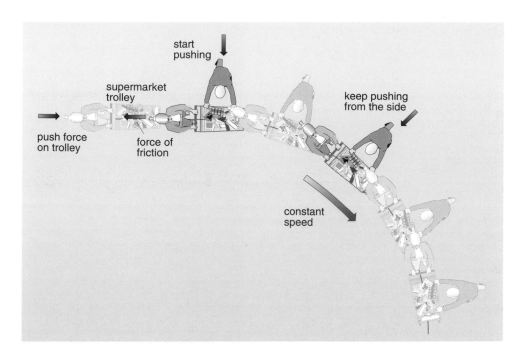

speed. It is you who steer it around the corner, and, as you can readily discover, you have to push the trolley sideways as shown in Figure 4.8. You can *feel* the force you have to exert on the trolley, so it can easily be a part of everyday experience that an unbalanced force causes a change of direction, even at constant speed.

Another example is that of someone running around a bend in a road. In order to change their direction they have to push sideways on the road. The road surface becomes slightly distorted, and as a result it pushes sideways back on their shoes. Runners can *feel* the sideways push they have to exert on the road, and the road responds by pushing sideways back on them. On ice (with normal shoes) the necessary sideways force cannot be set up, and consequently they can't take a bend.

A further example of an unbalanced force causing a change of direction is when you swing an object around on the end of a piece of string, as in Figure 4.9. In this case you can feel the force you are exerting on the object through the string, as a result of which the object moves around in a circular path.

Figure 4.9 An object being whirled around a circular path.

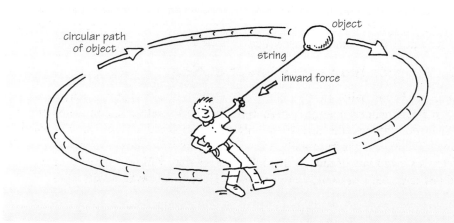

⬤ What would happen if you let the string go?

○ The object would shoot off.

Were it not for the Earth's gravity that makes the object fall to Earth, and the friction of the atmosphere, the object, once released, would travel in a straight line at constant speed. We shall return to an object being swung around in Section 4.4, where it is used as an analogy for a planet orbiting the Sun, or a star orbiting the Galactic centre.

We can thus see that there is indeed an unbalanced force acting when there is a change in direction at constant speed. We had already seen that an unbalanced force is acting when there is a change in speed with no change in direction. It follows that there is also an unbalanced force acting on an object when it changes its direction *and* changes its speed. One example is a car going around a bend at increasing or decreasing speed.

Velocity

It has become clear that the motion of an object has two attributes — speed and direction. These are the two attributes of what is called the **velocity** of a body. In everyday speech, velocity and speed are used interchangeably. In science, speed is just one of the two attributes of velocity, namely its magnitude. This is the numerical value of the velocity. The other attribute of velocity is its direction. Thus it is correct to say that the speed of a car is $22 \, \text{m s}^{-1}$, and that the velocity of the car is $22 \, \text{m s}^{-1}$ in the northwest direction. It is incorrect to say that the velocity of the car is $22 \, \text{m s}^{-1}$, or that the speed of the car is $22 \, \text{m s}^{-1}$ in the northwest direction.

⬤ Does force have two comparable attributes?

○ Yes. Force has a strength — a magnitude — and a direction.

Now that we have introduced velocity, we can restate Newton's first law of motion in a more compact form:

An object moves with constant velocity unless it is acted on by an unbalanced force.

The case of an object at rest is covered in this restatement, because such an object has zero velocity, which is certainly a constant velocity.

Question 4.3   The oil tanker in Question 4.1 is again moving through the sea at a constant speed in a straight line. A side wind springs up that does not reduce the speed. Why does this wind cause a change in velocity? ◄

4.1.3   Towards the second law of motion

An unbalanced force will cause a change in velocity, i.e. a change in speed, or a change in direction, or a change in both. But what is the precise relationship between an unbalanced force and the corresponding changes in speed and direction? Newton's first law only tells us that there will be changes but not what these changes will be. It is Newton's *second* law of motion that tells us what they will be, but before the second law is given, it is useful to restate the first law in terms of acceleration.

Acceleration in a straight line

Figure 4.2a is reproduced in Figure 4.10a along with a graph which we will discuss shortly. In Section 4.1.1 you showed that the speed of the car in Figure 4.2a is constant, with a value of $14\,\mathrm{m\,s^{-1}}$. In Figure 4.10b the speed is clearly not constant, but is increasing. We say that the car is accelerating. To examine the acceleration more closely we show the motion in each case as a graph of speed at various times. For the case of constant speed the graph is the horizontal line in Figure 4.10a. At every time shown, the value of the speed is $14\,\mathrm{m\,s^{-1}}$. For the case of acceleration the graph is again a straight line but it is no longer horizontal (Figure 4.10b): it shows that the speed is increasing.

○ What is the speed at 2 seconds, and at 6 seconds?

○ Reading from the graph in Figure 4.10b (using the guide lines), the speed at 2 seconds is $14\,\mathrm{m\,s^{-1}}$, and at 6 seconds is $22\,\mathrm{m\,s^{-1}}$.

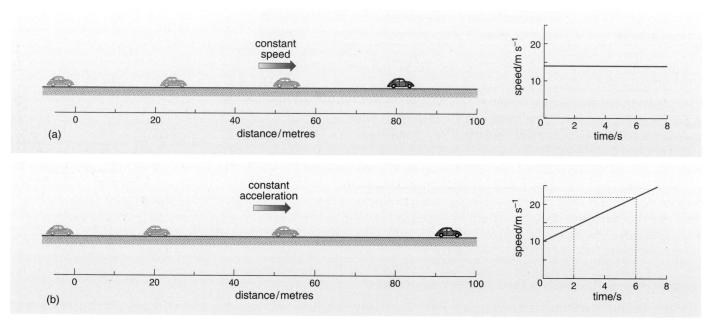

Figure 4.10 Snapshots at 2-second intervals, along with graphs of speed versus time: (a) a car moving in a straight line at constant speed; (b) a car moving in a straight line at constant acceleration: the speed increases by equal amounts in equal time intervals.

Recall that speed is given by:

$$\text{speed} = \frac{\text{distance travelled}}{\text{time interval}} \tag{3.1}$$

It is thus the rate at which distance is covered. Likewise, the acceleration in Figure 4.10b is given by:

$$\text{magnitude of acceleration} = \frac{\text{change in speed}}{\text{time interval}} \tag{4.1}$$

(The use of 'magnitude' implies that acceleration also has direction, a point to which we return shortly.) The magnitude can be obtained by choosing any time interval along the time axis in Figure 4.10b and reading off the corresponding change in speed.

● Calculate the magnitude of the acceleration in Figure 4.10b by determining the change in speed for the time interval between 2 s and 6 s.

○ The speed at 2 s is $14\,\mathrm{m\,s^{-1}}$, and at 6 s it is $22\,\mathrm{m\,s^{-1}}$. Thus, from Equation 4.1:

$$\text{magnitude of acceleration} = \frac{22\,\mathrm{m\,s^{-1}} - 14\,\mathrm{m\,s^{-1}}}{6\,\mathrm{s} - 2\,\mathrm{s}}$$

$$= \frac{8\,\mathrm{m\,s^{-1}}}{4\,\mathrm{s}}$$

$$= 2\,\mathrm{m\,s^{-1}\,s^{-1}}$$

$$= 2\,\mathrm{m\,s^{(-1-1)}}$$

$$= 2\,\mathrm{m\,s^{-2}}$$

(Refer to Block 2, Box 6.2, *Calculations involving powers of ten*, for numerical examples of the sort of manipulations of powers here.)

In words, this is 'two metres per second, per second', where 'metres per second, per second' or $\mathrm{m\,s^{-2}}$ is the SI unit of acceleration. For a small family car, $2\,\mathrm{m\,s^{-2}}$ is good acceleration.

For the graph in Figure 4.10b you can show that, regardless of where the time interval is placed, and regardless of how large it is, the magnitude of the acceleration is always $2\,\mathrm{m\,s^{-2}}$, and so in every second the car's speed increases by $2\,\mathrm{m\,s^{-1}}$. This is called constant acceleration (in a straight line in this case). From the graph in Figure 4.10a it is clear that the change in speed is zero, and so the acceleration is zero. Had the car been losing speed we would have said it was decelerating. Figure 4.11 shows constant deceleration. In every second the speed decreases by $2\,\mathrm{m\,s^{-1}}$, as you can see by reading off the graph. The magnitude of the deceleration is thus $2\,\mathrm{m\,s^{-2}}$. Scientists call this an acceleration of $-2\,\mathrm{m\,s^{-2}}$ ('minus two metres per second per second' or 'negative two metres per second, per second').

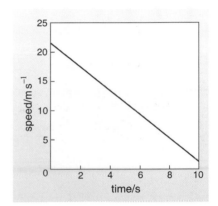

Figure 4.11 Constant deceleration: the speed decreases by equal amounts in equal time intervals.

Acceleration around a circle

Consider again the case of an object going around in a circle *at constant speed* at the end of a piece of string, as in Figure 4.12 (*overleaf*). If it is travelling at constant speed then you might think that it is not accelerating. This is not so! The proper definition of **acceleration** is that it is the rate of change in velocity. Velocity has a speed attribute and a direction attribute. Therefore, any departure from motion at constant speed in a straight line is an acceleration. You have already met the case of a change in speed with no change in direction, but there are the further cases of a change in speed and a change in direction, and, as in the example of the object on the string, a change in direction with no change of speed. If there were no change in direction of the object on the string, then the object would move along the straight line shown in Figure 4.12 at the same speed at which it is following its circular path. To follow the circular path we have to continuously change the direction of motion. So the object is continuously accelerating.

Thus, an acceleration occurs whenever there is a change in speed, or a change in direction, or a change in both. More compactly, as we said earlier, an acceleration is a rate of change in velocity. Like velocity, acceleration has a magnitude, and a direction. For example, 'The car accelerated at $2\,\mathrm{m\,s^{-2}}$ in a southerly direction'.

Figure 4.12 An object moving around a circle at constant speed: the distances between successive positions are equal, and are traversed in equal times. There is nevertheless an acceleration (towards the centre of the circle).

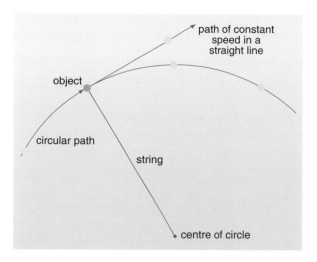

A restatement of Newton's first law of motion

We originally stated Newton's first law of motion in the form 'an object remains at rest or moves in a straight line at constant speed unless it is acted on by an unbalanced force'. In terms of acceleration we can restate this law as follows:

> An object does not accelerate unless it is acted on by an unbalanced force. Equivalently: if an object is acted on by an unbalanced force it will accelerate.

This makes a very useful link with Newton's second law of motion, which tells us by how much the object accelerates, and in what direction.

Question 4.4   Which of the following are changes in velocity? Which of them are accelerations? In which cases is an unbalanced force acting? Justify your answers.

(a) A train slows down on a straight track.

(b) A car goes around a bend at constant speed.

(c) A shark turns to chase its unfortunate prey and increases its speed as it does so.

(d) A plane descends along a straight flight path at constant speed. ◀

4.2   Newton's second law of motion

Newton's second law of motion states:

> magnitude of the unbalanced   =   mass of object × magnitude
> force on an object   of acceleration of object   (4.2)
>
> the acceleration being in the same direction as the unbalanced force.

The first thing to note about the second law is that it gives precise meaning to mass. In Block 1, Box 3.1, you learned that mass is a measure of the 'quantity of substance' in an object and that it is measured in kilograms (in SI units). Equation 4.2 shows that **mass** is no more and no less than the link between an unbalanced force acting on an object and the resulting acceleration. For an unbalanced force of given magnitude, the greater the mass of an object the smaller the acceleration. Conversely, the smaller the mass of an object the greater the acceleration. Equation 4.2 gives the precise relationship.

● If the mass is doubled, as in Figure 4.13, and the unbalanced force is kept the same, then by what factor does the magnitude of the acceleration change?

○ If the mass doubles, then the acceleration must halve, so that the product of the mass times the acceleration stays the same.

This means that mass is a property of an object that expresses its 'reluctance' to accelerate: the greater the mass, the smaller the acceleration for a given unbalanced force. This is in accord with everyday experience of the forces required to accelerate objects of different mass. The scientific name for this 'reluctance' to accelerate is **inertia**. So mass is a measure of inertia.

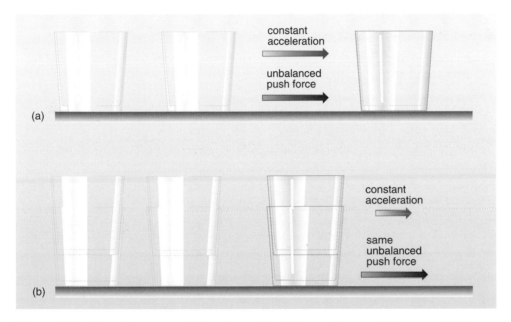

Figure 4.13   Snapshots at equal time intervals of (a) one glass, and (b) two stacked identical glasses being accelerated along a surface by an unbalanced force.

The second thing to note about Newton's second law is that it defines the unit of force: the unit of force is the unit of mass multiplied by the unit of acceleration. If we use SI units for mass (kg) and acceleration (m s^{-2}), then the SI unit of force is kg m s^{-2}. In words this is kilogram metre per second, per second. This mouthful cries out for a special name, and it's got it! The SI unit for force is also called the **newton**, symbol N (named after Isaac Newton). Thus, a force with a value of 1 kg m s^{-2} is the same as a force with a value of 1 newton, or 1 N. A couple of examples will give you an idea of the size of this unit.

● In the motoring example in Figure 4.10b the car accelerates at 2 m s^{-2}. If the mass of the car and occupants is 900 kg, calculate the magnitude of the unbalanced force.

The magnitude of the unbalanced force is given by Equation 4.2.

magnitude of unbalanced force = mass of car plus occupants × magnitude
of the acceleration

$= 900 \, \text{kg} \times 2 \, \text{m s}^{-2}$

$= 1800 \, \text{kg m s}^{-2}$

$= 1800 \, \text{N}$

$= 2 \times 10^3 \, \text{N}$ to one significant figure

Another example: to prevent an apple of mass of 0.1 kg from falling because of the downward force of gravity near the Earth's surface, you have to pull or push upwards on it with a force of about 1 N.

4.2.1 Using the second law of motion

The second law of motion (Equation 4.2) can be used to calculate any one of

- the mass of an object
- the magnitude of its acceleration
- the magnitude of the unbalanced force acting on it

provided that we know the other two. This requires Equation 4.2 to be rearranged to make the required quantity the subject of the equation, as described in Box 3.1. The second law also gives one other vital piece of information. It tells us the direction of the acceleration: this is the same as the direction of the unbalanced force.

Question 4.5   A family car plus two occupants has a mass of 1 100 kg (to three significant figures). It accelerates at a constant rate in a straight line along a level road from 0 to 26.8 m s^{-1} in 10.0 seconds. What are the magnitude and the direction of the unbalanced force acting on the car? ◄

If you have doubts about your ability to rearrange the sort of equations you saw in Box 3.1, you should work through the package on CD-ROM 3A. 'Algebraic manipulation'.

Question 4.6   The oil tanker in Question 4.1 meets a following wind during a particular voyage that exerts an unbalanced force of magnitude 4.0×10^6 N. The oil tanker has a mass of 2.0×10^8 kg (200 000 metric tonnes). Calculate the magnitude of the acceleration of the tanker, and state the direction of the acceleration. (If you are unsure how to rearrange Equation 4.2 you should re-read Box 3.1.) ◄

In Question 4.5, and in Question 4.6, the acceleration involved an increase in speed along a straight line, and the unbalanced force, which must be in the same direction as the acceleration, was in the direction of motion. The unbalanced force caused no change in direction: to do so it would have had to have been at an angle to the direction of motion.

What about those cases we discussed in Section 4.1.2 of an unbalanced force causing a change in direction at constant speed — the supermarket trolley, the runner taking a bend, the object on a string? What is the second law telling us now? It is telling us that there is *still* an acceleration and that it is *still* in the direction of the unbalanced force. In each of these cases the unbalanced force is directed across the direction of motion, as shown in Figures 4.8 and 4.9. It follows that the acceleration is also directed across the direction of motion. In the case of the object on the string (Figures 4.9 and 4.12) the unbalanced force is along the string, which is towards the centre of the circular path, and so this is also the direction of the acceleration. Note that this force, directed towards the centre, is always perpendicular to the circular path, i.e. it makes an angle of 90° to the path. Consequently the force causes no change in the speed around the path, only a change in direction.

○ What is the necessary condition for an unbalanced force to change a speed?

○ It must *not* be perpendicular to the direction of motion.

An unbalanced force that is neither perpendicular to the direction of motion nor along the direction of motion will cause both a change in speed *and* a change in direction.

How do we quantify acceleration due to a change in direction? The details are beyond the scope of this block, but the more strongly curved the path and the faster the object is following the curved path, the greater the acceleration. From Newton's second law of motion this means that the more strongly curved the path and the faster the object is following the curved path, the greater the sideways force must be. This is reasonable: if a car takes a certain curve at ever increasing speeds then the sideways force must get bigger and bigger if the car is going to stay on the road. Also, going around a tight bend at $30 \, \text{m s}^{-1}$ requires a bigger sideways force than for going around a gentle bend at the same speed.

4.2.2 Newton's second law of motion in symbols

Up to now, all equations relating physical quantities have been given in the form of words. For example, Newton's second law has been given as:

magnitude of the unbalanced force on an object	=	mass of object × magnitude of acceleration of object	(4.2)

the acceleration being in the same direction as the unbalanced force. We can state this law much more compactly if we replace each phrase by a single letter. If the magnitude of the unbalanced force is represented by the letter F, the mass of the object by m, and the magnitude of the acceleration by a, then Newton's second law of motion can be written much more compactly as:

$$F = m \times a \tag{4.3}$$

the acceleration being in the same direction as the unbalanced force. Equation 4.3 is read 'eff equals em times ay', or 'eff equals em multiplied by ay', or 'eff equals em ay'.

It is very common in science to use letters, or some other symbols, to represent quantities. Box 4.1, *The use of symbols for scientific quantities*, discusses the scientific use of symbols.

Box 4.1 The use of symbols for scientific quantities

When we use a symbol to represent a quantity, it clearly results in a saving of space. This is particularly useful when we often refer to a quantity. The use of symbols also makes it easier to see what we are doing when we rearrange equations, or have a lot of equations to consider. The use of symbols, however, carries the penalty that we have to remember what each symbol stands for. In this respect it clearly helps if the symbol is reminiscent of the full name, such as m for mass. It would not be very sensible to write Equation 4.3 as:

$$j = P \times t$$

The symbols used in Equation 4.3 are fairly standard, though variants do exist. Note that in printed text it is usual to italicize symbols, though this italicization does *not* extend to symbols for units, such as m for metres. This restriction helps us to distinguish between a symbol that represents a quantity and one that represents a specific unit.

The problem with symbols is that we run out of them, even when we use capitals, lower case, and the Greek alphabet, and so the same symbol can stand for several different words or phrases. For example *d* can stand for distance, and it can also stand for diameter. It is therefore important to state what a symbol stands for when it is first introduced.

When using symbols it is common to drop multiplication signs, and so Newton's second law of motion is usually written:

$$F = ma$$

From now on we will normally use symbols to represent quantities, particularly in equations. This use and rearrangement of symbols in equations is known as algebra, and you will become more familiar with it as the course progresses.

Question 4.7   Write Equation 3.1 in suitable symbols, and then rearrange it to make the time interval the subject. ◀

If the use of symbols in science seems a bit daunting then you should study Sections 1 and 2 in Chapter 5 of the *Sciences Good Study Guide*.* (Note that this guide does not always italicize the symbols that you will find italicized in this course.)

That completes our account of Newton's second law of motion. There is just one further Newtonian law of motion, called, unsurprisingly, Newton's *third* law of motion. In several places you have met the notion that if one object exerts a force on another object, then the second object will exert a force back on the first object. For example, when runners take a bend they push on the road, and the road pushes back on them. Newton's third law is about the relationship between these two forces. It states that if one object pushes on a second object with a certain force, then the second object pushes back on the first object with a force of the same magnitude, but in the opposite direction. We shall not explore Newton's third law of motion, principally because, unlike his first and second laws of motion, it is not needed in order to understand the motion of planets in the Solar System, and stars in the Galaxy. We do need, however, to explore another of Newton's laws — his law of gravity.

4.3   Newton's law of gravity

Gravity is a force that attracts one object (with mass) to another — any object to any other object. You are pulled towards the surface of the Earth by the gravitational attraction that the Earth's mass exerts on your mass and, because of this gravitational attraction, the best athletes can jump only a couple of metres away from the surface of the Earth. If you climb stairs, you lift yourself against the Earth's gravitational attraction and it takes a lot more effort than walking along a horizontal surface. Were it not for the considerable assistance that our technology gives us, in the form of aircraft, rockets etc., we would be trapped close to the Earth's surface.

Though you are being pulled gravitationally towards the Earth's centre, you will not accelerate towards the centre if you are standing on the solid Earth, or on a rigid structure resting on the Earth. This means that there is no unbalanced force in the vertical direction.

*Northedge, A., Thomas J., Lane, A. and Peasgood, A. (1997) *The Sciences Good Study Guide*, The Open University. (This guide is referred to as *SGSG* later in the book.)

○ Why is this?

○ Gravity is not the only force acting on you. Just as, in Section 4.1, there was an upward push of the table on the glass, and an upward push of the road on the car, so there is an upward push of the surface beneath your feet on you.

Newton's law of gravity states that the gravitational force between two objects increases when either of their masses increases or when they are brought closer together. These are intuitively reasonable features. Consider distance first. For spherical bodies like the Earth and the Sun, the distance is measured from their centres. You are about 6 370 km from the centre of the Earth. If you boarded a spacecraft and travelled to the outer reaches of the Solar System you would expect the gravitational attraction of the Earth on you to decrease, and indeed it would. Considering the mass of two objects, if you now journeyed to a point half way between the Earth and the Sun so that you were the same distance from each, you would expect the gravitational attraction of the massive Sun on you to exceed that of the far less massive Earth, and again it would. The exact relationship between the gravitational force that one object exerts on another, the masses of the objects, and their distance apart, was given by Newton, who also realized that gravity is a universal force, not just confined to attraction of objects to the Earth (Box 4.2, *Newton and the apple*). The direction of the force on one object is *towards* the other object.

Question 4.8 (a) Imagine that some aliens (with rather advanced technology) came and stole much of the interior of the Earth. Why would the gravitational force of the Earth on you decrease?

(b) Why is the gravitational force of the Earth on an astronaut in a space shuttle less than the gravitational force of the Earth on the same astronaut on the ground? ◀

Box 4.2 Newton and the apple

Isaac Newton (Figure 4.14) was born on Christmas Day 1642 at Woolsthorpe Manor in Lincolnshire. He was educated at Grantham Grammar School and then at Trinity College, Cambridge, from where he graduated in 1664. He stayed on at Cambridge, but in 1665 and 1666 England was ravaged by the Great Plague. Consequently many people spent as much time as they could in the country, where the chance of catching the deadly infection was lower. Thus it was that when the University was closed Newton returned to rural Lincolnshire.

During these years Newton pondered the nature of gravity, and came to the conclusion that the same force that drew a ball back to the Earth also kept the Moon in its orbit. It is likely that his deliberations were provoked in part by his observation of the fall of an apple in the garden of Woolsthorpe Manor, hence the famous tale that Newton formulated his theory of gravity after being hit on the head by a falling apple. Whatever part the apple played, the outcome was his theory of universal gravitation, which he expounded first in 1684 in the book *De motu corporum in gyrum* ('On the motion of bodies in an orbit'). The theory was given more completely in 1687, in *Philosophiae naturalis principia mathematica*, ('Mathematical principles of natural philosophy') along with his three laws of motion.

Figure 4.14 Isaac Newton, painted a few years after he published his theory of gravity.

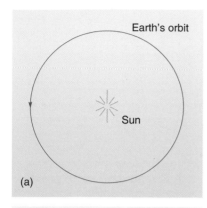

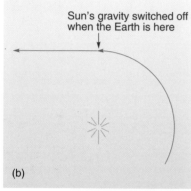

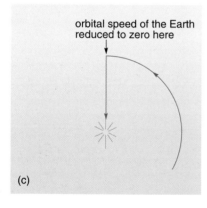

Figure 4.15 (a) The Earth's orbit around the Sun. (b) The effect of 'switching off' gravity. (c) The effect of suddenly reducing the orbital speed to zero.

4.4 Orbital motions in the Solar System and in the Galaxy

Because any object is gravitationally attracted by any other object, the Earth is gravitationally attracted by the Sun. This force of gravity on the Earth is not balanced by any other force, so what stops the gravitational force of the Sun on the Earth from pulling the two bodies into a collision? The answer is the 'sideways' motion of the Earth around the Sun. The Earth is in a roughly circular orbit around the Sun and for our purposes it is a good enough approximation to assume that the orbit is a circle with the Sun at the centre and with the Earth moving around the orbit at a constant speed (Figure 4.15a). Let's do a thought experiment in which the gravitational force of the Sun on the Earth is suddenly switched off. To answer the question 'What happens next?' we apply Newton's first law of motion. If the gravitational force becomes zero, then the acceleration becomes zero, meaning that there is no change in speed or direction (i.e. no change in velocity). The Earth must head off along the straight line in Figure 4.15b at the same constant speed as it had in its orbit. Thus the effect of gravity is to turn the Earth's path towards the Sun: the Earth is always falling towards the Sun but its sideways motion means that it always misses. Indeed it stays at very nearly the same distance from the Sun throughout its orbit.

There are strong parallels here with the astronaut in orbit around the Earth in Question 4.8, and also with the object on the string in Section 4.1.3. The Earth is accelerating towards the Sun in just the same way as the object on the string was accelerating towards the centre of its circular path. In the case of the object on the string, there was a force on the object exerted by the string. In the case of the Earth, there is the force of gravity exerted on the Earth by the Sun.

Further insight into the orbital motion of the Earth can be obtained by means of another thought experiment, in which we suddenly reduce the Earth's orbital speed to zero, as in Figure 4.15c. The Earth momentarily has zero speed. The Earth would still be acted on by the same gravitational force of the Sun as before, and therefore it would continue to accelerate towards the Sun at the same rate as before. But now, without the benefit of sideways motion, it would move directly towards the Sun, and collide with it 58 days later.

So far you have seen how the force of gravity explains the circular orbit in Figure 4.15a. None of the planets has an orbit quite like this: the orbits are slightly non-circular, and the Sun is not quite at the centre. An extreme case is the orbits of comets, and Figure 4.16 shows the orbit of comet Hale–Bopp. In non-circular orbits it is still the case that, at all points in the orbit, the Sun's gravitational force on the object is directed towards the Sun, and therefore the acceleration is also directed towards the Sun. However, at most points in the orbit the force is *not* perpendicular to the direction of motion. Therefore the speed of the comet in the orbit changes as well as the direction, and so the overall acceleration is partly due to the change of direction, and partly due to the change of speed.

○ For the orbit in Figure 4.16, what is the condition for the comet's acceleration to be due only to a change of direction, and not a change in speed?

○ This is when the gravitational force of the Sun on Hale–Bopp is in a direction perpendicular to the comet's direction of motion.

In Figure 4.16b you can see that this happens only when the comet is at its closest to the Sun. The comet increases in speed to this point, and decreases in speed thereafter. The gravitational force of the Sun on Hale–Bopp is again in a direction perpendicular to the orbit when it is furthest from the Sun, but this is much too far off to be shown in Figure 4.16.

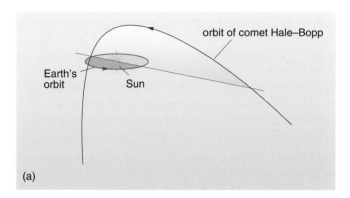

(a)

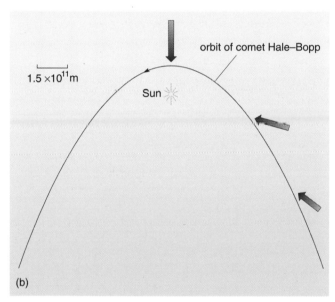

(b)

Figure 4.16 (a) The orbit of comet Hale–Bopp with respect to the orbit of the Earth. Hale–Bopp (discovered in 1995 by two American amateur astronomers, Alan Hale and Thomas Bopp) passed through the inner Solar System in 1997. Its orbital period is 2 500 years and it will recede to a maximum distance from the Sun equal to 370 times the average distance of the Earth from the Sun. (b) A face-on view of the orbit of comet Hale–Bopp. The arrows denote the direction of the gravitational force of the Sun on the comet at various points in the comet's orbit.

Newton's laws of motion and his law of gravity provide an excellent explanation of motions in the Solar System. The laws allow astronomers to calculate the orbits of the planets, comets, spacecraft, and other bodies, to many significant figures.

Newton's laws explain motions beyond the Solar System too. Consider the orbit of the Sun around the Galactic centre (Section 3.2.2). It turns out that the gravitational forces on the Sun of all the matter in the Galaxy further from the Galactic centre than the Sun approximately balance: the pull on the Sun in one direction (very nearly) equals the pull in the opposite direction. The unbalanced gravitational force due to this more distant matter is therefore zero. For the matter in the Galaxy *nearer* the Galactic centre than the Sun, it turns out that the net gravitational force on the Sun is much as if all of the mass were concentrated at the Galactic centre. We can therefore explain the orbital motion of the Sun, as you will see in Question 4.9.

Question 4.9 By drawing an analogy with the Solar System, explain in about 50 words why the Sun is in a roughly circular orbit around the Galactic centre. ◀

The motion of much of the matter in the Galactic disc can be accounted for in the same way as the motion of the Sun in Question 4.9.

In the next section we return to the Solar System, to look at the individual bodies more closely, rather than at their orbits.

4.5 Summary of Section 4

Newton's first and second laws of motion are as follows:

First law

An object remains at rest or moves in a straight line at constant speed unless it is acted on by an unbalanced force.

Second law

magnitude of the unbalanced   =   mass of object × magnitude
force on an object   of acceleration of object

the acceleration being in the same direction as the unbalanced force.

In symbolic form the second law is $F = ma$, the acceleration being in the same direction as the unbalanced force.

Acceleration is the rate of change of velocity. An object will be accelerating if its speed is changing, or if its direction of motion is changing, or if both are changing.

Force, velocity and acceleration all have both a magnitude and a direction associated with them.

The SI unit of force is the newton, N, and $1\,N = 1\,kg\,m\,s^{-2}$.

Gravity is a universal force, acting between all objects with mass. According to Newton's law of gravity, the gravitational force increases the greater the mass of the objects and the closer they are together. The direction of the force on one object is towards the other object.

Objects in the Solar System orbit the Sun because of the gravitational force of attraction that the Sun exerts on the object. The stars and interstellar matter are in orbit around the Galactic centre because of the gravitational attraction of the matter inside the orbit.

By using symbols to represent quantities, equations relating these quantities can be written concisely and rearranged easily.

The Solar System

5

The layout of the Solar System is summarized in Figure 3.3, which shows the orbits of the major planets, and in Figure 4.16, which shows the orbit of a particular comet. In this section we look more closely at the bodies themselves. Figure 5.1 shows the relative sizes of the Sun and of the major planets. Planetary satellites are not shown, though some of these, such as the Earth's Moon, are a bit larger than the smallest major planet, Pluto. The remaining satellites, the minor planets, and the comets, are smaller than Pluto, in many cases a good deal smaller. The Sun is clearly by far the largest body in the Solar System. It is strikingly different from the rest in other ways too, so we shall look at the Sun first.

5.1   The Sun

You have already seen that the Sun is a luminous body with a high surface temperature, about 5 500 °C. The luminous surface of the Sun is called the **photosphere**. This is a 'fuzzy' surface, with radiation from the photosphere reaching us from a range of depths, and so it is rather like looking into a bank of cloud, with whatever lies beyond always hidden from our direct view. The photosphere is about 500 km thick, just 0.07% of the 696 000 km from the photosphere of the Sun to its centre. The Sun gradually gets hotter and denser as we go deeper into it, the density ranging from about 1 kg m^{-3} around the photosphere to about 1.5×10^5 kg m^{-3} at the centre. To get a feel for these values, note that the density around the photosphere is about the same as that of the Earth's atmosphere at sea-level, and that the density at the centre is about 150 times greater than the density of tap water (which is about 10^3 kg m^{-3}).

The material at the centre of the Sun has a density corresponding to about the mass of an adult human crammed into a half-litre jug! You might expect such a dense substance to be solid, but it is not. This is because the temperature at the centre of the Sun is a mighty 1.5×10^7 °C or so. Under these extreme conditions the material is fluid, and can be regarded as a *very very* dense, *very very* hot gas.

Elsewhere in the Solar System, the centre of Jupiter comes closest to the densities and temperatures in the solar interior, but at 2×10^4 °C and with a density about 20 times that of tap water, it's not really in the same league.

Question 5.1   Explain why there is a depth in the Sun at which the density is the same as that of tap water, but no depth at which the temperature is 10^8 °C. ◄

5.1.1   The Sun's source of energy

It is the sustained high temperature of the solar interior that maintains the high luminosity of the Sun. Were the interior to cool, then the solar surface would cool and the Earth, which is heated by the Sun, would freeze over. To sustain the interior temperature there must be a source of energy, just as to keep the water in an electric kettle on the boil you must keep the kettle connected to the mains electricity supply. To understand the nature of the Sun's energy source, you need first to know a bit about its chemical composition.

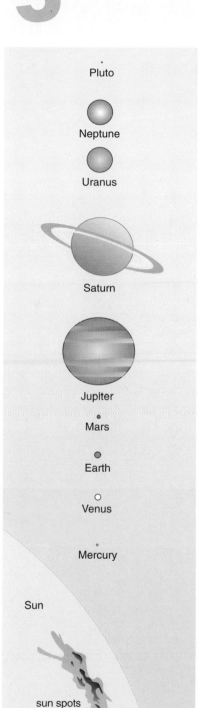

Figure 5.1   The relative sizes of the Sun and the nine major planets. The radius of Jupiter is 71 490 km (7.149×10^7 m). The planets are shown in order of increasing distance from the Sun, but the distances between the various bodies are not to scale: they are separated by far larger distances than are shown.

In Book 2, Section 6.3.1, you learned that there are over 100 chemical elements, each defined by the type of atom that comprises it. Different atoms have different mass. The hydrogen atom has the smallest mass. In order of increasing atomic mass the next element is helium, which you met earlier as a constituent of some planetary atmospheres (Book 2, Section 6.4.4 and Figure 6.15). It is familiar in gaseous form in its use to fill small balloons and airships. The atoms of the remaining elements are more massive still. You will see later, in Blocks 6 and 7, that for any particular element the atoms don't all have exactly the same mass, but broadly speaking we can say that helium is a more massive element than hydrogen, that carbon is yet more massive, and so on. In this context it is usual to use the terms 'heavier' and 'lighter' rather than 'more massive' and 'less massive'. For example, we say that helium is a lighter element than carbon, and that hydrogen is the lightest element of all. All the other elements are heavier than hydrogen.

The Sun is markedly different in composition from the Earth. Whereas the substances that make up our planet are dominated by the element iron and the common rock-forming elements (silicon, oxygen, plus various other elements), the Sun consists almost entirely of the two lightest elements, hydrogen and helium. At its birth about 73% of the mass of the Sun was hydrogen, about 25% was helium, and only about 2% was accounted for by all the 100 or so other chemical elements. The key to the Sun's energy source is what has been happening to some of these elements since the Sun's birth.

You might think that a chemical element can't change into another element. If this were true, then if we had certain masses of, say, oxygen and hydrogen, it would follow that, regardless of the processes they undergo, we would always have the same masses of each of these elements.

 Is this true for elements involved in chemical reactions?

 This is certainly true of chemical reactions, as stated in Book 2, Section 6.3.1.

In chemical reactions, atoms are joined or separated from different atoms, but the chemical elements stay the same. Indeed until about 100 years ago that was thought to be the end of the story. We now know that it is not, and that one chemical element *can* be converted into a different chemical element. It is one such conversion process that is the Sun's energy source: the process is called **nuclear fusion**. This involves the fusing together of atoms to make new types of atom. This is distinct from chemical reactions, in which molecules are produced when atoms combine.

In nuclear fusion, lighter chemical elements are converted to heavier chemical elements. In the case of the Sun, nuclear fusion converts hydrogen to helium. Though hydrogen is abundant throughout the solar interior, the fusion of hydrogen is concentrated in the Sun's core. This is because the rate at which fusion occurs increases as temperature increases, and temperature increases as we go deeper into the Sun. It is only below a certain depth that the solar temperatures are high enough for the fusion of hydrogen to occur at a significant rate. The threshold temperature is about 10^7 °C.

In the central core of the Sun the temperatures first exceeded 10^7 °C about 4 600 Ma ago, at the birth of the Sun. These high core temperatures were the result of the contraction of the Sun from a cloud of interstellar gas — this process will be discussed in Block 11. The fusion of hydrogen gives out energy, and as soon as the fusion of hydrogen started, this generated sufficient internal pressures to halt the contraction. The temperature was then maintained without further contraction. The Sun thus became self-sustaining, and has remained so ever since. It is this nuclear fusion that sustains the Sun's radiation.

The fusion of helium to form yet heavier elements also gives out energy. However, the temperatures required for the fusion of helium are even higher than those for the fusion of hydrogen, and the core of the Sun is not hot enough for helium fusion to be important. Fusion involving the elements that make up the remaining 2% of the Sun's mass is insignificant. Hydrogen in the core of the Sun is thus the Sun's sole significant nuclear fuel.

The Sun's core contains so much hydrogen, and the energy yield from the fusion of hydrogen to helium, per kilogram of hydrogen, is so enormous, that the Sun will sustain its luminosity for a long time before it runs out of fuel. Nevertheless, the hydrogen in the core is being relentlessly used up, and consequently the amount of helium in the core is building up. Eventually the hydrogen fuel will be gone and the Sun will then undergo enormous changes. One consequence will be the destruction of life on Earth (Block 2, Section 10.4). Fortunately, the Sun will not run out of hydrogen until about 5 000 Ma from now, and so it is only about half way through the hydrogen-fuelled phase of its life.

We have glossed over the fascinating details of nuclear fusion. We would be taken too far into the internal structure of atoms to explore the matter further here. Atomic structure is a subject for Block 7, and Block 11 will consider nuclear fusion in the Sun in more detail. All stars derive their energy from nuclear fusion, with the exception of stellar remnants that can be regarded as dying embers, slowly cooling into oblivion. Perhaps the best short definition of a **star** based on internal processes is that it is a celestial body that is (or has been) sustained by nuclear fusion in its core. (In Section 2.3, a star was defined in terms of *external* observation.)

Question 5.2   Why is the fusion of hydrogen an insignificant source of energy in (a) the interior of Jupiter, and (b) the Sun's photosphere? ◀

5.2   The planets (and their satellites)

The **planets** are much smaller and much less massive than the Sun (Figure 5.1) and their surface temperatures are far lower, ranging from below –200 °C to no more than a few hundred °C. Consequently, at visible wavelengths they shine by reflecting solar radiation, rather than by emitting their own (Section 2.2).

A more fundamental distinction between a planet and the Sun (and all stars except for stellar remnants) is that a planet's interior is always too cool for nuclear fusion. Indeed, this is why their surface temperatures are far lower. Planets do have internal energy sources, and you will meet these later in the course in relation to the Earth, but nuclear fusion is ruled out because their interiors never get hot enough. It can be shown that this is a consequence of the lower masses of the planets.

We will now have a brief look at the variety of planets in the Solar System. This will also help to place the Earth in a broader context.

5.2.1   Diameter, density, and composition

On the basis of diameter, Figure 5.1 suggests a broad division into two types of planet.

● Divide the nine major planets into two types on the basis of diameter.

○ There is a group of five small planets: Mercury, Venus, Earth, Mars, Pluto. There is a group of four large planets: Jupiter, Saturn, Uranus, Neptune.

Unsurprisingly, the four large planets are called **giant planets**. Four of the five small planets are called **terrestrial planets**, meaning Earth-like planets. These four are Mercury, Venus, Earth and Mars. In Figure 3.3 you can see that the terrestrial planets occupy the inner zone of the planetary domain, whereas Pluto is on its outer edge. This is one reason to exclude Pluto from the terrestrial group. But there is a more fundamental reason to exclude Pluto, and it emerges if we consider the densities of the planets. Density indicates interior composition, because different substances have different densities.

You should recall that the density of any object is its mass divided by its volume (Block 2, Section 5.2.1).

● Write the equation for density in symbols, using m for the mass, V for volume, and the Greek letter ρ (rho, pronounced 'roe') for density. (Note the use of capital V for volume, which distinguishes it from v for speed. The symbol ρ is conventionally used for density because d is used for distance, or diameter.)

○ The word equation is density = $\dfrac{\text{mass}}{\text{volume}}$, and so in symbols this equation is:

$$\rho = \frac{m}{V} \tag{5.1}$$

The volume of a planet can be calculated from its radius, which can be obtained directly from astronomical observations, as can the mass — the details are unnecessary here. Table 5.1 lists the radius, mass and density for most of the major planets. There are two gaps, which you should now fill by doing the following question.

Table 5.1 Properties of the major planets[a]

Major plant	Radius/km[b]	Mass/10^{20} kg	Density/kg m^{-3}
Mercury	2 440	3 302	5 43*0*
Venus	6 052	48 69*0*	5 24*0*
Earth	6 378	59 740	
Mars	3 397	6 419	3 94*0*
Jupiter	71 490	18 990 *000*	1 33*0*
Saturn	60 270	5 685 *000*	700
Uranus	25 56*0*	866 200	1 30*0*
Neptune	24 765	1 028 *000*	1 76*0*
Pluto	1 15*0*	150	

[a]*Non*-significant figures are *italicized*. Note that for the radii of Neptune and Pluto, the right-hand digit '5' comes from dividing diameters of 49 53*0* km and 2 3*00* km by 2. Therefore, the radius of Neptune is known to 4 significant figures, but that of Pluto is known only to 2 significant figures.
[b]The radius is the measured value at the equator.

Question 5.3 Calculate the densities of the Earth and Pluto, using the masses in Table 5.1, and given that their volumes are respectively 1.082×10^{21} m³ and 6.4×10^{18} m³. Enter your answers in the table. ◄

The completed Table 5.1 (Question 5.3) shows that Pluto has a substantially lower density than the terrestrial planets, indicating a different composition, and this is another reason for excluding it from the terrestrial group.

The inference of the composition of a planet from its density is possible because of the great differences in density of substances that are serious candidates for making up an appreciable proportion of the mass of a planet. In the broadest terms, there are just three categories of substance. First, there are the substances that dominate the Sun, the two lightest elements hydrogen and helium. Second, there are **rocky materials**. As their name suggests, these comprise the sorts of materials that make up rocks (and this includes metals, notably iron). Finally there are **icy materials**, such as water. The term 'icy materials' can be misleading because 'icy' suggests cold solids. However, it is the name astronomers use for a group of chemical substances, and though they do occur frozen in some planetary interiors, they also occur as very hot liquids. Likewise rocky materials can be solid or liquid.

Hydrogen and helium have low densities, even when compressed into liquids in planetary interiors. Icy materials have intermediate densities, and rocky materials high densities. Under conditions at the Earth's surface, liquid or solid water has a density of about 1 000 kg m⁻³, and rocky materials have densities in the approximate range 3 000 to 8 000 kg m⁻³.

● In which of the planets are rocky materials likely to dominate? What is the evidence?

○ In the terrestrial planets; these have densities in the range quoted above for rocky materials.

Figure 5.2 (*overleaf*) shows plausible models of the interiors of the major planets in terms of the three categories of material and ignoring many details of internal structure. Each planet is shown in cross-section, though only as a segment in each case. The giants are distinguished by having massive cores of icy and rocky materials overlain by hydrogen and helium as major or dominant components. You might wonder why the densities of Jupiter and Uranus are so similar (Table 5.1), even though Jupiter has a higher proportion of hydrogen and helium. The reason is the much greater pressures in Jupiter than in Uranus. The greater the pressure the greater the compression of a given substance to higher densities. The greater pressures in Jupiter are a consequence of Jupiter's greater mass.

The terrestrial planets consist almost entirely of rocky materials. In Figure 5.2 no internal layering is shown at all, though all of the terrestrial planets are intricately layered, and the layering of the Earth is known in considerable detail, as you will see later in this block. Pluto is the odd one among the major planets in that icy materials account for a greater fraction of its mass than is the case for any other major planet. However, Pluto finds companions in some of the large satellites that are of comparable size and are comparably icy. It could even be that some of these satellites were once planets in their own right, subsequently captured by neighbouring planets in some cataclysm. By contrast, other large satellites (including the Moon) are rocky in composition. The smaller satellites are variously rocky, or icy and rocky mixtures.

Figure 5.2 Plausible models of the interiors of the major planets in terms of three categories of material. The radii of the planets are all drawn to the same scale. Pluto is too small to show at this scale. Note that all the composition boundaries in the giants are probably 'fuzzy', and not as sharp as shown here.

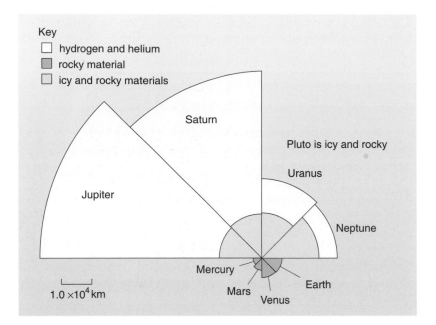

Key
☐ hydrogen and helium
▨ rocky material
☐ icy and rocky materials

Saturn

Pluto is icy and rocky

Uranus

Jupiter

Neptune

1.0 ×10⁴ km

Mercury

Mars
Venus

Earth

These broad compositional differences, with terrestrial planets in the inner Solar System, and giant planets in the outer Solar System, hold important clues to the formation of the Solar System, described briefly in Section 5.4.

Question 5.4   On the basis of Figure 5.2, justify the creation of a subdivision of the giant planets, called subgiants, and comprising Uranus and Neptune. ◀

5.2.2 Surfaces and atmospheres

The surfaces and atmospheres of the planets are as varied as their interiors. We will visit briefly some of the planets, ending with the Earth, with the aim of highlighting some of the Earth's unique features.

The atmospheres of Neptune and Uranus are broadly similar, so we shall take Neptune to represent the subgiants. An image of Neptune is shown in Figure 5.3. The view is dominated by a deep haze, with a few cloud features buried in the haze. The planet can be regarded as having a deep atmosphere of hydrogen and helium (plus traces of other substances) with a surface beneath consisting of a planet-wide ocean of rocky and icy materials, notably water. These surface materials extend to the centre (Figure 5.2).

Figure 5.4 shows Jupiter, where we are seeing the top of the uppermost of several layers of cloud. The uppermost layer consists of small crystals of ammonia, richly coloured by traces of other substances. The cloud patterns are the result of atmospheric winds. There is really no distinction between atmosphere and interior: the atmosphere has much the same composition as the interior (except near the centre — see Figure 5.2), and as we go deeper the atmosphere gets hotter and denser until it is a hot ocean of hydrogen and helium, with no surface ever having been encountered. Saturn's atmosphere is broadly similar to that of Jupiter, and it lacks a surface for the same reason. A well-known distinction between the two planets is that Saturn is surrounded by an extensive system of rings. These are made up of small bodies, typically a few centimetres to a few metres across, which have an icy–rocky composition, and which are travelling in circular orbits around the planet.

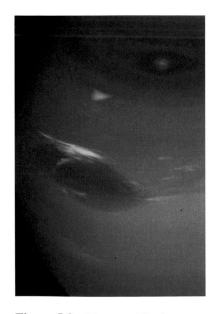

Figure 5.3   Neptune. The image is dominated by a deep haze in the thick atmosphere. The radius of the planet is 24 765 km.

The terrestrial planets do have surfaces, and they are rocky. The surface of Mercury (Figure 5.5), like that of the Moon, is heavily cratered by the impacts of small rocky bodies from space, accumulated throughout Solar System history. That there are so many craters shows that the surface of Mercury has not, for a long time, been reworked by geological processes (such as volcanic activity) that erase craters. The surface is overlain by a negligible atmosphere.

Figure 5.4 Jupiter. The rich patterns are created by the winds in the upper cloud layer that consists of ammonia crystals coloured by traces of other substances. The radius of the planet is 71 490 km.

Figure 5.5 The surface of Mercury, heavily cratered by impacts. The radius of the planet is 2 440 km.

By contrast, the surface of Venus is overlain by an atmosphere about 100 times as massive as that of the Earth and consisting mainly of carbon dioxide. Though it has by far the most massive atmosphere of the terrestrial planets, the atmosphere of Venus is still just a thin veneer, accounting for a negligible fraction of the planet's mass. High in the atmosphere is a planet-wide layer of cloud, consisting largely of sulphuric acid droplets, and this hides the surface from direct visual scrutiny. The surface is everywhere very hot, with a global mean surface temperature (GMST) of about 460 °C, whereas the GMST of Mercury is about 170 °C.

○ Why is the surface temperature of Venus higher than that of the surface of Mercury, even though Venus is further from the Sun?

○ The high surface temperature is a consequence of the powerful greenhouse effect sustained by the massive atmosphere consisting largely of the greenhouse gas carbon dioxide (Block 2, Section 6.5).

Though the surface of Venus is shrouded in cloud, radar has been used to obtain images of its surface. Volcanoes and evidence of volcanic activity seem to be widespread. This explains the scarcity of impact craters: they have been covered by the products of volcanic eruptions.

Mars also has an atmosphere consisting mainly of carbon dioxide, but it is about 60 times *less* massive (per unit area of planet) than the Earth's atmosphere. It is also a very dry atmosphere. The greenhouse effect is therefore weak; with Mars being 1.5 times further than the Earth from the Sun, the GMST is about −60 °C. There are polar caps consisting largely of permanent deposits of water ice overlain by a layer of carbon dioxide frost, which for the northern cap is present only in the winter. Clouds are common, though they are not so widespread as on Earth, and as well as water ice crystals they also consist of carbon dioxide crystals. In one hemisphere ancient impact craters still survive in abundance, but in the other hemisphere they have been obscured by volcanic activity. In the older cratered hemisphere there appear to be dry river valley systems (Figure 5.6) — evidence that long ago Mars was a wetter, warmer place than it is today. Whether life became established during that distant time is an area of intensive investigation, as you will see in Block 12.

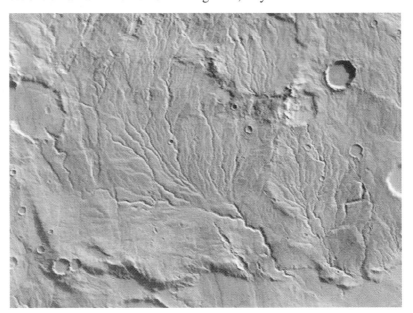

Figure 5.6 Dry river valleys on the older hemisphere of Mars, indicating that warmer, wetter conditions once prevailed. The width of this image is about 200 km.

And so we come to our Earth (see the title page). The Earth's surface and atmosphere are remarkable in four ways. First, as you saw in Block 2, the atmosphere contains a significant amount of oxygen. Second, most of the rocky surface is covered by oceans of liquid water, and the atmosphere is rich with clouds of water droplets or ice crystals. Third, though the rocky surfaces of all the terrestrial planets have been shaped by a variety of geological processes, some of those that are shaping the Earth's surface might be unique in the Solar System. A fourth distinctive feature of the Earth is that it harbours life. The Earth's surface, its geological processes, and its interior, will be explored in more detail in Sections 6 onwards.

Question 5.5   State two ways in which the Earth (a) resembles, and (b) differs from the other terrestrial planets. ◀

5.3 The small bodies in the Solar System

Figure 4.16 shows the orbit of the comet Hale–Bopp, which passed through the inner Solar System in 1997, and put on a fine show. Though comets are small, irregularly-shaped solid bodies, rarely more than a few tens of kilometres across, they are transformed in the inner Solar System by solar electromagnetic radiation and by a thin wind of atomic particles from the Sun. The radiation and the wind drive some of the readily vaporized material (such as water) from the comet, along with entrained dust particles, to form two or more huge tails. Figure 5.7 shows the tails of Hale–Bopp. In the outer Solar System cometary tails are not present, and the solid comets are so small that they cannot normally be detected much beyond the orbit of Saturn. The composition of comets is inferred from the composition of their tails, which reveals the comets to be loose aggregates of icy and rocky materials.

Another main class of small body in the Solar System is the minor planets (asteroids). These are rocky bodies, the largest, Ceres (pronounced 'series'), being 914 km in diameter, and there are about 10^5 asteroids that are larger than 100 m. The smaller ones are irregularly shaped, and so it is more appropriate to refer to a typical distance across the body (as 'size') rather than to their diameters. The smaller the size the greater the number of bodies, and there are so many rocky bodies smaller than 100 m, and they have sufficiently varied orbits, that every day some of the very smallest enter the Earth's atmosphere, where they are seen as meteors (informally known as 'shooting stars', although this term is quite erroneous as they are totally unrelated to stars). A further population of meteors are comet fragments, and a small number are pieces of the surfaces of Mars and the Moon, blasted off those bodies by the impacts of rocky bodies from space. If a meteor escapes complete vaporization in our atmosphere, and survives to reach the Earth's surface, it is called a meteorite. A great number of meteorites have been found, providing astronomers with important samples of extraterrestrial Solar System materials.

5.4 The origin of the Solar System

The striking differences between the various bodies in the Solar System, and the layout of the Solar System, can be explained by a widely accepted theory of its origin. In this theory, the Solar System formed from a rotating disc of gas composed mainly of hydrogen and helium, plus a small proportion of dust. The centre of the disc was the site of the Sun's formation, as illustrated in Figure 5.8 (*overleaf*), and the Sun's chemical composition was the same as that of the disc.

⬤ How does this account for the chemical composition of the Sun?

◯ The disc was mainly hydrogen and helium. Therefore, so too was the Sun.

The planets formed from the remainder of the disc, which probably had a mass of about 10% of that of the Sun, and was prevented by its rotation from contracting into a single object. In the inner part of the disc the dust had a rocky composition, and this dust gathered together to form the terrestrial planets.

⬤ Is this in accord with the composition of the terrestrial planets?

◯ Yes, the terrestrial planets have a rocky composition.

The later stages of formation of the terrestrial planets took the form of the gathering up of small solid bodies, peppering the planetary surfaces with impact craters.

Further from the Sun the disc was cooler, and so the dust also contained icy materials, notably water. This extra icy component led to the formation of four icy-rocky bodies. These were so massive that the gas in the disc was gravitationally captured by them, and so the giant planets were formed. The capture was brought to an end by radiation from the newly active Sun, which drove the remaining disc gas out into interstellar space.

Figure 5.7 The tails of comet Hale–Bopp during its spectacular passage through the inner Solar System in 1997. The blue tail consists largely of hot gas, and the other tail largely of dust. The bar is ten times the apparent diameter of the Sun in the sky. This image was obtained on 1 April 1997 when the comet was at its closest to the Sun (1.4×10^{11} m) and when it was about 2×10^{11} m from the Earth. The solid nucleus is at the heart of the fuzzy head, far too small to be visible, and in any case obscured by the head.

Figure 5.8   Artist's impression of the formation of the Solar System. The circular disc of gas (plus a trace of dust) is viewed obliquely here.

The formation of the Solar System was largely completed by about 4 600 Ma ago; the time it took the Solar System to form was very much less than 4 600 Ma.

The comets and the minor planets are left-over fragments that escaped incorporation into a major planet. Most of the comets now orbit the Sun far beyond Pluto, though there are a number closer in, and Pluto itself might be the largest example of these icy-rocky left-overs. The minor planets are not the original left-overs. Most of the original bodies aggregated into larger bodies, many of which were later disrupted by collisions among themselves, to yield today's minor planet population. The gravitational effect of Jupiter has been responsible for preventing a large planet from forming in the minor planet region. The subsequent impact of some of these bodies onto the surfaces of major planets (and their satellites) has added to the initial endowment of impact craters, or has replaced craters lost through geological activity.

There is a lot of evidence in support of this theory for the origin of the Solar System, not only from within the Solar System, but in recent years from the discovery of discs of gas and dust around very young stars, and of giant planets in orbits around not so young stars. Whether there are any Earth-like planets around other stars, and whether these support life, are questions that might be answered within a few decades.

Activity 5.1   The giant planets

In this activity you will write a brief account that describes how the theory of the origin of the Solar System, outlined above, explains the composition of the giant planets and their location in the outer part of the Solar System. ◄

5.5 Summary of Section 5

The Solar System is believed to have formed about 4 600 Ma ago from a disc consisting of gas (mainly hydrogen and helium) and dust. In the inner Solar System the dust consisted of rocky materials that gave birth to the terrestrial planets. In the outer Solar System the dust consisted of a mixture of rocky and icy materials that formed bodies massive enough to capture disc gas, resulting in the giant planets.

The Sun is composed mainly of hydrogen and helium. In its central core nuclear fusion is converting hydrogen to helium, which releases the energy that sustains the Sun's luminosity. In about 5 000 Ma, the Sun will have exhausted its hydrogen supply. Other stars are also sustained by nuclear fusion.

The planets are much less massive than the Sun, and as a consequence their interiors can never be hot enough for nuclear fusion: this is a fundamental distinction between a planet and a star. Planetary interiors are therefore much cooler than that of the Sun, and so their surfaces are cooler. Cool surfaces emit little visible radiation, so we see planets by reflected sunlight.

An indication of the interior composition of a planet is given by its density. Two of the giant planets, Jupiter and Saturn, are dominated by hydrogen and helium, whereas the other two giants, Uranus and Neptune, have a greater proportion of icy and rocky materials compared to hydrogen and helium. Pluto is dominated by icy and rocky materials, and the terrestrial planets by rocky materials alone. The planetary satellites are variously rocky, or icy-rocky.

All four giants have massive atmospheres consisting largely of hydrogen and helium. Venus has a massive atmosphere, largely of carbon dioxide, that sustains an enormous greenhouse effect. The atmosphere of Mars is also carbon dioxide, but is much less massive than the atmosphere of Venus. The Earth has an atmosphere of intermediate mass, and it is unusual in having a significant amount of oxygen.

The Earth is also unusual in having much of its surface covered by oceans of water. Mars has polar caps, and seems to have had liquid water on its surface in the distant past. Mercury is covered in impact craters, as is one hemisphere of Mars. The other martian hemisphere has been resurfaced by geological activity, as have the surfaces of Venus and the Earth.

The comets are small icy–rocky bodies, and the minor planets are small rocky bodies. Both sorts of body are fragments that have escaped incorporation into a major planet.

6 The Earth's surface

The rest of this block concerns the planet we live on; what it is made of, how its outer surface is shaped, and how its interior functions. As our first step in studying the Earth, it is useful to recognize that the Earth comprises a number of different parts, some of which can be seen from space (see the title page of this book). They include the atmosphere and the solid, rocky, land. We are also familiar with the oceans, lakes and rivers; these make up the **hydrosphere** — the part of the Earth composed of water. It is also possible to define the biosphere as that part of the Earth inhabited by life. Although the Earth can be 'taken apart' and split into these individual components, we have already seen in Block 1 that life on Earth is inextricably linked to the Earth's water supply, and in Block 2 that the atmosphere and hydrosphere are linked by the water cycle. It is these interactions between component parts, rather than just the presence of the components themselves, which make Earth such an interesting planet to inhabit.

The Earth's component parts are far from static. In fact, the Earth is an amazing hive of activity in which things are moving around all the time. Even something as straightforward as falling raindrops provides an instructive example. Rain plays a role in maintaining the water cycle, and this involves the hydrosphere, biosphere and atmosphere. Rain is also an example of a moving liquid (rather than a moving solid or gas) and without it life and the water cycle would cease to function. Signs of activity within the Earth's component parts and between those parts can be recognized all around us.

Activity 6.1   Describing examples of activity on planet Earth

This activity asks you to identify activity in the Earth's component parts from your own knowledge and experience. ◀

The Earth is clearly an active planet, and science provides a way of understanding this activity. Some of the most obvious examples of activity occur in the atmosphere (for example, weather) and the oceans (for example, waves, tides and water currents) so let us start with these parts of the Earth, before considering its solid surface and, in later sections, the processes that shape its surface.

6.1   The Earth's atmosphere and oceans

There are many reasons why scientists are interested in the atmosphere and the oceans. Some scientists are driven by natural curiosity — 'why does the wind blow?'. Others are motivated by a need to understand and then solve problems of concern to society, such as the control of air pollution and the effect of ocean circulation on climate. Already in this course (Blocks 1 and 2) we have discussed a number of aspects of the Earth's atmosphere. For example, the chemical composition of the atmosphere is critical in determining the global mean surface temperature (GMST).

Question 6.1   Using what you learnt in Block 2, explain in 50 to 100 words why the wind blows. ◀

We will not go into any more detail about the atmosphere than we did in Block 2. There, you found that the atmosphere consists of a number of layers. In the lowermost layer, temperature decreases with height; this layer is called the troposphere and is about 10 km thick. It is this layer that contains weather systems, driven by unequal heating across the Earth's surface and the transfer of energy associated with evaporation, condensation and precipitation of water.

In the rest of this section, we shall investigate the oceans, and then review how the atmosphere and oceans are linked. Let's start by looking at the temperature of the water in the oceans.

6.1.1 Temperature in the oceans

Imagine that a scientist decides to measure the temperature at several depths beneath the sea surface as follows. First, the scientist arranges to be aboard a ship anchored at sea. Over the side of the ship is lowered a long piece of rope with a heavy weight and a mercury-in-glass thermometer attached to the end. The intention is then to wait a few minutes, pull up the rope and read from the thermometer the water temperature for the depth corresponding to the length of the rope. By repeating this procedure for different depths a series of readings will be obtained showing how temperature varies with depth.

● The design of any scientific experiment should ensure that the results are reliable and not likely to give a misleading impression. Do you think this method will give reliable results? Explain your answer.

○ No. There are several problems. First, a mercury-in-glass thermometer is delicate and could easily break while it is being hauled around; the high pressures at depth, due to the mass of overlying water, could also break the instrument. Second, if the thermometer passed through warmer or colder water while it was being pulled to the surface then the temperature that was read would be different from that at depth. In short, this is a badly designed experiment.

The methods we have just described were essentially those used when the scientific exploration of the oceans was starting in the early 1800s. Not surprisingly, the results led to confusion and some very heated debate about the reliability of the measurements, which prevented any agreement being reached on what the measurements actually meant. The practical problems were gradually acknowledged and then overcome by designing new instruments. The present practice for obtaining reliable measurements is to lower an electronic temperature sensor that sends the measured temperatures to a computer on board the ship. The results are best presented on a graph such as Figure 6.1 in which the vertical axis represents depth increasing downwards. This might seem a rather unconventional way of drawing a graph but it has the advantage of letting us follow temperature *downwards* into deeper waters.

Question 6.2   Summarize how the seawater temperature varies with depth in Figure 6.1. Consider:

(a) the difference between temperatures at the surface and at the deepest levels measured;

(b) the way in which temperature changes with depth — does it change at a constant rate, or, if the rate is not constant, over what depth range does it change most rapidly? ◀

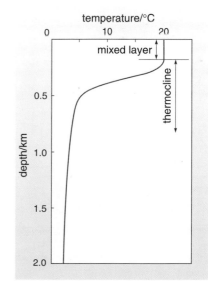

Figure 6.1   Graph showing how temperature typically varies with water depth in the uppermost 2 km of the ocean in mid-latitudes.

So, the measured temperature structure of the ocean shows that it comprises two layers in which temperature changes only slightly with increasing depth, separated by a layer in which temperature decreases by several degrees over a few hundred metres (the exact thickness of this layer varies from place to place). The water in the warm uppermost layer is stirred by the action of wind and waves, so this layer of water is called the mixed layer. This layer is where phytoplankton live and, as Block 2, Section 8, showed, this makes it an important reservoir in the global carbon cycle. Below it lies the zone of steep temperature change, called the thermocline (combining the Greek words *therme*, 'heat', and *klinein*, 'to lean'). The temperature of the deep ocean hardly varies.

○ Why is the water in the mixed layer warmer than deep ocean water?

○ Energy from the Sun is absorbed by the surface water which therefore becomes heated. This energy is distributed throughout the uppermost few hundred metres by mixing. The mixing does not penetrate to the deep ocean, so deep ocean water remains colder.

Because of the Sun's influence we might expect to find a seasonal variation in surface water temperature. This is indeed the case — a swim in the North Sea in summer is not as chilling an experience as it is in midwinter. Different amounts of solar energy reach polar and equatorial parts of the Earth and this also influences the temperature of the surface water, such that surface water near the Equator is about 20 to 25 °C warmer than Arctic and Antarctic surface water.

6.1.2 Ocean currents

In the troposphere, winds transport heat and moisture around the atmosphere. In the oceans, the equivalent of winds are ocean currents. By tracking the paths of buoys and other floating markers, ocean scientists have identified currents in the upper part of the ocean, involving the mixed layer. These surface currents, such as the Gulf Stream, are shown in Figure 6.2a. In the North Atlantic Ocean the surface currents form a roughly clockwise circulation pattern. The prevailing winds in this region also travel in the same direction, so is there a connection of any sort between the motion of the surface current and the overlying atmosphere? It turns out that there is; surface currents are driven by prevailing winds, with the seawater being 'dragged along' and set in motion by the moving air.

There are also currents in the deep ocean, beneath the thermocline, and these transport cold polar water towards the Equator by flowing beneath warmer water. This involves the vertical as well as horizontal flow of water, so the deep currents are best illustrated on a cross-section rather than on a map (Figure 6.2b). These currents are driven by the differences in the density of the seawater which result from differences in temperature and/or salt content (salinity) — relatively dense water flows down and beneath less dense water. Although the variations in density are tiny, being measured in tenths of one percent, they are able to cause significant circulation in the ocean. In this way, water (and hence heat) is constantly being moved around the ocean, much as air is constantly being moved around the atmosphere. As well as redistributing heat, the oceanic circulation system also redistributes salt in the ocean.

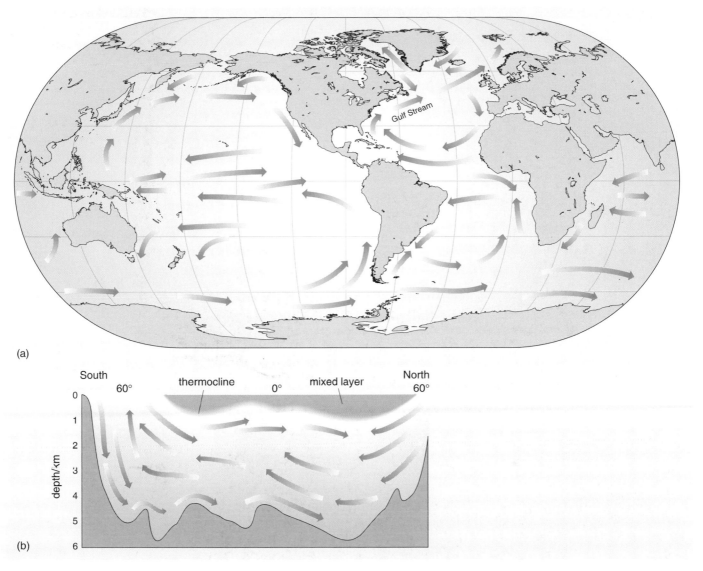

(a)

(b)

What processes can you think of that would change the salinity of seawater?

Fresh water is added to seawater, reducing its salinity, when rain falls into the sea, where rivers flow into the sea, and when ice melts into the sea. When fresh water is removed by evaporation this increases the salinity of the seawater because the salt is left behind in the ocean as the water evaporates (Block 1, Section 4.5).

You'll notice that these effects involve more than the oceans alone. The role of the atmosphere is critical, and the importance of interactions between the atmosphere and ocean cannot be overestimated. Water, carbon dioxide and other atmospheric gases move between the two (Block 1, Section 4.5, and Block 2, Sections 7 and 8). Energy is also exchanged between the atmosphere and ocean, for instance in the form of heat, and when the wind drives surface mixing and ocean currents.

Figure 6.2 (a) Map of surface ocean currents. (b) Deep currents in the Atlantic Ocean illustrated on a north–south cross-section.

6.2 The solid Earth

The Earth's atmosphere and oceans are constantly on the move, fuelled by energy from the Sun. However, as we saw in Activity 6.1, the solid Earth is also a very active place. Not only are there obvious signs of this activity such as earthquakes and volcanoes, but the surface of the Earth also moves under our feet without most of us ever noticing. This is because the Earth's surface is composed of a dozen or so separate interlocking blocks (known as 'plates') which are constantly moving around the globe — albeit very slowly. This movement is fuelled by energy stored in the Earth's hot interior and it accounts for a great many of the observations we can make about the solid parts of the Earth. For much of the remainder of this block we will be investigating the solid Earth, and the observations we make will lead us to an explanation of the movement and interaction of the plates — plate tectonics — one of the great scientific discoveries of the 20th century.

Our starting point is the large-scale shape of the Earth's surface, shown on the poster 'The Earth's surface'. Before continuing with this section you need to lay out the poster on a large table in front of you, or have it pinned to a wall next to where you are sitting. The political geography map of the world in the Study File (see Activity 6.2), or an atlas may also be helpful.

The poster shows the shape of the Earth's solid surface as if the oceans had been drained. Green, yellow, reddish-brown and grey shades indicate progressively higher land, and deepening shades of blue indicate increasing depth of the ocean floor. Probably the most familiar features are the coastal outlines of the land masses and the major mountain belts such as the Alps in Europe and the Himalayas in Asia. To help you to appreciate the shape of the Earth's undulating surface, the map is shaded as if illuminated from the left-hand side of the poster. This means that surfaces that slope down to the west are lit and appear bright, whereas eastward facing slopes are 'in shadow' and appear dark. This applies both over the land areas and on the ocean floor. Thus, the ocean floor slopes down to the west off the western coast of Africa, showing up as a white, illuminated, band. The eastern side, however, appears dark and in shadow even though the depths are the same as on the west side.

○ Does the poster show the entire area of the Earth?

○ No. The latitudes beyond 75° North and 75° South have been left off, as can be seen from the labelled latitude scale on the left- and right-hand edges of the poster.

Our reason for neglecting the polar regions stems from the difficulty of representing on a flat surface the true shapes and relative sizes of every geographical feature that lies on a sphere, as explained in Box 6.1, *Map projections*. On the poster map, all lines of latitude have the same length as the Equator (so that the map has a rectangular shape) whereas in reality lines of latitude get shorter and shorter as the poles are approached. The effect of this is to make areas far from the Equator look unrealistically large. Very close to the poles the distortion is so large as to make the map almost meaningless, which is why the polar regions have been cropped from the poster.

The poster map shows a considerable amount of detail, so it makes sense to concentrate on particular parts rather than try to deal with everything at once. We'll start with the land surface.

Box 6.1 Map projections

In everyday life we encounter many maps of the world; in newspapers, on TV, in advertising and even in this course. All of these representations of the Earth are distortions of the truth, however, because the Earth is not flat, but a three-dimensional object, with a 'front' and a 'back' when viewed from space. Representing the distribution of features on the surface of a sphere on a flat surface provides a challenge. There is no way of doing this and arriving at a map in which relative distances between places *and* the shapes of areas are both represented truthfully at every point on the map. This box describes various attempts to do this and illustrates the similarities and differences between two of the common types of world map used in S103.

There are many ways of tackling the challenge of making a flat map of a spherical planet. One simple way of doing this was devised by the German mathematician J. H. Lambert in 1772. His idea can be envisaged as surrounding the Earth with a sheet of paper and projecting each feature horizontally onto the paper (Figure 6.3a). Unrolling the cylinder of paper then reveals a map of the whole world (Figure 6.3b). Although this method allows the spherical surface of the Earth to be represented on a flat surface or plane, it produces a map with considerable north–south compression and east–west stretching at the poles. For example, every line of latitude (Block 2, Section 9) has the same length as the Equator, whereas, in reality, lines of latitude become shorter and shorter the further they are from the Equator. This stretching effect reaches an extreme at the poles, such that the *point* that is the North Pole appears as a *line* the length of the Equator at the top of the map (the same effect is true for the South Pole).

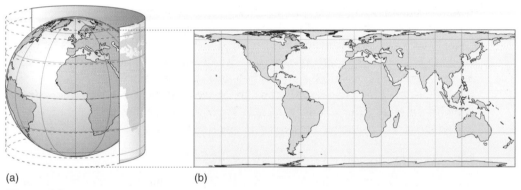

(a)　　　　　　　　　　(b)

Figure 6.3

(a) Visualization of how to represent the surface features of the Earth on a cylinder of paper which is then unrolled to provide the map shown in (b). This map projection is called Lambert's cylindrical equal-area projection. Grid lines are at every 30° of latitude and longitude.

A similar problem afflicts one of the most commonly used map projections — Mercator's projection, which is shown in Figure 6.4a and is used in the poster. In this projection, lines of longitude as well as latitude get stretched lengthways nearer the poles. This has the advantage that the shapes of small regions are represented correctly. But there is a disadvantage in that areas become more and more magnified the closer they are to the

North or South Pole. To get a sense of this distortion, it is useful to consider a specific example. Take Greenland and South America. Which of these has the greater surface area in Figure 6.4a? Actually South America is ten times the area of Greenland, but on Mercator's projection the distortion of Greenland is so great that it appears to be larger than South America! Such grossly distorted geography is so unrealistic that it is more sensible to miss the polar regions out, as we have done with the poster, and in fact the poles themselves would have infinite area on a Mercator's projection so they can never be displayed.

Other projections can be designed partially to overcome these problems. One example is shown in Figure 6.4b; note how the relative sizes of Greenland and South America are more realistic. This is the Eckert III projection and it is used widely in S103.

Figure 6.4 Two of the common map projections used in this course: (a) Mercator. (b) Eckert III. Grid lines are at every 30° of latitude and longitude.

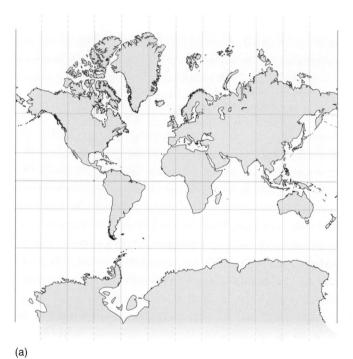

(a)

(b)

6.2.1   Mountain belts

The mountainous regions of the Earth are notable features of the land. On the poster they are identified in shades of reddish-brown which identify places of more than about 2 000 m elevation above sea-level. Many of these regions extend over many thousands of kilometres; they are known as **mountain belts**. Dramatic examples occur along the western side of North America (the Rocky Mountains), the western side of South America (the Andes), and there is a chain running east from the European Alps, through the Middle East and the Himalayas. The Earth's highest point is the summit of the Himalayan peak Mount Everest, which is 8 848 m above sea-level. (Measuring the height of a tall mountain is not straightforward and every now and then a new technique or an improved version of an old technique is applied to the problem, typically coming up with a slightly different value.) In northwest Africa, along the coast, lies another mountain belt — the Atlas mountains. Slightly lower mountain belts are found along the east coast of the USA (the Appalachians), across Norway and Sweden, and running north–south in central Russia (the Urals).

Mountain belts are more than scenic attractions, however, because they influence the climate by interrupting the flow of air across the surface of the Earth. Mountainous obstacles force air to rise to high altitudes, causing it to cool. As a result, water vapour in this air condenses into clouds and then falls as precipitation (Block 2, Section 7.1). Precipitation supplies rivers which return water to the ocean. For example, the Himalaya–Tibet region, which contains all but one of the world's peaks higher than 7 000 m, supplies about 10% of the river water flowing into the oceans. Rivers with their headwaters in these mountains supply freshwater for more than one-fifth of the world's population.

6.2.2   The ocean floor

The poster map shows the shape of the ocean floor, and it is quite a triumph of science and technology that such information is available for virtually all of the oceans. One simple way of obtaining this information is described in Box 6.2, *Measuring the depth of the ocean*.

Box 6.2   *Measuring the depth of the ocean*

The first measurements of ocean depth relied on seafarers lowering weighted ropes to the ocean floor. Clearly, this is not a very efficient way to get detailed coverage of the 3.6×10^8 km^2 of ocean floor, so it was not until the emergence of suitable echo-sounding technology, and a military interest in defining the oceanic environment in which to wage submarine warfare, that it became possible to make detailed maps of the ocean floor. The principle of echo-sounding is as follows.

Whenever we make a noise, sound waves carry the noise away from us. The waves bounce off any objects they encounter and these reflected waves may travel back to us, in which case we hear an echo a short time after the original noise was made. This effect is most noticeable whenever the sound has to travel a long distance, say several hundred metres, before being reflected. The time delay (t) between making the noise and hearing the echo depends on the speed at which the sound travels (v) and the total distance travelled by the sound (d) according to the word equation (which you met in Section 3.3):

$$\text{speed} = \frac{\text{distance travelled}}{\text{time interval}} \tag{3.1}$$

This can be expressed more concisely in symbols as

$$v = \frac{d}{t} \tag{6.1}$$

To find the distance travelled, Equation 6.1 must be rearranged to make d the subject of the equation. This is done by multiplying both sides of the equation by t (Box 3.1) to get $vt = d$ and hence:

$$d = vt \qquad (6.2)$$

Note that the total distance travelled, d, is the distance from the source of the sound to the reflector and back, i.e. twice the distance between them.

Figure 6.5 shows a shipborne echo-sounder emitting a pulse of sound that travels to the ocean floor and is reflected back to the ship. The time taken between the sound being emitted and the echo being received is measured electronically by the echo-sounding equipment. The speed of sound in seawater is approximately $1\,500\ \mathrm{m\ s^{-1}}$.

So, for example, if the time taken is 4.0 s, then applying Equation 6.2, the sound has travelled a total distance of $d = vt = 1\,500\ \mathrm{m\ s^{-1}} \times 4.0\ \mathrm{s} = 6\,000\ \mathrm{m}$, or 6.0 km. The depth of the ocean is half of this, i.e. 3.0 km.

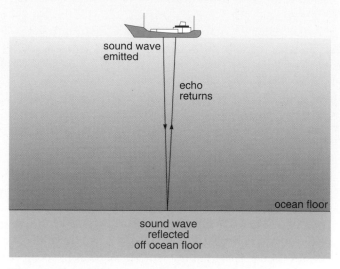

Figure 6.5 The use of echo-sounding to measure the depth of the ocean.

Around each continent is a region shaded on the poster in pale blue. This is the **continental shelf**, defined as being where the ocean floor lies no more than 200 m below the ocean's surface. Many oil and gas deposits are found in the rocks that form the continental shelf. Deeper water lies beyond the continental shelf, shown on the poster by the deep blue colours of much of the ocean basins.

○ How variable is the width of the continental shelf (pale blue on the poster)?

○ The width of the continental shelf varies considerably. For example, the continental shelf is much narrower around Africa than it is around the British Isles, where the North Sea is part of the continental shelf. (Note that this is not an effect of the stretching caused by the map projection, because the width of the continental shelf varies along any one line of latitude, for example along the Equator.)

Question 6.3 Consider a voyage across the Atlantic Ocean from the British Isles to North America. In three or four sentences, describe in qualitative terms (i.e. numerical values of depth are not required) how the ocean depth changes with distance as you travel westwards. ◀

An alternative, pictorial, way of describing the shape of the ocean floor is to draw a cross-section through the Earth. Such a diagram shows the undulations of the Earth's surface along a line between two places on the surface.

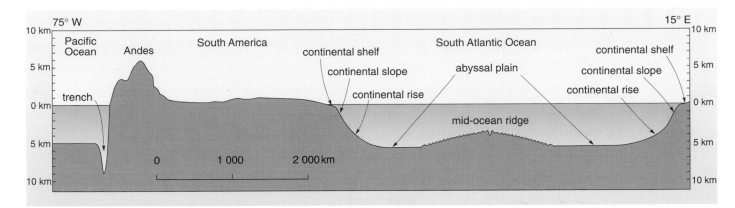

Figure 6.6 Labelled cross-section between 20° S, 75° W and 8° S, 15° E.

Figure 6.6 shows the specific example of a section between the eastern Pacific Ocean and western Africa. It illustrates the relief along a roughly west–east line that crosses South America and the South Atlantic Ocean. The continental shelf on the west coast of Africa is labelled on the extreme right-hand side of this diagram. Immediately to the west of the continental shelf lies a much steeper part of the ocean floor, called the **continental slope**. This in turn lessens in slope as the deep ocean floor is approached; this region is called the **continental rise**. In Figure 6.6 it appears as if these features slope quite steeply, but in fact the actual slopes are very gentle. The continental shelf, slope and rise have average slopes of just 0.1°, 4° and 0.5° respectively. (You may want to remind yourself about degrees of arc by looking back to Block 2, Section 9 and Figure 9.4.) To put these figures in context, a slope of 4° amounts to a change in height of 7 m over a horizontal distance of 100 m, whereas a slope of 0.1° amounts to a change of just 17 cm over the same 100 m distance. The reason the slopes look so much steeper in Figure 6.6 is that the vertical scale on this cross-section is much greater than the horizontal scale. On the horizontal scale, a distance of 1 cm represents 500 km.

⬤ What distance is represented by 1 cm on the vertical scale?

◯ Measuring the vertical scale with a ruler shows that 1 cm represents 5 km.

The ratio of these two scales is 500 km to 5 km, or 100 : 1. This means that the vertical scale has been stretched out, or exaggerated, by a factor of 100, making gentle slopes appear precipitous. The reason for drawing the cross-section with such pronounced vertical exaggeration is that it allows the topography, or shape of the surface, to be visible on a small diagram.

Beyond the continental rise, and several hundred kilometres from the coastline, lies a flat expanse some 4 to 6 km below sea-level, as shown by the deeper blue tones on the poster. These areas are called the **abyssal plain**; 'abyssal' because they are deep, and 'plain' because they are so flat and extensive. But the abyssal plain does not extend uninterrupted across the Atlantic to the continental rise of South America. The ocean floor shallows considerably to form a broad elevated region in the mid-Atlantic. This is the same feature you encountered in the North Atlantic when answering Question 6.3. On the poster, you'll see that this feature snakes its way along the mid-Atlantic from south to north, meeting Iceland on the way. This is the Mid-Atlantic Ridge.

Question 6.4   (a) What is the width of the Mid-Atlantic Ridge in the South Atlantic Ocean shown in Figure 6.6? (You can assume that the cross-section cuts the ridge at right-angles to its length and therefore shows the true width rather than an oblique section.)

(b) What is the water depth at the ridge crest and at the adjacent abyssal plain?

(c) What is the height of the ridge above the adjacent abyssal plain? ◄

It is not only the Atlantic Ocean that contains a large, symmetric ridge. As the poster map shows, a system of **mid-ocean ridges** extends around the Earth. These ridges extend for about 65 000 km and form the Earth's most spectacular mountain ranges, yet their full extent was not known until the 1960s. The locations of the mid-ocean ridges are shown in Figure 6.7 along with their names.

Question 6.5   On the poster map, follow the Mid-Atlantic Ridge south until it intersects two other ridges. Follow the mid-ocean ridge system eastwards around the map on Figure 6.7 and on the poster, noting the names of the most prominent ridges (these are named on Figure 6.7). Are there any mid-ocean ridges to be seen on Figure 6.7 or the poster which are not connected to the system you have followed? ◄

Activity 6.2   A summary map of the Earth's major features

Now that you have identified some of the key features on the map of the Earth's surface, this activity will help you to summarize their positions by sketching them onto a blank map of the Earth. ◄

Figure 6.7   Locations of the major mid-ocean ridges (light blue), ocean trenches (dark blue) and island arcs (red). Trenches and arcs are explained later in the text.

In following the mid-ocean ridge system on the poster map while answering Question 6.5 and completing Activity 6.2, you probably noticed that the crest of the ridges is not continuous, but is frequently displaced to one side or the other. On the Mid-Atlantic Ridge, these displacements are quite closely spaced but on the East Pacific Rise, for instance, they are more widely spaced. The significance of these

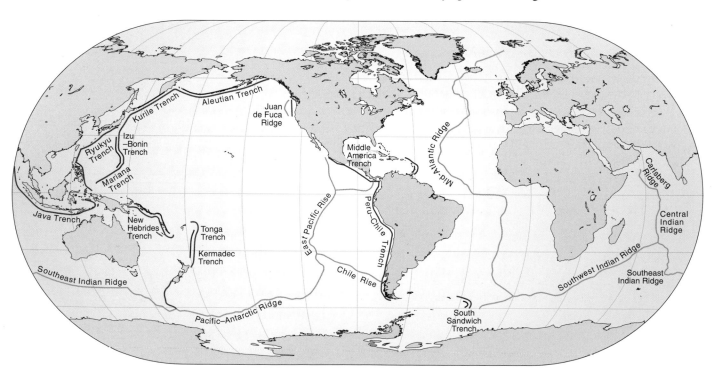

displacements will be considered later in this block. For the time being we simply make the observation that they are a feature of the global mid-ocean ridge system.

Now return to the cross-section in Figure 6.6 and consider the ocean floor at the edges of ocean basins.

○ In what ways is the ocean floor along the Pacific coast of South America different from that along the Atlantic coast?

○ Off the Pacific coast of South America, the continental shelf, slope and rise appear to be absent or at least very much narrower than on the Atlantic coast. Also, the abyssal plain, at about 5 km depth, is separated from the land by a trench some 9 km deep. There is no trench along the east coast of South America.

The name of the deep trench is the Peru–Chile Trench. It is visible on the poster as a narrow dark blue band, about 1 mm wide, running along the eastern margin of the Pacific Ocean adjacent to South America. The western side of the trench is dark, being 'in shadow', whereas the eastern side is 'illuminated' and bright.

The **ocean trenches** are extremely long troughs in the ocean floor, extending from the depth of the abyssal plains to the greatest depths of the oceans. The major trenches are named in Figure 6.7. The Mariana Trench, in the western Pacific Ocean, contains the deepest known point in the oceans (the Challenger Deep) where the ocean floor is 11 034 m below sea-level.

○ How does the depth of the Challenger Deep compare with the height above sea-level of Mount Everest?

○ The Challenger Deep is over 2 km deeper than Everest is high!

Activity 6.2 (continued)

Return to your sketch map and add the ocean trenches that you can identify on the poster. ◀

6.2.3 Island chains and island arcs

Within the ocean basins lie many small islands and conical submarine mountains (seamounts). Some are isolated patches of land, but others are arranged together along lines thousands of kilometres long. On the poster map, chains of islands and seamounts are particularly noticeable in the Pacific Ocean. Some extend roughly east–west at about 20–30° S. Another prominent chain defines a large 'L'-shape in the northwest Pacific. Still other chains of islands lie alongside some ocean trenches. The chains that lie next to ocean trenches are curved and so are referred to as **island arcs**. Examples are found in the Caribbean, the Aleutian Islands (between Alaska and Siberia) and in the western Pacific, for instance north of New Zealand (Figure 6.7). All of these island arcs contain many active volcanoes, of which more in Section 8.

Activity 6.2 (continued)

Add the island arcs to your sketch map. As you do so, notice which ocean trenches have neighbouring island arcs and which do not. ◀

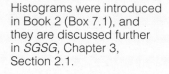

Activity 6.3 Describing your sketch map in writing

This activity helps you to develop the skill of translating from diagrams to words. It requires you to summarize in words the information on your sketch map (from Activity 6.2) about the distribution of the Earth's major surface features. ◀

6.3 Heights and depths

So far, we have been considering those parts of the Earth above sea-level separately from those parts below sea-level. But in reality the Earth's solid surface is distributed continuously between the highest point on the continents (8 848 m above sea-level) and the lowest point in the oceans (11 034 m below sea-level), a total height difference of almost 20 km.

○ It might seem likely that the height of the Earth's solid surface is equally distributed between these two extremes. From your examination of the poster, do you think that this is correct?

○ No. The abyssal plains, with water depths of 4 to 6 km, cover large proportions of the ocean floor, so it seems likely that, roughly speaking, there may be two main levels for the Earth's solid surface —the low-lying land (coloured green on the poster) and the deep ocean floor.

To find out if this is really the case, requires us to find out how much of the Earth's surface area actually lies above, below or between given levels. Figure 6.8 gives a pictorial representation of this information, in the form of a histogram. The length of each bar gives the percentage of the surface area (read from the vertical axis, although in this case the values are also written above each bar) within each 1 km interval. For example, 4.5% of the Earth is at an altitude of between 1 and 2 km above sea-level.

Histograms were introduced in Book 2 (Box 7.1), and they are discussed further in *SGSG*, Chapter 3, Section 2.1.

Figure 6.8 A histogram showing the percentage of the Earth's surface area lying within given intervals of height and depth. The percentages of the Earth's surface above 5 km altitude and below 7 km depth are too small to show at this scale. This type of histogram is known as a hypsometric plot.

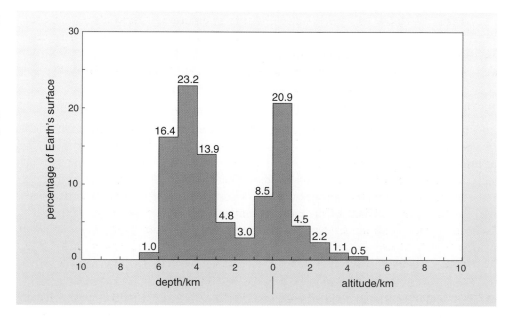

Rather than referring to Figure 6.8 as a histogram of the heights and depths of the Earth's solid surface, which is a bit of a mouthful, it is more convenient to use a shorthand term. So, combining the two Greek words *hypsos*, 'height', and *metron*, 'measure', Figure 6.8 is called a hypsometric plot.

○ Does the shape of the hypsometric plot indicate that the level of the Earth's surface is evenly distributed between the deepest and highest points?

○ No, there are two peaks, one centred on 0 to 1 km height and the other centred on 4 to 5 km depth. These peaks indicate that much of the Earth's surface lies within these two height/depth ranges.

○ What is the significance of the trough between the two peaks?

○ The trough means that there is only a small portion of the Earth lying at depths between those of the two most common levels. This portion includes the mid-ocean ridges.

○ How do these observations compare with the picture of the Earth's surface presented in Figure 6.6?

○ They compare well — the most common heights or depths apparent on Figure 6.6 are, on the one hand, the vast expanse of the abyssal plains between 4 and 6 km depth, and, on the other hand, the areas of land and the continental shelves that lie near sea-level (between 1 km deep and 1 km high).

In summary, the hypsometric plot illustrates that a substantial proportion of the Earth lies between 3 and 6 km below sea-level, and a second large proportion lies between 1 km depth and 1 km high. Extremely deep regions (ocean trenches) and extremely high regions are rare and do not show up on Figure 6.8.

Despite the familiar division of the Earth into areas lying above and below sea-level, the two peaks on the hypsometric plot suggest an alternative division placed between 1 and 2 km depth within the continental rise, not at sea-level. Thus, in this case, the continental shelf, such as that beneath the North Sea and to the west of the British Isles, is really part of the continents rather than the ocean floor. During the last glaciation (Block 2, Section 3), when sea-level was some 130 m lower than today, large areas of the continental shelf were actually dry land.

The difference between the deep ocean floor and the continents (including the continental shelf and slope) is not only one of elevation but extends to the type of material they are made from. The deep ocean floor is covered in mud, but beneath it lies a dark-coloured rock called basalt, which has a relatively high density (about $3.0 \times 10^3 \, \text{kg m}^{-3}$) compared with most rocks. The continents also contain some basalt rock, for example the Giant's Causeway in Antrim, but a host of other rock types are also found on the continents. Some, such as sandstone, limestone and granite, will be familiar from their use as building stones quarried from various places around the British Isles. The uniting aspect of these rocks is that, on average, they are less dense than basalt, the characteristic rock of the deep ocean basins. The rocks on the continental landmasses have an average density of about $2.8 \times 10^3 \, \text{kg m}^{-3}$. To an Earth scientist, the difference between the ocean basins and the continents is not that one is submerged by seawater, but that they are made of different types of rock having different densities. In other words, the hypsometric plot reveals that the Earth has two geological domains, the continents and the ocean floor, and the boundary between these lies beneath the continental rise, not at sea-level. It so happens that seawater covers the boundary between oceanic and continental rocks. At the present time about 25% of the continental area is actually covered by the sea.

6.4 Summary of Section 6

The Earth has many active parts; these include the atmosphere, oceans and solid parts of the Earth.

Like the atmosphere, the ocean has a layered structure. Ocean surface currents are driven by the prevailing wind, whereas deep currents are driven by differences in the density of seawater caused by differences in both the temperature and the salinity (saltiness) of seawater. The atmosphere and ocean exchange energy and materials.

The Earth's solid surface comprises extensive areas of rather flat terrain, principally the abyssal plains and much of the continental areas. The main linear physical features of the Earth's surface are the mid-ocean ridge system, oceanic trenches, volcanic island arcs, and mountain belts.

A hypsometric plot shows that the Earth's surface is distributed about two average heights representing continental and oceanic areas. The boundary between these areas does not coincide with sea-level, but lies beneath the continental rise. The 'oceanic' areas are made from basalt, whereas 'continental' areas are made from a wide range of rock types whose mean density is lower than that of basalt.

Earthquakes

7

As we saw at the start of Section 6, the Earth is an active planet, with activity occurring in the oceans, in the atmosphere and in the solid Earth itself. This section, and Section 8, look at two dramatic examples of solid Earth activity: earthquakes and volcanoes.

7.1   What happens during an earthquake?

You probably have some idea from newspapers, television or perhaps personal experience, of just how powerful earthquakes can be. In a matter of minutes earthquakes have devastated cities and killed a quarter of a million people. I was in only a medium-sized earthquake in 1978, but even that had the power to throw me out of bed onto the floor and make the building sway from side to side; an awesome experience.

One of the most destructive earthquakes of the 1990s occurred near Kobe, Japan, on 17 January 1995. This killed over 5 000 people, injured 25 000 and made a quarter of a million homeless. It was the most destructive Japanese earthquake since the one that killed 143 000 people in Tokyo in 1923.

Activity 7.1   Using a newspaper report on the Kobe earthquake

In this activity you will use an eyewitness news report of the Kobe earthquake to describe what happens during an earthquake. ◀

7.1.1   Earthquake-triggered landslides and tsunami

As well as being highly destructive in their own right, earthquakes can also trigger two other very destructive natural hazards. One of these is a landslide. This is a rapid movement of earth materials down a slope, the materials ranging from huge boulders to soil. Landslides can involve the movement of just a small amount of material or enough to bury whole towns in their path. They can have a number of causes, of which earthquakes are just one. The shock of an earthquake may be sufficient to start the slide. One of the most destructive earthquake-induced landslides occurred in Peru in 1970, as described in Box 7.1, *The 1970 Mount Huascaran landslide*.

Box 7.1   *The 1970 Mount Huascaran landslide*

On 31 May 1970, there was a large earthquake beneath the Pacific Ocean about 25 km from the coast of Peru. The ground shaking produced by the earthquake loosened rocks and ice on Mount Huascaran, one of South America's highest mountains, 130 km away from the earthquake. This initiated a gigantic landslide, which increased in speed and size as it moved down the mountain, reaching a speed of over 200 km h^{-1}. It swept along the valley at the foot of the mountain, filling it with rock, mud and ice, and partially destroying the town of Ranrahirca, 12 km from the mountain. Part of the landslide branched off to one side, swept over a ridge and roared through the village of Yungay. The village was obliterated; only a few of its inhabitants managed to escape by running to higher ground as the landslide approached. Survivors described the landslide as like a gigantic ocean wave with a deafening roar and rumble. The earthquake also triggered many other smaller landslides in the region, destroying thousands of buildings and causing even more deaths. The final toll was 67 000 dead and 800 000 homeless, making this the worst earthquake-induced disaster in the Western Hemisphere.

The second natural hazard that can be triggered by earthquakes is that of **tsunami** (pronounced 'tsoo-nam-ee'). Tsunami are ocean waves caused by movement of the ocean floor by an earthquake beneath the ocean. The water is moved as if it were being pushed by a giant paddle, producing powerful waves that spread out from the region of the earthquake across the ocean. Tsunami are hardly detectable in the open ocean, having only a low wave height, 1 m or less, but when they reach shallow water at a coastline their wave height increases significantly, reaching over 10 m, with disastrous effects.

Tsunami is a Japanese word meaning bay or harbour wave, and is particularly apt as it is only along the shore that they become noticeable or destructive; in the open ocean they do no harm to ships. The term 'tidal wave' is sometimes used in newspaper reports of tsunami but this is inaccurate as they are not related to tides (which are generated on the Earth's surface by the gravitational attraction of the Moon and the Sun) so scientists use the term 'tsunami'. The Japanese word is particularly appropriate because Japan has suffered greatly from the destructive effects of tsunami. Box 7.2, *The 1964 'Good Friday' tsunami*, describes the effects of one of the most damaging tsunami, triggered by an earthquake near Alaska.

Box 7.2   The 1964 'Good Friday' tsunami

A major earthquake occurred on 27 March 1964 (which happened to be Good Friday) beneath the Pacific Ocean just to the south of Alaska. People on Chenega Island, a mainly fishing and hunting community in the Gulf of Alaska, felt the earthquake and, concerned that a tsunami might follow, looked towards the shoreline. One of the islanders, Nicholas Kompkoff, noticed that water was receding from the beach. He quickly ran to his three young daughters who were down by the island's pier, and ran with them towards higher ground. As they were running, a huge wave arrived, sweeping 30 m up the hillside, carrying away people, the church and every home on the island. Two of Nicholas Kompkoff's daughters were carried away by the wave and killed. Nicholas and the other child were carried further up the hill and knocked unconscious, but miraculously they survived. 23 of the 80 islanders were killed by the tsunami.

About four hours after the tsunami struck Chenega Island, it reached Crescent City, on the coast of northern California about 2 600 km away. A tsunami warning had been sent out to the county sheriff in Crescent City, and he notified people in the low-lying areas to evacuate. The first wave of the tsunami to arrive rose to a height of only 1 m, and did no damage, so some of the people returned to the waterfront area, thinking that the danger was over. This was a fatal action, as during the next few hours several more tsunami waves arrived, up to 6 m high. The third and fourth waves caused massive destruction, washing more than 500 m inland and killing 11 people. The waves overturned cars (Figure 7.1), moved and destroyed houses and sank boats in the harbour.

The tsunami also caused death and damage at ports and coastlines along other parts of the North American coast between Alaska and California, causing 119 deaths and $104 million of damage.

Figure 7.1   Wreckage in Crescent City, California, from the 1964 Good Friday tsunami.

7.2   Why do earthquakes occur?

What causes the apparently solid and rigid Earth to move and so produce an earthquake? Earthquakes mainly occur when the different blocks or plates that make up the Earth's surface move relative to each other (Figure 7.2a), causing distortion in the rock (Figure 7.2b). The distortion builds up very slowly, over tens or hundreds of years. When rocks are distorted very slowly they behave as if they were springs, or pieces of elastic, in being able to store energy when they are stretched or compressed. Prior to an earthquake, the area is like a spring-loaded system waiting to go off. Eventually the distortion is enough to cause the rock to break and move, releasing energy in the form of an earthquake. The break is called a **fault**. It starts as a small fracture (Figure 7.2c), but grows rapidly (Figure 7.2d). In general, the larger the area of the fault, the greater is the size of the earthquake. The fault length (the length of the break along which rocks are displaced) can vary from metres for a small earthquake to about 1 000 km for a very large earthquake.

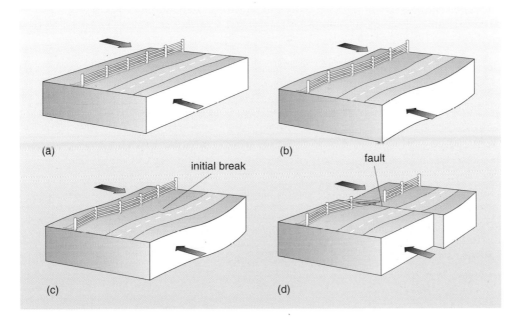

Figure 7.2   The cause of an earthquake. These are *block diagrams*, illustrating both the surface of the Earth and the Earth in cross-section.

(a) Part of the Earth where forces (shown by arrows) are trying to move the rock in opposite directions.

(b) Before a fault breaks, the rocks stretch.

(c) When the distortion is enough to cause the rocks to break, the break starts at one point.

(d) The break spreads rapidly along the fault, releasing energy.

Note that faults are not always vertical, and the forces causing movement can sometimes result in the rocks on either side of the fault moving up or down.

Question 7.1 Figure 7.3 is an aerial view of part of the San Andreas Fault in California.

(a) What is the evidence for a fault in this photograph?

(b) What are the relative directions of motion of the blocks on either side of the fault? ◀

Figure 7.3 An aerial view of the San Andreas Fault in California, looking northwest.

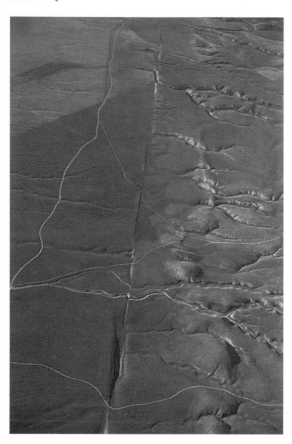

What is the real place of origin of an earthquake? As the initial break propagates, it releases energy along the fault, so in a sense the earthquake originates from the entire fault — which may be 1 000 km long. However, it is useful to refer to one part of the fault as the place of origin of an earthquake, and this is taken as the initial break. It is called the **focus** (plural foci) of the earthquake. This is usually below (not at) the Earth's surface. The point on the Earth's surface directly above the focus is called the **epicentre** (Figure 7.4).

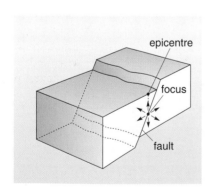

Figure 7.4 The focus and epicentre of an earthquake.

A large earthquake is frequently followed by a series of smaller earthquakes on the same fault, called aftershocks. These can continue for months after the main earthquake. They are caused by readjustment in the positions of the rocks following the main earthquake, releasing smaller, localized buildups of energy on the fault. Sometimes the main earthquake is preceded by one or more smaller foreshocks, although these cannot be identified as foreshocks until after the main earthquake has occurred.

A 1989 earthquake in California had a sequence of aftershocks that revealed the size and orientation of the fault. This earthquake occurred on 17 October 1989 with the epicentre about 100 km southeast of San Francisco, and is usually referred to as 'the

Loma Prieta earthquake' after the mountain just to the east of the epicentre. The earthquake involved movement on a fault about 40 km in length. It was large enough to cause destruction not only in the nearby town of Santa Cruz but also in San Francisco and its surroundings, where some buildings, bridges and raised roads collapsed.

Figure 7.5a is an epicentral map (a map showing the location of the epicentres) for the Loma Prieta earthquake and its aftershocks. The earthquake and aftershocks occurred along a well-known fault in California — the San Andreas Fault (shown in Figure 7.3). Figure 7.5b is a vertical cross-section of this area along the fault, from point B to point B′ on Figure 7.5a. This shows the positions and *depths* of the earthquake and aftershocks, i.e. their foci.

○ Over what length of the fault did the aftershocks occur?

○ Over about 70 km.

○ What was the depth of the main earthquake, and what was the maximum aftershock depth?

○ The main earthquake had a depth of 17 km and the maximum depth of the aftershocks was 21 km.

Figure 7.5c is a cross-section showing the foci on the fault beneath the line joining point C to point C′ on Figure 7.5a.

○ Is the fault vertical?

○ No. The earthquake foci become deeper towards the southwest, indicating that the fault slopes down to the southwest (at about 25° to the vertical).

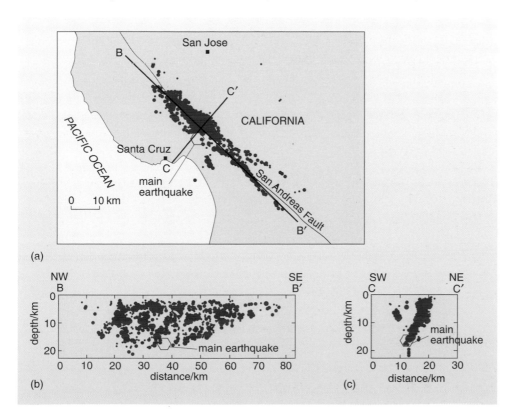

(a)

(b)

(c)

Figure 7.5 (a) Epicentral map, and (b) and (c) cross-sections, showing the foci for the main earthquake and aftershocks of the Loma Prieta earthquake, California, 1989. BB′ and CC′ on (a) are the locations of cross-sections in (b) and (c), which show foci parallel to (in line with) and perpendicular to (at right-angles to) the fault. Larger earthquakes are shown by larger red dots.

81

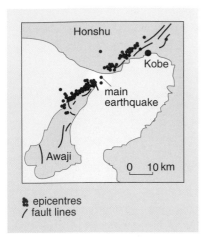

epicentres / fault lines

Figure 7.6 The epicentres for the 1995 Kobe earthquake and its aftershocks.

The San Andreas Fault is the largest and possibly most active of many faults in California. As well as the Loma Prieta earthquake, movement along the fault has caused other large earthquakes, including a major San Francisco earthquake in 1906. This resulted in the almost total destruction of the city by fire, following the rupture of gas mains; rupturing of the water mains made it impossible to put out the fires. The land to the west of the fault moved as much as 6 m north relative to the other side during this earthquake.

Now we know a bit more about what causes earthquakes, we can return to the first earthquake we considered (Kobe, 1995) to look at it in terms of movement along a fault. The epicentre was about 30 km to the southwest of the city of Kobe (Figure 7.6). The rocks moved up to 1.5 m horizontally over a 10 km length of a northeast–southwest fault along the northern coast of the island of Awaji. Aftershocks occurred on this fault, and to the northeast, over about 50 km. The only previously recorded significant earthquake along this fault was in 1916, and that was much smaller than the 1995 earthquake. The fault was thought to be moving only very slowly, enough to cause a large earthquake every thousand years or so. Unfortunately for Kobe, 1995 turned out to be the year in a thousand.

7.3 Where do earthquakes occur?

How deep in the Earth do earthquakes occur? Most earthquake foci are within a few tens of kilometres of the surface. Earthquakes less than 70 km deep are classified as *shallow-focus*. Earthquakes with foci 70–300 km deep are classified as *intermediate-focus* and those below 300 km are *deep-focus* (Figure 7.7). Shallow-focus earthquakes occur more often than deeper ones; about 75% of the total energy released from earthquakes is from shallow-focus ones. Unfortunately, the shallower an earthquake, the more damage it can produce at the surface; intermediate and deep-focus earthquakes are rarely destructive. No earthquakes are known to have occurred below about 700 km. At greater depths the rocks are very hot and under high pressure so they deform by flowing rather than breaking and faulting.

Do earthquakes occur everywhere, or only in some parts of the Earth? So far, this section has discussed earthquakes in Japan and California, and in the Pacific Ocean near Alaska and near Peru. You may also recall hearing of earthquakes in Italy, Armenia, Mexico City, China and even Britain. Figure 7.7 shows the global distribution of earthquakes.

Activity 7.2 Comparing information on different maps of the Earth

(a) Use Figure 7.7 to describe the main patterns of the geographical distribution of earthquakes.

(b) Use Figure 7.7 and the poster map to identify which surface features on the Earth appear to have (i) shallow, and (ii) deep earthquakes associated with them. ◀

Earthquakes are largely confined to specific areas of the Earth, called **seismic zones** (derived from *seismos*, the Greek word for 'shaking'). Most of the rest of the Earth is relatively free of earthquakes, or at least free of large earthquakes (Figure 7.7). However, even the UK has some small earthquakes (Box 7.3, *Earthquakes in the UK*).

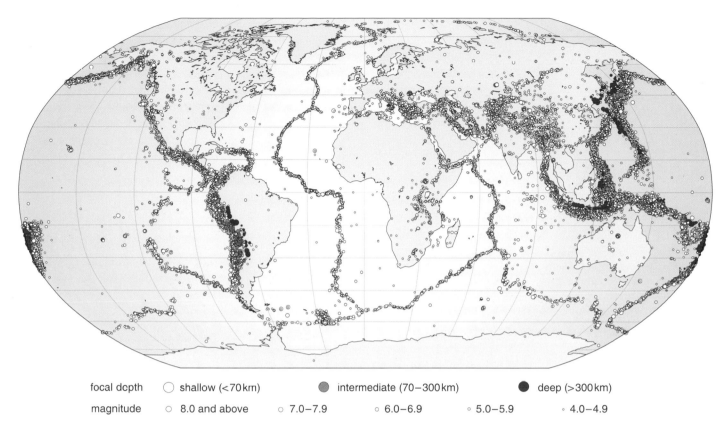

focal depth ◯ shallow (<70 km) ⬤ intermediate (70–300 km) ⬤ deep (>300 km)

magnitude ◦ 8.0 and above ◦ 7.0–7.9 ◦ 6.0–6.9 ◦ 5.0–5.9 ◦ 4.0–4.9

Figure 7.7 Global earthquake epicentres for 1980–1996. Shallow-focus earthquakes are white circles, intermediate-focus earthquakes are light red circles and deep-focus earthquakes are deep red circles. Only earthquakes of magnitude 4 and above are included. The significance of earthquake magnitude is discussed in Section 7.4. Data from the British Geological Survey World Seismicity Database, Global Seismology and Geomagnetism Group, Edinburgh. (> means 'greater than'; < means 'less than'.)

Box 7.3 Earthquakes in the UK

Earthquakes do occur in and around the UK, but they are usually fairly small; the largest one recorded (in 1931) had about a thousand times less energy than the 1906 San Francisco earthquake, for example. This 1931 earthquake occurred under the North Sea but was felt over most of the UK. Two earthquakes just a little smaller occurred in the Dover Straits in 1382 and 1580, causing significant damage in London, the latter killing two apprentices in Newgate. In 1863, Charles Dickens experienced shaking caused by an earthquake and was moved to write to *The Times* describing its effects (Figure 7.8).

All UK earthquakes occur at shallow depths; the greatest recorded depth is 42 km.

Figure 7.8 Charles Dickens' letter about the 1863 Hereford earthquake.

THE EARTHQUAKE.

TO THE EDITOR OF THE TIMES.

Sir,—As you may think any accurate observation of the shock of earthquake which was felt in various parts of England last Tuesday morning worth publishing I send you mine.

I was awakened by a violent swaying of my bedstead from side to side, accompanied by a singular heaving motion. It was exactly as if some great beast had been crouching asleep under the bedstead and were now shaking itself and trying to rise. The time by my watch was 20 minutes past 3, and I suppose the shock to have lasted nearly a minute. The bedstead, a large iron one, standing nearly north and south, appeared to me to be the only piece of furniture in the room that was heavily shaken. Neither the doors nor the windows rattled, though they rattle enough in windy weather, this house standing alone, on high ground, in the neighbourhood of two great rivers. There was no noise. The air was very still, and much warmer than it had been in the earlier part of the night. Although the previous afternoon had been wet, the glass had not fallen. I had mentioned my surprise at its standing near the letter "i" in "Fair," and having a tendency to rise. It is recorded in the second volume of the *Philosophical Transactions* that the glass stood high at Oxford when an earthquake was felt there in September, 1683. Your faithful servant,

CHARLES DICKENS.

Gad's-hill place, Higham by Rochester, Kent, Oct. 7.

You will have seen in Activity 7.2 that most earthquakes are associated with certain features of the Earth's solid surface — mid-ocean ridges, ocean trenches, and some mountain belts. We can also see that deeper earthquakes are characteristic of ocean trenches whereas shallower earthquakes are more typical of mid-ocean ridges. This relationship between the surface features of the Earth, and the movement of blocks of the Earth that causes earthquakes, is one of the observations of the active Earth that can be explained by the theory of plate tectonics — introduced in Section 6.2 and explained later in this block, in Section 13. For now, however, we will continue looking specifically at earthquakes.

7.4 The size of earthquakes

Why are some earthquakes more destructive than others? There are three main reasons: location (an earthquake with a focus under an ocean at a large distance from land, for example, is not usually destructive, unless it generates a tsunami), depth (shallower earthquakes can be more devastating), but, most importantly, the *size* of the earthquake.

7.4.1 Earthquake intensity

A straightforward way to measure the size of an earthquake is to look at the damage it caused. This is a measure of the strength of the ground shaking caused by an earthquake, and is called the earthquake **intensity**. To estimate the intensity of an earthquake at a single place, descriptions of what happened to people and structures during the earthquake are collected, and the description compared to a scale of earthquake effects, such as 'objects fall off shelves' or 'most chimney pots fall off'. The descriptions are given numbers on a 12-point intensity scale, with intensity 1 being not felt, 8 including 'most chimney pots fall off' and 12 being total devastation. The intensity scale is a *qualitative* scale because it is not based on specific measurements, even though it has numbers.

It is important to realize that intensity refers to the damage caused *at a particular place* by an earthquake. An earthquake will have different intensities in different places. It is therefore wrong to refer to *the* intensity of an earthquake; it is necessary to state the intensity in, say, Los Angeles, or 'the maximum intensity'. The intensity at the epicentre of the 1989 Loma Prieta earthquake was intensity 8, but the maximum intensity (and damage) was in parts of San Francisco and Oakland, about 100 km to the northwest of the epicentre, where intensity 9 was recorded. This was mainly due to the presence of a loose sand layer at the ground surface in the San Francisco Bay area which did not support structures as well as the solid rock nearer to the epicentre.

Intensity scales have two major disadvantages; they are no use for earthquakes under the oceans and no use for uninhabited areas. Even in inhabited areas, building standards vary in different areas, so earthquake effects are different. To overcome these problems in measuring the size of earthquakes, a different way of measuring earthquake size, using instruments, is often used instead of intensity.

7.4.2 Earthquake magnitude

The **magnitude** of an earthquake is a measure of the amount of *seismic energy* released by it, so it is a *quantitative* scale. The scale of earthquake magnitude is called the **Richter scale**. Its development is described in Box 7.4, *Charles Richter and the Richter earthquake magnitude scale*. The Richter magnitude is calculated by first measuring the size of the largest ground motion recorded by a seismometer, a sensitive instrument that detects the ground movements produced by earthquakes. This is then corrected for the distance from the earthquake, since the closer the seismometer is to the earthquake, the larger the ground motion will be.

Box 7.4   Charles Richter and the Richter earthquake magnitude scale

Many scientists contributed to the evolution of the earthquake magnitude concept, but it was Charles Richter, a professor at the California Institute of Technology, who set up a scale on the basis of many years of observations and applied it to well-known earthquakes. He explained the scale in a now classic paper published in 1935. Professor Richter modestly never attached his own name to the scale. He even refused to call it the Richter scale in his papers, long after the press and public had made 'Richter scale' synonymous with 'earthquake magnitude scale'.

Professor Richter often had trouble explaining to people that the Richter scale is a mathematical scale involving measurements and calculations on paper. 'They seem to think it is some sort of instrument or apparatus. Every year they come by wanting to look at my scale', he once said in an interview. Richter borrowed the term 'magnitude' from astronomy, in which he had an amateur interest. In astronomy the brightness of stars is measured on a magnitude scale.

Unlike earthquake intensity, any earthquake has only *one* Richter magnitude. The Richter scale is also *quantitative*, being based on numerical measurement. The Richter scale has no upper limit, but in reality the Earth itself provides an upper limit due to the strength of rocks. The largest earthquakes ever recorded had Richter magnitudes of 8.9.

The sizes of earthquakes vary enormously, so the size of the ground motion produced can differ by thousands or even millions from earthquake to earthquake. In order to deal with such enormous variation, the Richter scale is based on powers of ten, which means that an increase of one unit on the scale implies a tenfold increase in the amount of ground motion. For example, a magnitude 2 earthquake produces 10 times more maximum ground motion than a magnitude 1 earthquake. A magnitude 3 earthquake produces 10 times more again, which is $10 \times 10 = 100$ times greater maximum ground motion than a magnitude 1 earthquake.

⬤ What is the difference in maximum ground motion between a magnitude 3 earthquake and a magnitude 6 earthquake?

○ Magnitude 6 is 3 points more on the Richter scale than magnitude 3, so a magnitude 6 earthquake has $10 \times 10 \times 10 = 1\,000$ (or 10^3) times greater maximum ground motion than a magnitude 3 earthquake.

Similarly, the difference between earthquakes of magnitude 3 and 7 (4 points on the Richter scale) will be 10^4 in maximum ground motion. What appears at first to be a small change in Richter magnitude of an earthquake (say from 3 to 7, 4 points) really represents a very large change in earthquake size.

Activity 7.3 *Investigating links between earthquake magnitude and location*

In Activity 7.2 you established links between the depths of earthquake foci and the location of the earthquake epicentre. In this activity you will investigate links between magnitude and location. ◄

7.4.3 Seismic energy

It is also possible to relate magnitude to the seismic energy released by an earthquake. An increase of one unit on the Richter scale represents an increase of about 40 times in the amount of seismic energy released.

Question 7.2 What increase in (a) the maximum ground motion, and (b) the energy released is involved between an earthquake that measures 6.1 on the Richter scale and one that measures 8.1? ◄

Earthquakes with magnitudes of 8 and greater occur rarely, but when they occur they can lead to almost total devastation over a large area (Table 7.1). Smaller earthquakes occur more frequently, but their combined energy release is small compared with that from one great earthquake; it would take about 3 million earthquakes of magnitude 4 to release as much seismic energy as a single magnitude 8 earthquake. Earthquakes with the highest Richter magnitudes are not necessarily the most devastating, nor do they necessarily cause the greatest loss of life. The damage depends on the depth; as mentioned previously, shallow earthquakes are more destructive than deeper ones. It also depends on other factors such as population density, the rock types, soil conditions and local building standards.

Table 7.1 Earthquake numbers and effects.

Richter magnitude	Average number per year	Radius of region of strong ground shaking/km	Effects of shallow earthquake
>8.0	<1	80–160	almost total destruction
7.0–7.9	15	50–120	serious/great damage
6.0–6.9	140	20–80	considerable damage
5.0–5.9	900	5–30	slight damage
4.0–4.9	8 000	0–15	felt by many

Finally in this section, it is interesting to compare the energy produced by earthquakes with other energy sources. The amount of energy released by the Hiroshima nuclear bomb was about 10^{12} J, whereas the largest earthquake ever recorded (magnitude 8.9) released about 10^{18} J of seismic energy (Figure 7.9). This is a million times more energy (i.e. a factor of 10^6) than the Hiroshima bomb. The amount of energy used every day in the UK is somewhat more than 10^{16} J (Figure 7.9), and this is more than 100 times greater than the seismic energy released by the largest UK earthquake. However, the seismic energy (responsible for ground motion and the resulting damage) is only a few per cent of the total earthquake energy. The rest is involved in breaking and crushing rocks around the fault, moving the adjoining blocks of the Earth, and heating the rocks.

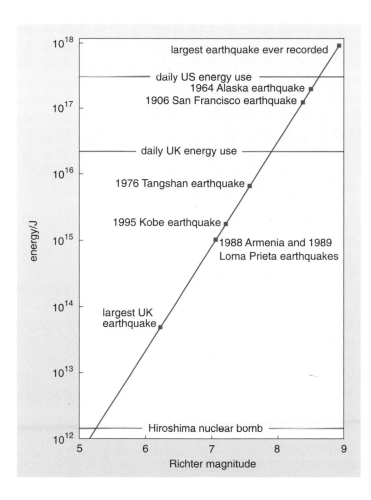

Figure 7.9 The seismic energy released by earthquakes, compared with the Hiroshima nuclear bomb and the UK and US daily energy use. Energy is given in joules. Each step on the vertical scale represents a tenfold increase in energy.

7.5   Summary of Section 7

Earthquakes shake the ground surface, can cause buildings to collapse, disrupt transport and services, and can cause fires. They can trigger landslides and tsunami.

Earthquakes occur mainly as a result of plate tectonics, which involves blocks of the Earth moving about the Earth's surface. The blocks of rock move past each other along a fault. Smaller earthquakes, called foreshocks, may precede the main earthquake, and aftershocks may occur after the main earthquake. Earthquakes are mainly confined to specific areas of the Earth known as seismic zones, which coincide mainly with ocean trenches, mid-ocean ridges, and mountain ranges.

The point of origin of an earthquake is called the focus. The epicentre is the point on the Earth's surface directly above the focus. Most earthquake foci are within a few tens of kilometres of the Earth's surface. Earthquakes less than 70 km deep are classified as shallow-focus. Intermediate-focus earthquakes are 70–300 km deep, and deep-focus earthquakes more than 300 km deep. Shallow-focus earthquakes occur in all of the Earth's seismic zones, but intermediate- and deep-focus earthquakes are almost exclusively associated with seismic zones near ocean trenches.

The destructiveness of an earthquake depends on the size, the depth (shallow ones are more destructive) and the location. Earthquake size can be stated in terms of the damage caused (the intensity) or the amount of ground motion and the energy released by the earthquake (related to the Richter magnitude).

8 Volcanic activity

Whereas earthquakes involve the movement of solid parts of the Earth, volcanic eruptions entail the movement of molten rocks from the Earth's interior to the surface and are yet another reminder that we live on an awe-inspiringly active planet (Figure 8.1). If you have had the thrill of observing a volcanic eruption at first hand, or you recall seeing pictures of eruptions in the news media, then you will be only too aware of the hazards they pose to life, property and society. Volcanoes have other effects on the Earth too, because they contribute to the water and carbon cycles by injecting water vapour and carbon dioxide into the atmosphere. Some volcanic eruptions produce aerosol particles of sulfuric acid which reflect solar radiation, leading to a reduction in heating of the Earth's surface. There are about 1 500 volcanoes on Earth that have erupted at least once in the last 10 000 years and have the potential to erupt again. These are regarded as 'active volcanoes' and, apart perhaps from Venus, the Earth is the only terrestrial planet with active volcanoes.

Figure 8.1 An explosive eruption of Etna in 1969 hurls red hot lumps of molten rock 80 m into the air.

8.1 Volcanoes and their eruptions

Although in popular imagination a volcano is envisaged as a majestic cone which every now and then suddenly explodes catastrophically, this is not always the case. For example, some volcanoes in Iceland and Hawaii are rather flat instead of being steep cones; and in some eruptions the molten rock oozes out of the ground very slowly rather than bursting out violently. To make sense of such a wide range of different phenomena, a fruitful approach is to work out the common attributes of various eruptions and to use these to classify the eruptions into a number of types or classes. This has the advantage of reducing a large number of observations to a handful of basic behaviours, with the hope that each can be readily explained.

Classification has several uses. First, the name of a class is a shorthand specification of the properties that all members of that class share. Second, a detailed study of a few members of a class enables us to learn something about the other members. The process of making observations and classifying them so as to help in explaining them is widespread in science. For example, in Section 5 we classified the planets in the Solar System according to their composition and found that this helped in building a theory for the origin of the Solar System. You will meet many examples of scientific classification in this and later blocks.

One example of classification is the classification of the materials that are erupted by volcanoes. We need to consider these materials before observing the spectacular volcanic eruptions in Activity 8.1. The first type of material to consider is **magma**, the technical term for molten rock. When magma is disgorged from a volcano it may flow out to form a stream of **lava**, in which case the eruption is described as an **effusive eruption**. The hot molten lava eventually cools, changing from a liquid to a solid. In other cases, Figure 8.1 for example, the magma erupts explosively, sending lumps of broken rocks and magma known as **pyroclasts** into the air. (The word pyroclast comes from the two Greek words *pyros*, 'fire', and *klastos*, 'shattered', so it means 'broken by fire'. But volcanic eruptions and magmas have nothing to do with burning; it is just that magma is extremely hot, anything from about 700 to 1 200 °C.) Explosive eruptions are often described as **pyroclastic eruptions**.

Many pyroclastic eruptions are caused when hot gas at high pressure bursts out of the erupting magma, tearing the molten magma apart into frothy blobs which solidify in mid-air, and it is this gas that is the second important type of material produced by volcanic eruptions. The hot mixture of water vapour, carbon dioxide and other gases escapes into the atmosphere, leaving air-filled bubbles in pyroclasts such as pumice. Although gas is a small proportion of the material produced in an eruption it is an impressive source of natural air pollution. For example, an eruption of the Philippine volcano Pinatubo in June 1991 injected 2×10^{10} kg of sulfur dioxide into the atmosphere in less than a day. This is about one-seventh of the annual global output of sulfur dioxide from all power stations and other industrial sources. The aerosols that formed from Pinatubo's gas seem to be the most likely explanation for an approximate 0.5 °C lowering of the global mean surface temperature (GMST) in 1991–2.

A third type of material involved in some eruptions is the pre-existing rock that can be ripped out of the ground in explosive eruptions.

Although the ingredients for a volcanic eruption can be classified into three classes: magma, gas and pre-existing rock, the proportions of these components vary widely between eruptions and between volcanoes, with the result that eruptions occur in a variety of styles.

◯ Would you expect magmas that don't contain much gas to erupt effusively or explosively?

◯ Explosive eruptions result when magma is torn apart by the violent expansion of hot pressurized gases, so eruptions of gas-poor magma would be expected to be effusive rather than explosive.

Thus, the gas content of a magma may determine how violently it erupts.

Clearly, volcanic eruptions are something that happen above the ground, but every volcano has a hidden underground part where magma is stored and transported. The key parts of the underground system are sketched in Figure 8.2, in particular the **magma chamber** which stores magma several kilometres below the surface between eruptions. At many volcanoes, the ground surface swells slightly before an eruption, indicating that the magma chamber is inflating with new magma from below, like a balloon about to burst. During eruptions, a conduit opens up between the chamber and the surface, and the magma flows along the conduit to erupt from the vent, which may be in a crater. Dramatic examples of this are the subject of Activity 8.1.

Figure 8.2 A model of a volcano depicted in cross-section showing the sub-surface parts of the volcano and the surface features. Not drawn to scale.

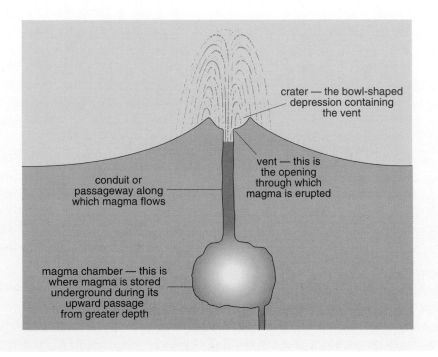

crater — the bowl-shaped depression containing the vent

vent — this is the opening through which magma is erupted

conduit or passageway along which magma flows

magma chamber — this is where magma is stored underground during its upward passage from greater depth

Activity 8.1 Observing, classifying and explaining volcanic eruptions

This activity involves you in studying video of several volcanic eruptions. You will use a classification scheme to summarize the features of these eruptions and then relate them to the processes that cause them. ◀

8.2 Where do volcanoes occur?

Figure 8.3 shows the locations of the world's active volcanoes.

○ Referring to Figure 8.3 and maps of the Earth's surface features (such as the poster map, your summary map from Activity 6.2, and Figure 6.7), can you see a relationship between the distribution of volcanoes and major topographic features?

○ A great many of the volcanoes are arranged in long narrow 'chains' along island arcs (Section 6.2.3) and along the edges of some continents. In both cases, these 'chains' of volcanoes lie beside ocean trenches.

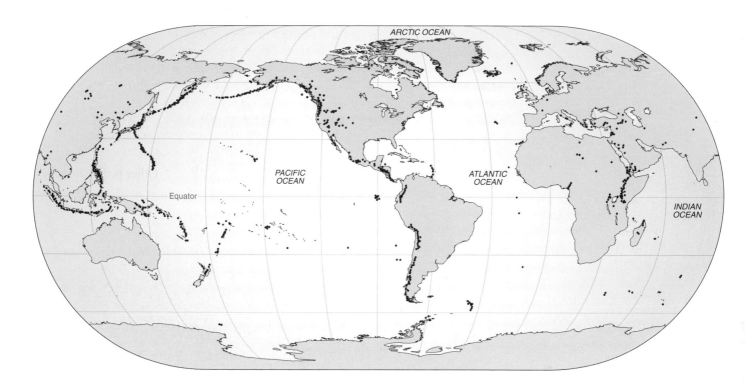

These chains of volcanoes alongside trenches are called volcanic arcs; they lie a few hundred kilometres away from the trench but the association is striking. Examples are the Aleutians (an island arc) and the volcanoes of the Andes in South America.

Volcanoes are also associated with mid-ocean ridges, as in the case of Iceland and the Galapagos Islands. But not all volcanoes are part of an arc or mid-ocean ridge; some can be found in the deep ocean (e.g. Hawaii) and on the continents (e.g. East Africa).

We know where volcanoes occur, but explosive volcanic eruptions are obviously much more dangerous than effusive eruptions, so if humans are to understand the dangers posed by volcanoes, one point to consider is whether all volcanoes have the potential to be equally dangerous. Use the evidence from the volcanoes you investigated in Activity 8.1 to answer the following question.

Question 8.1 Is there a connection between the style of an eruption (explosive versus effusive) and the location of the volcano? ◄

The number of examples provided by Activity 8.1 is small so it might be premature to conclude that we have found a general rule. When much more information is brought to bear, for instance by including other volcanoes from Figure 8.3 that have produced famous explosive eruptions, such as Krakatau (1883, Indonesia), Mont Peléc (1902, West Indies) and Tambora (1815, Indonesia), then the idea that explosive eruptions tend to be associated with volcanoes in island arcs and at the edges of continents alongside ocean trenches becomes more convincing. Many of these explosive volcanoes are found around the edge of the Pacific Ocean, and this concentration of explosive volcanoes has been dubbed the Pacific Ring of Fire. Coincidentally, large numbers of people live in these regions, and many of the world's major cities lie near volcanoes that have produced explosive eruptions in the past. In Europe, the most threatening volcano is Vesuvius, which sits beside Naples (population 1.2 million). It was a pyroclastic flow from Vesuvius that destroyed the town of Pompeii in AD 79.

Figure 8.3 Map showing the locations of active volcanoes (indicated by red dots).

Volcanoes that lie within ocean basins, and that are not associated with ocean trenches, tend to have fewer explosive eruptions, often producing only lava flows. Some examples are the volcanoes on Hawaii and the Galapagos Islands in the Pacific, and Iceland in the Atlantic Ocean.

8.3   Volcanoes and earthquakes

Volcanoes and earthquakes are prime examples of activity within the solid Earth, but are these two phenomena linked in any way?

○ Compare a map of the world showing the locations of volcanoes (Figure 8.3) with a map of earthquake distribution (Figure 7.7). Are volcanoes and earthquakes found in the same places?

○ There is often a link, for example around the Pacific Ocean basin and on parts of the mid-ocean ridge system. Sometimes they are not associated; for instance, in the Himalayas there are many earthquakes but no volcanoes.

The maps of volcanoes and earthquakes show that there are not always volcanoes where there are earthquakes. But there *are* earthquakes wherever there are volcanoes. What does this mean?

Section 7.3 described how earthquakes are caused when rocks move past each other along faults, typically as a result of plate-tectonic movements. The occurrence of volcanoes in many of the same places as earthquakes (for instance near ocean trenches) suggests that many volcanoes may also be associated with plate-tectonic movements — of which more in Section 13. As well as this association, some small earthquakes are caused at active volcanoes when rocks are forced apart by magma moving into the magma chamber and conduits beneath the volcano. It is often the case that the number of shallow earthquakes at a volcano increases before an eruption, so monitoring earthquakes is a good way of anticipating that an eruption may be about to happen, though predicting exactly when the volcano will erupt is only very rarely possible.

8.4   Summary of Section 8

Volcanoes erupt mixtures of molten magma, hot gas and, in some cases, lumps of rock which were already part of the volcano or the underlying rocks.

Volcanic eruptions can be classified according to the behaviour of the erupting mixture of magma, gas and rock. When the magma breaks violently into blobs which solidify in mid-air, the eruption is said to be explosive (or pyroclastic). When the magma forms a molten river of lava, the eruption is said to be effusive. Explosive eruptions can be divided into two types depending on whether the erupted mixture is lighter than air, becoming lofted in a tall eruption column high into the atmosphere, or is denser than air and flows at high speed across the ground as a pyroclastic flow.

Explosive volcanic eruptions are typically associated with volcanoes in island arcs and volcanic chains at the edges of certain continents, such as around the Pacific Ring of Fire. These volcanic arcs lie parallel with ocean trenches. Effusive eruptions are typically associated with volcanoes on islands within ocean basins.

Earthquakes occur beneath volcanoes when rocks get forced apart by magma moving in the magma chambers and conduits beneath volcanoes. Other earthquakes near volcanoes are caused by rocks moving along faults that are present in the area.

Classification is an important aspect of science since it allows a large number of objects or observations to be divided into a smaller number of classes, each with properties in common. Studying a few members of a class enables us to learn about the other members.

How rocks are formed

So far we have not said much about the rocks making up the surface of the Earth. In this section we redress the balance and show that the rocks around us are actually another manifestation of the Earth's activity. This seems obvious in the case of rocks produced in volcanic eruptions, but it is true for all rocks.

Although rocks are mainly to be seen in cliffs and road cuttings, solid rocks also lie below the vegetation and soil in every landscape. Some of these rocks are useful as building stones, others are sources of metals needed to make many of the trappings of civilization that we take for granted such as coins, railway tracks or the wiring inside computers. Although rocks often appear to be permanent features of the landscape, we have already found, in Block 2, that at least some rocks become formed and destroyed during the gradual operation of the water and carbon cycles. And, of course, active volcanoes are producing new rocks right now. Far from being immutable bits of scenery, rocks are testimony to the fact that ours is a dynamic planet.

Different types of rock form in different ways, and the processes involved leave their marks on the rocks they produce. The purpose of this section is to use the set of rock samples provided in the Practical Kit to explore the link between processes occurring on the Earth and their rock products. First, it is necessary to elaborate on the meanings of two key terms — rocks and minerals.

9.1 Rocks and minerals

We need to be clear about what we mean by a rock and by a mineral, and the distinction between the two. A **mineral** is a solid material, formed by natural processes and with a chemical composition that falls within certain narrow limits. Its constituent atoms are arranged in a regular three-dimensional array or pattern and because of this, minerals form crystals with a characteristic shape.

The five common minerals in Figure 9.1 provide us with some examples to look at. They range in shape from cubes (pyrite) and thin sheets (mica) to more complex shapes. This is because each is built from atoms of different chemical elements, and different combinations of atoms fit together into differently shaped structures. You can also see that they have different colours and that their appearance varies from glassy to metallic to matt. These differences also come about because of the minerals' different chemical composition and atomic structures. Although in this block there is no need to know the details of these minerals' chemical compositions, we can note that quartz, mica and feldspar are common examples of the many kinds of minerals that contain silicon and oxygen atoms — the two most common atoms at the Earth's surface. Quartz contains only silicon and oxygen atoms. Pyrite contains iron and sulfur atoms. Calcite contains calcium, carbon and oxygen atoms — it is calcium carbonate, the main constituent of limestone that, as you learned in Block 2, is part of the largest reservoir of carbon on Earth.

There are several thousand different kinds of minerals and some are very common; for example, most of the sand grains on a beach or in a desert are grains of quartz. Others, such as gemstones and the minerals that are used to supply metals are rather rare, and are usually the most valuable.

Figure 9.1 Crystals of some common minerals. From left to right: back row: mica, calcite, quartz; front: feldspar and two cubes of pyrite.

A **rock** is a solid assemblage of mineral grains. The mineral grains may be fragments of crystals or intact crystals and their size can range from a few micrometres to a few centimetres. A rock may consist of only one type of mineral but more usually it consists of several different minerals. For example, in the piece of granite shown in Figure 9.2 some of the grains are white, others are grey and glassy, and others are black with a shiny appearance. It is therefore an assemblage of several minerals: these are the black shiny mineral mica, the grey glassy mineral quartz and the white mineral feldspar, all of which are shown individually in Figure 9.1.

Figure 9.2 A piece of granite, shown at approximately true size.

Now that some of the important terms have been defined, let's consider the dynamic processes occurring on the Earth that actually make different types of rock.

Activity 9.1   An introduction to rocks and their origins

This practical work provides experience in handling, observing, recording and critically inspecting specimens of Earth materials. It will help you to relate features of rocks to the processes involved in their formation. ◀

Activity 9.1 revealed that rocks may be classified into three types, reflecting the three different types of process that form rocks on the Earth:

1   **Igneous rocks** are formed from molten rock (magma) that becomes solid when it cools, either after a volcanic eruption at the Earth's surface, or deep underground. (The word igneous comes from the Latin *ignis*, 'fire'.)

2   **Sedimentary rocks** are laid down as sediment in layers (for example sand on a beach, or mud on a river bed) at the surface of the Earth.

3   **Metamorphic rocks** are existing rocks that have 'changed form' (metamorphosed) by the action of high pressure and/or temperature, for example after burial deep in the Earth.

The following sections describe how each of the three major rock types is formed.

9.2   The formation of igneous rocks

Igneous rocks are defined as having solidified from a molten state, either inside the Earth or on the surface. The lavas and pyroclasts produced by volcanoes (Section 8) are called *extrusive* igneous rocks, because they are formed by the extrusion of magma on to the Earth's surface. Other igneous rocks, such as granite, however, are formed deep underground; these are called *intrusive* igneous rocks, formed where magmas have cooled within the Earth (Figure 9.3).

When magma cools, crystals of different minerals start to grow from the liquid. The number and size of the crystals depend on the amount of time available for their growth. In the case of extrusive rocks, the amount of time is short — anything from a few seconds for a lump of volcanic ash flying through the air, to a few years for the interior of a thick lava flow. Rapid cooling results in small crystals (see the specimen of basalt in the Practical Kit). For intrusive rocks, the cooling rate is much slower and the magma has time to grow larger crystals and become completely crystallized (see the specimen of granite in the Practical Kit and Figure 9.2). (The magma at depth cannot be observed in the way that volcanic eruptions can, so the time required for intrusive rocks to crystallize is not known for sure but may be up to several thousand years.) Generally speaking, the slower the cooling, the bigger the crystals.

Intrusive igneous rocks form several kilometres below the Earth's surface, so how is it that intrusive rocks such as granite can be found at the surface, for example as the Red Hills of Skye (Figure 9.4) or tors on Dartmoor? The explanation is that all the rocks originally on top of the granite have been gradually worn away and removed as sedimentary grains, to be deposited elsewhere. This process can lead to the formation of sedimentary rocks.

(a)

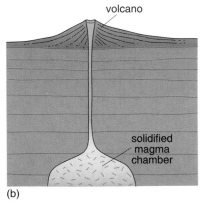

(b)

Figure 9.3   (a) Rocks, such as lava flows, formed when magma erupts on to the Earth's surface from a volcano are called extrusive rocks. (b) Rocks, such as granite, that form where magmas cool underground are called intrusive rocks. Note that the magma chamber is several kilometres below the Earth's surface.

Figure 9.4 The Red Hills of Skye are composed of granite, an intrusive igneous rock.

9.3 The formation of sedimentary rocks

Sedimentary rocks have been formed by the laying down, or deposition, of layers of sediment. For example, when sediment is transported by flowing water in rivers or seas, it can settle to the bottom in the same way as tea leaves or coffee grounds settle to the bottom of a cup. The deposition of sediment can be seen operating today in rivers, on beaches, near glaciers and in deserts.

○ Where has all this sediment come from?

○ The sediment has been carried by flowing water, ice or air from locations where erosion is taking place.

So, as well as laying down sedimentary grains (deposition), the formation of most sedimentary rocks also involves the grains being eroded and then transported from one place to another. These grains are liberated when rocks at the Earth's surface are slowly broken up by exposure to rain, wind and frost in the processes collectively termed **weathering**. It is weathering that causes the facing on stone monuments and buildings to degrade slowly over time, making ancient gravestones more difficult to read than newer ones. Once a rock has been broken up by weathering into small rock fragments and individual mineral grains, these particles can be transported by water, wind or glaciers to be deposited elsewhere as roughly horizontal layers of sediment.

With time, these accumulations of sediment may themselves get washed or blown away. Alternatively, they may become compacted under the weight of overlying sediment and new minerals may grow in the spaces between grains. In this way, loose sedimentary grains are effectively cemented together, forming a solid sedimentary rock, such as sandstone. The layers of sedimentary rock are called **beds** or **strata** (Figure 9.5).

○ Are all sediments composed of fragments of rock and minerals eroded from pre-existing rocks?

○ No, some sedimentary rocks also contain fossils of plants or animals which were living at the time the sedimentary material was deposited (Block 2, Section 3).

Figure 9.5 Layers of sedimentary strata, South Wales.

Many limestones form from the accumulation of shells and calcite skeletons of certain marine organisms. Chalk is a well-known type of limestone that is found extensively across southern England; it is almost pure calcite, and consists mostly of minute shells of countless billions of phytoplankton fossils. Limestones are, however, rarely so pure; usually some sand, silt or mud is deposited along with calcite, as you found with the limestone sample in the Practical Kit. Limestones with abundant fossils of large organisms, such as shells and reef-building corals, can form attractive ornamental stones.

Sedimentary rocks are useful in a variety of ways, not just as building stones. For example, limestones are an important source of calcium carbonate for making cement and fertilizer. Fragmentary rocks are often porous, with the individual pores being connected with each other. This means that liquids and gases can move through the rock, with the result that underground reservoirs of water, oil and gas are frequently contained within these sedimentary rocks (Block 2, Sections 7.4 and 8).

9.4 The formation of metamorphic rocks

The third group of rocks is called metamorphic, a word that means 'changed form'. Any type of rock can undergo a change of form, becoming metamorphic rock, if it is heated to temperatures of several hundreds of degrees Celsius, and/or if subjected to high pressure (because of the weight of overlying rocks).

An increase in pressure and temperature will come about if a rock becomes more deeply buried in the Earth as a result of earth movements, or if it is covered by a deepening layer of sedimentary deposits. Igneous and metamorphic rocks both have a crystalline texture and both form at high temperatures, but an important distinction is that metamorphism occurs in the solid state, whereas igneous rocks form from liquid (molten) rock.

During metamorphism, the atoms in the minerals making up the rock become reorganized, sometimes resulting in the regrowth of existing minerals (crystals), or in the formation of new minerals. As a result, the new rock may look very different from the original rock. The overall chemical composition of the rock normally remains about the same, however, with elements just rearranging themselves into new minerals that are more suited to the new temperature and pressure conditions. This is what happens during recrystallization and can often result in banding or alignment of the crystals in the rock. An example is the schist specimen in the Practical Kit.

You may already know of two other metamorphic rocks, slate and marble. Although the terms slate and marble are often used to describe construction and ornamental stones, the colloquial use of 'slate' and 'marble' covers a much wider range of materials than is covered by the strict definitions of these metamorphic rocks. Slate is a metamorphic rock with an extremely fine grain size; it is difficult to make out individual crystals even with a hand lens. It was originally laid down as a soft mud, but it has been recrystallized and the result is a hard, water-resistant rock that can be split into thin sheets. Marble is a metamorphic rock formed from limestone, but unlike schist and slate, marble doesn't always have a banded structure. This is because marble usually contains only one mineral, calcite, so there cannot be alternating bands of different minerals. This means that marble doesn't break along preferred directions like metamorphic rocks that contain minerals arranged in parallel bands. It therefore makes a good material for statues, as smooth surfaces can be carved in any direction. Any impurities in the marble tend to result in a mottled appearance.

9.5 Reviewing the features of different rock types

In this section we have investigated the links between the processes that form rocks and the textural features displayed by those rocks. The following activity allows you to focus on the distinctive features of the different rock types.

Activity 9.2   Summarizing the distinguishing features of different rock types

In this activity you will compile a table summarizing the properties of sedimentary, metamorphic, extrusive and intrusive igneous rocks. This draws together the content of Section 9. ◄

The features that we can observe within a rock do much more than allow us to classify it as sedimentary, igneous or metamorphic; they provide a window into the dynamic processes that shape the planet's surface. So, although there are no active volcanoes in Britain, both intrusive and extrusive igneous rocks are to be found — for example, the famous landmarks of the Dartmoor tors, the Red Hills of Skye (Figure 9.4), the Giants' Causeway in Antrim and Arthur's Seat in Edinburgh. These igneous rocks are evidence that Britain was volcanically active in the geological past. Similarly, the presence of metamorphic rocks (for example in much of the Scottish Highlands) indicates periods of past earth movements and burial of rocks, while sedimentary rocks are the record of ancient oceans, lakes, rivers, deserts and glaciers.

The insights into past conditions on the Earth provided by rocks, and also by fossils (Block 2, Section 3), give us information about the evolution of planet Earth. This theme will be taken up in Block 10, but for now we continue to concentrate on the Earth and its activity as we observe it at the present day by investigating the Earth's interior.

9.6 Summary of Section 9

Rocks are classified into three types according to how they were formed. Igneous rocks are formed from the molten state; sedimentary rocks are deposited at the Earth's surface from water, air or ice; and metamorphic rocks are rocks of any origin that have been subsequently transformed (metamorphosed) by heat and/or pressure, often several kilometres down in the Earth.

Rocks are generally either crystalline, i.e. formed of interlocking mineral crystals, or fragmental, i.e. formed of mineral or rock fragments compacted and cemented together by later mineral growth. Most igneous and metamorphic rocks are crystalline, whereas most sedimentary rocks are fragmental. Most metamorphic rocks can be distinguished from most igneous rocks because they show a characteristic banding or alignment of minerals. The presence of fossils usually indicates a sedimentary rock. The appearance and texture of a rock thus allows the processes that formed it to be deduced.

10 The Earth's interior

Our investigation of the Earth has, in the last four sections, concentrated on its surface features and the activity that affects its surface — earthquakes, volcanism, and the various igneous, sedimentary and metamorphic processes that form the rocks seen at the surface. It is now time to turn our attention to the interior of the Earth. Starting from the rocks that are known at the surface, how deep inside the Earth do these rocks extend — to the centre or only part of the way? If they do not extend all the way to the centre, what does? These are the questions that will be investigated in this section, as we develop a model of the Earth's interior. The term 'model' is being used in a new sense here: it is not a computer or mathematical model (like the climate model in Block 2, Section 9), nor a physical model (like a model aircraft, or the scale models of the Universe that were the subject of Activity 3.1) but a *description* that fits the observations.

10.1 How is the inside of the Earth investigated?

There is one technique that can be used to investigate the interior of the Earth directly, and that is by drilling into it and bringing samples of the rock at depth to the surface. Oil companies have drilled holes up to 8 km deep on land in their search for oil. Deeper holes have been drilled for research purposes; the deepest hole is 12 km deep in Russia. The deepest drill hole under the deep oceans is just over 2 km. All these drill holes have found rocks that are similar to the sedimentary, igneous and metamorphic rocks found at the Earth's surface, so these familiar rocks extend at least to those depths.

○ The mean radius of the Earth is 6 371 km. What percentage of this has been penetrated by the deepest drilling?

○ A 12 km drill hole reaches only $\dfrac{12}{6371} \times 100\% = 0.19\%$ (to 2 significant figures) of the distance to the centre of the Earth. (Box 2.4 in Block 1 deals with calculating percentages.)

So samples from drill holes are very limited in what they can tell us about the Earth's interior — drilling can only be used to investigate the rocks close to the surface. All the other techniques that can be used to investigate the interior of the Earth are *indirect* techniques, which use observations or measurements made at the surface to interpret what is inside the Earth.

○ Imagine that you were given a parcel, and want to find out what is inside the parcel without actually opening it. What might you do?

○ One of the simplest investigations would be to weigh the parcel, which would tell you whether the object inside was heavy or light, whether it had high or low density.

A similar investigation can be made for the Earth. Is the overall density of the Earth similar to the density of the rocks at the surface of the Earth? If it is not, this is an indication that the interior of the Earth is different from the surface. The overall (in scientific terms, the *mean*) density of the Earth was calculated in Section 5.2.1 (Question 5.3) as $5.52 \times 10^3 \, \text{kg m}^{-3}$. How does this mean density compare with the density of surface rocks? Ocean floor rocks have a density of around $3.0 \times 10^3 \, \text{kg m}^{-3}$

and the density of continental rocks is around $2.8 \times 10^3\,\text{kg m}^{-3}$ (Section 6.3), so the mean density of the Earth is almost twice the density of the surface rocks. An initial interpretation of this difference is that the interior of the Earth cannot be the same as the surface rocks, but before going any further with this interpretation we have to consider what the density of surface rocks would be if they were under the high pressure conditions inside the Earth. The pressure at the centre of the Earth is over a million times that at the surface, for example. Results from high-pressure experiments in the laboratory on surface rocks indicate that their density does increase at high pressures, but the increase is not sufficient to produce the calculated mean density of the Earth. So the initial interpretation is still correct: the interior of the Earth must be made of materials that are of higher density than the surface rocks.

But how do we find out what these materials might be? One useful clue comes from volcanoes that have erupted magma containing exotic lumps of green rock brought up from inside the Earth (Figure 10.1). These lumps are crystalline rocks called *peridotite* ('per-id-oh-tight'; they contain the olive-green mineral olivine, which is an impure variety of the gemstone peridot, hence the name peridotite). Peridotite is somewhat denser ($3.3 \times 10^3\,\text{kg m}^{-3}$) than the rocks normally found at the Earth's surface. Although peridotite is not dense enough to account for the higher mean density of the Earth, at least part of the Earth's interior must be made of peridotite.

Figure 10.1 Fragments of green peridotite up to 10 cm in size, surrounded by basalt. The peridotite was carried to the surface by a volcanic eruption of basalt on Lanzarote (Canary Islands) which lasted from 1730 to 1736.

Activity 10.1 *Summarizing different lines of evidence about the interior of the Earth*

Summarize, in one sentence for each, the main conclusions about the interior of the Earth that can be obtained from drilling, density measurements, and the occurrence of peridotite at the Earth's surface. ◄

10.2 The seismic structure of the Earth

Drilling, density measurements and the occurrence of peridotite provide useful information about the interior of the Earth, but the information is not very specific. What would also be useful is a technique that makes it possible to look inside the Earth in the way that X-rays make it possible to see inside the human body. X-rays cannot penetrate significantly into rock, so cannot be used to look inside the Earth, but there are other waves that do penetrate into the Earth, and that can be used to investigate it. These are **seismic waves**, the vibrations generated by earthquakes. The use of seismic waves is the most important technique for investigating the interior of the Earth, and because of this we will spend some time on the technique itself, as well as on discussing the results obtained.

10.2.1 Seismic waves

There are two main types of seismic waves — body waves and surface waves. **Body waves** are seismic waves that travel *within* the body of the Earth, spreading out from an earthquake focus in all directions, like sound waves in air. **Surface waves** are seismic waves that travel at and near the Earth's surface, like ripples spreading out from where a stone was thrown into a pond (Block 2, Figure 5.2). Surface waves usually shake the ground surface more than body waves, and are the most destructive waves in an earthquake. Body waves, however, are more useful than surface waves for investigating the Earth's interior because they travel within the Earth. Before we use seismic waves to investigate inside the Earth, it is necessary to find out a bit more about them, and this is done in Activity 10.2.

Activity 10.2 Investigating seismic waves

You should now study 'Seismic waves', the first part of the CD-ROM activity 'Journey to the centre of the Earth'. This activity will develop your understanding of the differences and similarities between the different types of seismic waves. ◀

10.2.2 The crust

So how are seismic waves used to investigate the Earth's interior? First of all, they must be recorded at the Earth's surface by a seismometer after they have travelled through the Earth. A seismometer consists of a heavy object that is suspended from a spring (Figure 10.2). The frame of the seismometer is attached firmly to solid rock. When a seismic wave moves the ground, the inertia of the suspended object makes it stay relatively still, whereas the frame moves with the ground. The relative motion between the object and the moving frame is traced by a pen, fixed to the object, onto a chart that moves with the ground, and is also recorded electronically. The paper record of ground motion with time is called a **seismogram** (Figure 10.3).

Figure 10.2 How a seismometer works. (a) A heavy object is suspended by a spring from a frame (attached to the ground). (b) When the ground moves upwards, the inertia of the object makes it stay relatively still and the attached pen moves down on the chart, which moves with the ground. (c) As the ground moves downwards the pen moves up on the chart. This seismometer measures vertical ground motion: a slightly different supporting system can be used to measure horizontal motion.

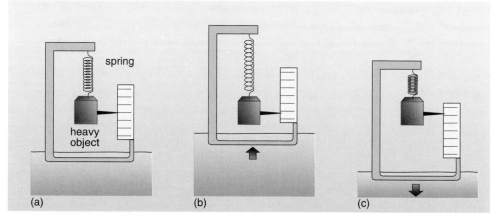

Figure 10.3 A seismogram. Time elapsed increases from left to right. The first arrival of each type of seismic wave is marked.

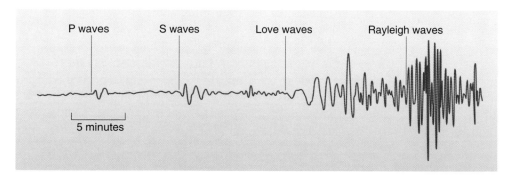

Before the seismic waves arrive at the seismometer, the ground is still, and the seismogram trace shows little or no motion (the far left-hand side of Figure 10.3). P waves travel faster than the other types of seismic waves, so arrive earliest at the seismometer. S waves arrive next (about 8 minutes later on this seismogram) and surface waves arrive last of all.

⬤ Which waves produce the largest ground motion?

◯ The Rayleigh waves. The ground motion caused by the Rayleigh waves is about 6 times the ground motion caused by S waves and about 11 times more than the P-wave ground motion.

⬤ Which of the waves would be used to calculate the Richter magnitude of the earthquake?

◯ The wave producing the largest ground motion (Section 7.4), which is the Rayleigh wave.

Question 10.1   Mark on the seismogram in Figure 10.4 the points where the P waves, S waves, Love waves and Rayleigh waves first arrive. ◀

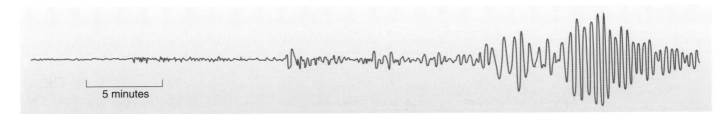

5 minutes

So now we can pick out on a seismogram the times that seismic waves from an earthquake arrive at a seismometer. However, a seismogram does not tell us when the earthquake *occurred*; it only records when the seismic waves *reached the seismometer*. Nevertheless, it is possible to use a number of seismograms, recorded at different locations, to find both when and where an earthquake occurred. (We will not explain here how this is done, as it is not necessary for our aim of investigating inside the Earth.)

Figure 10.4   Seismogram from an earthquake near Japan recorded at Hobart, Tasmania, in 1958. Time increases from left to right.

Armed with this information, it is then possible to work out the time taken for a seismic wave to travel from the earthquake focus to a seismometer. This is called the travel time. The travel times for seismic waves to reach seismometers at different distances from the epicentre can be used to calculate the speeds of the seismic waves, and these speeds turn out to be very informative. This is because the speeds of seismic waves depend on the type of material the waves pass through on their journey through the Earth. If we plot a graph of the travel times for one type of wave (let's start with a P wave) arriving at a number of seismometers up to a few hundred kilometres from a shallow-focus earthquake (Figure 10.5) against distance of the seismometer from the epicentre, we get a number of points that can be joined into a straight-line graph (Figure 10.6). We can use this graph to calculate the mean P-wave speed in the parts of the Earth that the waves have travelled through. This involves measuring the slope, or gradient of the line (see Box 10.1, *The gradient of a straight-line graph*).

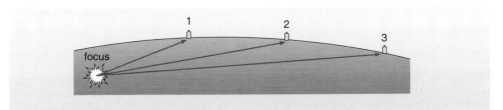

Figure 10.5   The paths of P waves from a shallow-focus earthquake to seismometers (1, 2 and 3) up to a few hundred kilometres away.

Figure 10.6 A travel time–distance graph for P waves at distances up to a few hundred kilometres from a shallow earthquake. Points 1, 2 and 3 correspond to the seismometers in Figure 10.5.

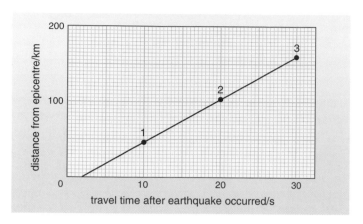

Box 10.1 The gradient of a straight-line graph

In everyday speech, the **gradient**, or slope, of a road is the amount the road goes up (or down) in a set distance. For example the gradient of a road might be signposted with a sign saying 'gradient 1 in 10', meaning that a change of 1 m in height occurs for every 10 m of horizontal distance. This definition is equally appropriate to describing the gradient of a straight line on a graph where we are interested in how quickly the quantity (in mathematical terms this is called the *variable*) plotted on the vertical axis changes for a given change in the value of the variable plotted on the horizontal axis (Figure 10.7).

The gradient of a straight line is therefore defined as:

$$\text{gradient} = \frac{\text{change in vertical value}}{\text{change in horizontal value}} \quad (10.1)$$

A useful way to remember this is to think of it as

$$\text{gradient} = \frac{\text{rise}}{\text{run}}$$

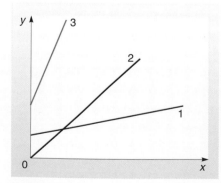

Figure 10.7 A graph of three lines with different gradients.

○ Which of the lines in Figure 10.7 has the largest gradient and which of the lines has the smallest gradient?

○ Line 3 has the largest gradient — this is the steepest slope. Line 1 has the smallest gradient — it has the smallest change in the vertical direction for any particular change in the horizontal direction.

Recall, from Section 4.1.3, that you worked out the acceleration of a car from a graph showing the change in its speed (i.e. a change in vertical position on the graph) against time (i.e. a change in horizontal position). This, as you can now see, was another example of interpreting the gradient of a straight line on a graph.

To work out the gradient of a straight line on a graph, the procedure is as follows. Let's refer to two points on the line we are interested in as P and Q (Figure 10.8). Now any point on a graph can be specified by its *coordinates*, the values of the point plotted on the horizontal axis (called the x axis) and on the vertical axis (called the y axis). The coordinates of point P are (x_1, y_1) and the coordinates of point Q are (x_2, y_2). Note that the coordinates are written in brackets, separated by a comma, and with the x, or horizontal, coordinate before the y, or vertical, coordinate. In moving from P to Q, when the value of x changes from x_1 to x_2, the value of y changes from y_1 to y_2. The gradient of the line joining them is defined, therefore, as:

$$\text{gradient} = \frac{\text{change in value of } y}{\text{change in value of } x} \quad (10.2)$$

The change in y is $y_2 - y_1$ and the change in x is $x_2 - x_1$, so

$$\text{gradient} = \frac{y_2 - y_1}{x_2 - x_1} \qquad (10.3)$$

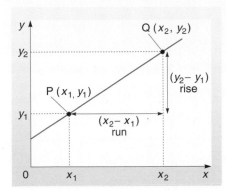

Figure 10.8 The gradient of the line joining the two points P and Q.

Note that P and Q can be any points on the line. To increase the precision of the calculation, they should be quite well separated.

To work out the gradient, the numerical values of x_1, x_2, y_1 and y_2 are substituted into this equation. For example, if the coordinates of P were $x_1 = 10.4$ s, $y_1 = 51.7$ km, and the coordinates of Q were $x_2 = 33.1$ s, $y_2 = 99.8$ km, these values would be used in Equation 10.3:

$$\text{gradient} = \frac{y_2 - y_1}{x_2 - x_1} \qquad (10.3)$$

$$= \frac{(99.8 - 51.7)\,\text{km}}{(33.1 - 10.4)\,\text{s}}$$

$$= \frac{48.1\,\text{km}}{22.7\,\text{s}}$$

$$= 2.12\,\text{km s}^{-1} \text{ (to 3 significant figures)}$$

In the special case of a straight line that intersects the origin (the origin has the coordinates (0,0); line 2 in Figure 10.7 would be such a line), the gradient is still defined by these equations, but the task of calculating the gradient can be simplified by choosing point P to be the origin (so $x_1 = 0$ and $y_1 = 0$). In this case:

$$\text{gradient} = \frac{y_2 - 0}{x_2 - 0}$$

so,

$$\text{gradient} = \frac{y_2}{x_2} \qquad (10.4)$$

SGSG Maths Help Section 10 also discusses how to measure gradients of graphs.

What is the gradient of the line in Figure 10.6? The line does not pass through the origin, so we have to use Equation 10.3. For the greatest precision in the calculation, it is useful to choose $(x_2 - x_1)$ to be as large as possible, for example $x_1 = 2$ s, $x_2 = 30$ s.

○ What are the values of y_1 and y_2 in Figure 10.6 corresponding to $x_1 = 2$ s and $x_2 = 30$ s?

○ The values are $y_1 = 0$ km and $y_2 = 160$ km.

$$\text{Gradient} = \frac{y_2 - y_1}{x_2 - x_1} \qquad (10.3)$$

$$= \frac{(160 - 0)\,\text{km}}{(30 - 2)\,\text{s}}$$

$$= \frac{160\,\text{km}}{28\,\text{s}}$$

$$= 5.7\,\text{km s}^{-1} \text{ (to 2 significant figures)}$$

The gradient has the unit of km s^{-1}, which is a unit of speed. We have divided distance (on the vertical axis) by time (on the horizontal axis). From Equation 3.1 (Section 3.3), this is speed:

$$\text{speed} = \frac{\text{distance travelled}}{\text{time taken}}$$

So the gradient of the graph in Figure 10.6 is the mean P-wave speed of the seismic waves along the paths through the Earth in Figure 10.5.

Figure 10.6 has the travel time plotted on the horizontal axis and the distance plotted on the vertical axis. This was done because then the gradient is the speed of the seismic waves. However when scientists draw graphs, they follow the convention of plotting the variable that is under the control of the investigator, called the *independent variable*, on the *x* axis, and the variable that depends on this, called the *dependent variable*, on the *y* axis. Thus, travel time–distance graphs are normally plotted, as shown in Figure 10.9, with distance on the *x* axis, as it is the independent variable (a seismometer distance), and travel time on the *y* axis, as it is the dependent variable (the measured time at a seismometer).

Figure 10.9 This is a travel time–distance graph (usually just called a travel time graph) for P waves at distances up to a few hundred kilometres from an earthquake. The graph is plotted according to scientific convention, with time on the vertical *y* axis and distance on the horizontal *x* axis. The data are the same as in Figure 10.6 and the points 1, 2 and 3 correspond to the seismometers in Figure 10.5.

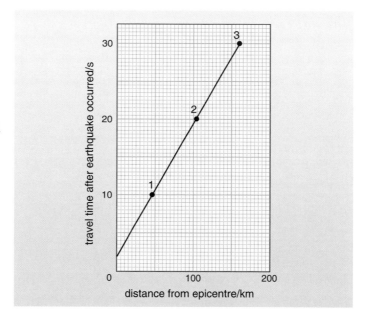

How can wave speed be calculated from the travel time graph in Figure 10.9?

First we need to calculate the gradient:

$$\text{gradient} = \frac{28\,\text{s}}{160\,\text{km}} \quad \text{or } 0.175\,\text{s km}^{-1}$$

The unit 's km^{-1}' is the *inverse* of the unit for speed (km s^{-1}); in other words:

$$\frac{1}{\text{km s}^{-1}} = \text{s km}^{-1}.$$

To get the speed value from the gradient on a travel time graph, we therefore have to invert it, which means 'turning the value upside down':

$$\text{speed} = \frac{1}{\text{gradient}}$$

$$= \frac{1}{0.175\,\text{s}\,\text{km}^{-1}}$$

$$= 5.7\,\text{km}\,\text{s}^{-1}\text{ (to 2 significant figures)}$$

As would be expected, this value of speed is the same as that calculated using Figure 10.6. So speed on a travel time graph is the *inverse* of the gradient (1/gradient). All seismic travel time graphs used subsequently in this section will have distance on the *x* axis, so remember that:

$$\text{speed} = \frac{1}{\text{gradient}}$$

Now that you know how to determine seismic wave speeds from travel time graphs, you can use them to investigate the structure of the Earth.

Activity 10.3   Travel time graphs

In this CD-ROM activity you will use travel time graphs to measure the P-wave speed in the upper layer of the Earth, and determine the depth of this layer. ◄

Your investigation of the Earth's structure in Activity 10.3 revealed a change in the properties of the Earth, at a boundary called the **Mohorovičić discontinuity**, or **Moho**. This is a *global* seismic discontinuity, existing all around the Earth. The layer above this discontinuity is the Earth's **crust** and the region below it is the **mantle**. The discontinuity occurs at about 7 km below the ocean floor. Beneath continents its depth is very variable, from 20 km to 80 km, averaging 35 km, and it is deepest below mountain belts and plateau regions (Figure 10.10). You should remember from Section 6.3 that the division between oceanic and continental *crust* is not the same as the coastline; it occurs offshore, generally beneath the continental rise (see the hypsometric plot in Figure 6.8).

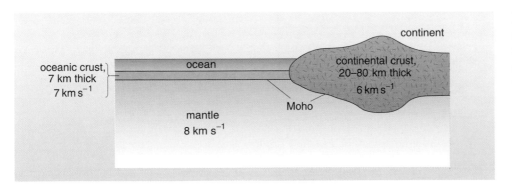

Figure 10.10   Seismic structure of the oceanic and continental crust and mantle. The seismic wave speeds shown are the mean P-wave speeds, to 1 significant figure.

Activity 10.4   Summarizing information about the crust in a table

This activity requires you to produce a summary of information about the crust in the form of a table. ◄

10.2.3 The mantle and core

To investigate the mantle, we need to look deeper into the Earth, using the travel times from seismometers at greater distances from the epicentre, thousands of kilometres instead of the hundreds of kilometres that we used to investigate the crust and Moho.

◯ What is the main difference between the travel time graph to 10^4 km (Figure 10.11) and the travel time graph to 200 km (Figure 10.9)?

◯ The graph to distances of 10^4 km is a *curve*, whereas the graph to 200 km is a straight line.

Figure 10.11 Travel time graph for earthquake P waves at distances up to 10^4 km from the epicentre. These are the times for the first P waves to arrive: other P waves arrive later. The label 'distance/10^3 km' means that each value on this axis should be multiplied by 10^3 km to obtain the actual distance in kilometres. The two boxes show enlargements of parts of the graph at distances of 2×10^3 km and 8×10^3 km; they show that for small distance intervals the graph is approximately a straight line. The 'epicentral angle' scale will be explained later.

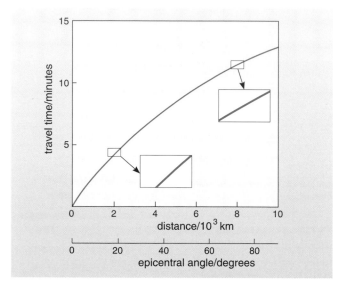

If the data from the 200 km travel time graph (Figure 10.9) were plotted on this graph, they would occupy just a small part of the line in the bottom left-hand corner of the graph. This small part of the curve will appear as an approximately straight line when enlarged — hence Figure 10.9 is a straight line travel time graph.

There are a number of reasons for the curved shape of the travel time graph.

1   The wave speed changes with depth.
2   The wave paths change by refraction due to encountering materials with different wave speeds.
3   The Earth's spherical shape affects travel times at greater distances.

◯ Does the gradient of the graph in Figure 10.11 increase or decrease with increasing distance? (Look at the two box enlargements.)

◯ It decreases. The gradient at a distance of 8×10^3 km is smaller (i.e. the curve is less steep) than the gradient at 2×10^3 km.

As the gradient of the travel time graph decreases with distance of the seismometer from the earthquake, this suggests that the P-wave speed *increases* with distance (remember that speed = 1/gradient). Waves that have travelled greater distances have usually travelled deeper into the Earth, so this suggests that P-wave speed generally *increases* with depth inside the Earth.

An alternative measure of the distance of a seismometer from an earthquake epicentre is the *epicentral angle*, the angle between radii from the centre of the Earth to the epicentre and to the seismometer (Figure 10.12). The maximum epicentral angle is 180°, for a seismic wave that has travelled right through the centre of the Earth. Epicentral angle, instead of distance around the Earth's surface, is usually plotted on the x axis of travel time graphs.

Figure 10.12 The distance between an earthquake epicentre and a seismometer can be represented by the epicentral angle. The locations of seismometers at epicentral angles of 80° and 150° are indicated.

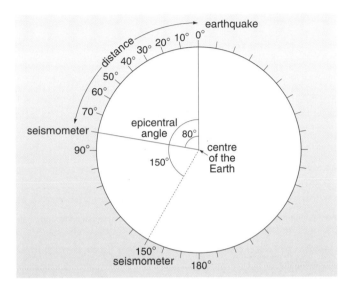

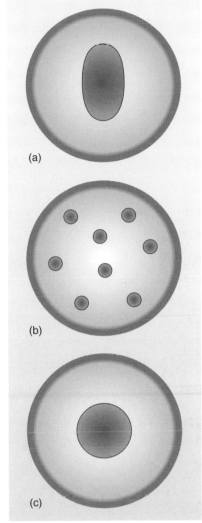

The travel time graph in Figure 10.11 is the same for *all* earthquakes (after correction for different focal depths), wherever the earthquake takes place, and wherever the seismometers are distributed. This fact provides useful information about the interior of the Earth, because if the position of an earthquake makes no difference to travel times, then the Earth's interior structure must be radially symmetrical. This means that the seismic properties at all points at a given distance from the centre of the Earth are the same. In other words, the variations in seismic properties are *concentrically arranged*.

○ Which of the models (a)–(c) in Figure 10.13 satisfies the concentric criterion?

○ Model (c). Models (a) and (b) are not concentric about the Earth's centre. These are therefore not possible models for the Earth's interior, since they are not consistent with seismic observations.

Figure 10.13 Hypothetical models of the Earth's interior seismic structure. The red areas have higher seismic wave speeds than the yellow areas.

Activity 10.5 Down to the centre

In this CD-ROM activity you will use travel time graphs to investigate deeper inside the Earth. ◄

Travel time graphs for the whole Earth, shown in Activity 10.5 and Figure 10.14, provide additional clues to the Earth's structure. From them we can deduce that the mantle is formed of peridotite, and that there is a liquid outer **core** about 2 900 km below the surface. You have therefore now located two major seismic discontinuities within the Earth, the Moho and the mantle–core boundary. There is one more, the outer core–inner core boundary. The study of seismic waves indicates that the inner core (unlike the outer core) is solid.

Figure 10.14 P-wave and S-wave travel time graphs for the whole Earth. There is a P-wave shadow zone from epicentral angles of 105° to 143°, and an S-wave shadow zone from 105° to 180°.

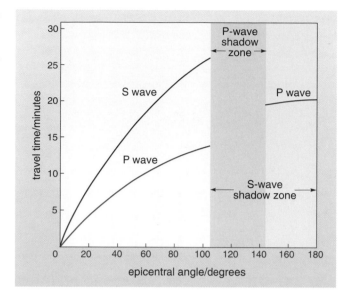

From travel time graphs like Figure 10.14, Earth scientists have developed models for the way in which seismic wave speed and density vary with depth in the Earth, and Figure 10.15 summarizes the results. Spend a few minutes studying the caption and interpreting the information in this complicated graph before answering the questions that follow.

Figure 10.15 The variation of wave speed (left vertical axis) and density (right vertical axis) with depth inside the Earth. The graph has two vertical axes, for wave speed and density, so that the changes in wave speed and density can be compared. The dark blue line is P-wave speed, the red line is S-wave speed and the turquoise blue line is density. S waves cannot travel in the liquid outer core, but can exist in the inner core, since part of the P waves can transform into S waves at the outer core–inner core boundary.

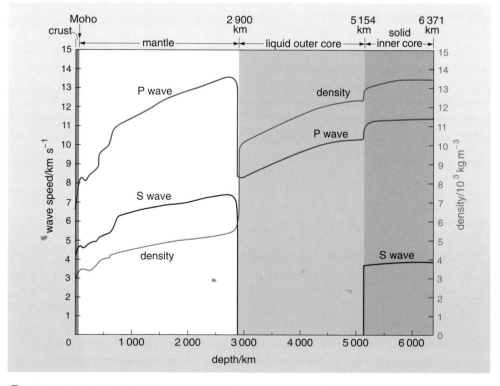

⬤ What is the depth of the outer core–inner core boundary?

◯ 5 154 km. (At this depth there are changes in both P-wave speed and S-wave speed.)

○ What happens to the P-wave speed at the mantle–core boundary, and at the outer core–inner core boundary?

○ The P-wave speed decreases significantly at the mantle–core boundary, and increases slightly at the outer core–inner core boundary.

10.3 Density, magnetism and meteorites

In this section we will have a brief look at other observations that can be used to provide information about the Earth's interior. Figure 10.15 summarizes how density varies with depth in the Earth. In Section 10.1 we noted that the mean density of the Earth is $5.52 \times 10^3 \, \text{kg m}^{-3}$. Various techniques indicate that the density of the core is greater than this, between $1.00 \times 10^4 \, \text{kg m}^{-3}$ and $1.36 \times 10^4 \, \text{kg m}^{-3}$, with a large difference in density between the mantle and the core; the core is over twice as dense as the mantle (Figure 10.15). This suggests that the core also has a very different composition from that of the mantle.

The Earth's magnetism (which causes a compass needle to point towards the North Pole) can also provide information about the interior of the Earth. Current theories for the origin of the Earth's magnetism (which we shall not investigate here) suggest that the Earth has a liquid outer core that has a metallic composition.

Additional evidence for the interior composition of the Earth comes from a source you might not have expected: space. More than a million kilograms of extraterrestrial rock fall towards the Earth from space each year. As discussed in Section 5.3, many of these vaporize completely as they pass through the atmosphere as meteors, but some do survive to reach the Earth's surface, and are then called **meteorites**. Most meteorites come from the region of the Solar System between the orbits of Mars and Jupiter, the location of the minor planets (the asteroids), although there are also a few that were once part of the Moon, Mars or comets. Meteorites are composed of peridotite and an iron–nickel metal (with typically 5–25% of nickel). Some are composed mainly of peridotite (called stony meteorites) and others are mainly iron–nickel (called iron meteorites). Because some meteorites come from the breakup of a terrestrial minor planet, they allow us to study material from *inside* an Earth-like planet. Their compositions indicate that peridotite and iron–nickel metal are important parts of terrestrial planets.

We are now in a position to draw together all these lines of evidence for the composition of the Earth, in order to produce a model of the Earth's interior that is consistent with each bit of evidence (Figure 10.16). The upper part of the mantle is similar to the specimens of peridotite we see at the Earth's surface, but deeper in the mantle there is a higher-density form of peridotite. The predominant element in the core is iron; we are fairly certain of that, but the more detailed composition is much less certain. The solid inner core may be pure iron, or it may be iron with a small amount of nickel. The liquid outer core is mainly iron, with around 10% of a lighter element, probably either oxygen or sulfur.

Figure 10.16   A model for the structure and composition of the Earth.

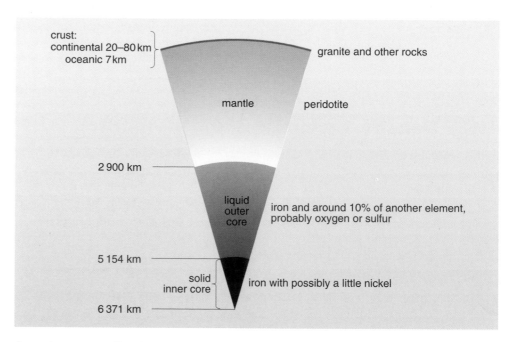

Question 10.2   Consider the following statements on Earth structure and composition and, for each, list which of the lines of evidence (seismic, density, magnetism and meteorites) would be used to make or support the statement. A statement may be based on more than one line of evidence.

(a)   The mantle–core boundary is at a depth of 2 900 km.

(b)   The outer core is liquid.   ◀

10.4   Summary of Section 10

There are a number of lines of evidence that are used to develop a model of the Earth's interior: drilling, density, seismic waves, magnetism and meteorites.

Drilling has found rocks similar to those at the surface down to a depth of 12 km.

The mean density of the Earth is about twice the density of crustal rocks, which indicates that part (at least) of the Earth at depth must be much denser than the crust.

There are major discontinuities in seismic wave speeds with depth in the Earth. The first of these is at a depth that varies between 7 and 80 km. This discontinuity is called the Mohorovičić discontinuity (the Moho). The surface layer of the Earth above it is called the crust, and the layer below it is called the mantle. The next seismic discontinuity is at 2 900 km, which is the boundary between the mantle and the core of the Earth. There is also an outer core–inner core seismic discontinuity. The outer core is in a liquid state, whereas the inner core is solid.

These seismic discontinuities are accompanied by major changes in density. The composition of meteorites suggests that part of the Earth's interior may be formed of peridotite, and that other parts are an iron–nickel alloy. The Earth's magnetism suggests that the liquid outer core is metallic.

Figure 10.16 is a model for the structure and composition of the Earth's interior that is consistent with these lines of evidence.

The gradient of a straight line on a graph of y plotted against x is defined as:

$$\text{gradient} = \frac{\text{change in value of } y}{\text{change in value of } x} = \frac{\text{rise}}{\text{run}}$$

Activity 10.6 Reviewing your study so far

You are now a little over halfway through Block 3. This activity allows you to review your progress against the study plan you made at the start of the block (Activity 1.1), and to reflect on the way you have used the different components in the block. The activity includes a short video on 'keeping up'. ◀

11 Continental drift: a theory for the Earth?

So far you have learnt numerous facts about the Earth, based on direct visual observations and on measurements recorded by instruments such as seismometers (Sections 6–10). You have learnt about the land surface, the ocean floor, the moving parts of the Earth, and the interior structure of the planet as a whole — but how can we explain such observations? Predicting earthquakes and volcanic eruptions, or finding new mineral and oil deposits, requires not just knowing that such things exist, but having some sort of understanding about why they occur, and why they occur in particular places or at particular times.

Seeking explanations for natural phenomena is something that humans have attempted to do for thousands of years. For instance, the ancient Greeks believed that the glowing cinders ejected from the fiery summit of Mount Etna (Figure 8.1) were sparks flying from the underground workshops of the god of fire Hephaistos. Many other cultures in volcanically active regions across the world have likewise attributed volcanic eruptions and the accompanying earthquakes to the doings of awesome gods.

In modern times, Earth scientists have sought to find an all-encompassing theory to explain their observations of the Earth. Starting with a relatively small number of observations, individual scientists propose a preliminary explanation — a scientific hypothesis — to account for the observations. This is part of the scientific process by which a hypothesis is erected and tested against new observations (Block 1, Section 7.1). For a hypothesis to be useful it must, therefore, account for all the observations and allow us to make new predictions that can be tested. (You might reflect that although the Greeks' idea about Hephaistos and volcanoes explains observations of volcanic eruptions, it is hardly a testable scientific hypothesis.) A testable hypothesis may be proved wrong, in which case it has to be abandoned or at least modified so that new evidence can be taken into account. A hypothesis that has been rigorously tested, and that survives intact, becomes elevated to a scientific theory.

It would be an impressive achievement to devise a theory that explains all the observations and workings of the Earth's surface. Many have tried, and some have almost succeeded. Ultimately, the theory of plate tectonics emerged as the successful theory, but along the way the hypothesis of continental drift was put forward. This section gives you the opportunity to test this hypothesis — is it worthy of being a theory for the Earth?

11.1 Continental drift

You may have noticed that, on a map of the world, the Atlantic coastlines of western Africa and eastern South America have similar shapes. If you could remove the southern Atlantic Ocean they would fit together remarkably well. (The fit is even better if the true border between continental and oceanic crust — such as the edge of the continental rise at a depth of 1 km below sea-level — is used instead of the coastlines; see Section 6.3.) Such a similarity is not obviously matched by any other continents, so is this a coincidence, or might it be a clue to something else? In particular, it looks as if the two continents might once have been joined. Do you think this is possible?

If you do, then you are not the first person to think so. As long ago as 1620 the English philosopher Francis Bacon recognized the similarities of the continental outlines. In 1858 an American called Antonio Snider also recognized this fit. He interpreted it as a fissure in an unstable landmass that existed on the fifth day of the Biblical creation. He believed that on the sixth day this landmass split apart, when a build-up of internal pressure vented volcanic vapours through the fissure, and the waters of the oceans rolled over the continents in a great flood. Fifty years later, in 1907, W. H. Pickering, an American astronomer, suggested that the Atlantic Ocean was created when the two continents were torn apart by the separation of the Moon from the Pacific Ocean basin.

Interpretations such as these are not generally believed today. Yet, all three men made the same initial observation as you did. This demonstrates that good observations remain valid even though the original interpretations to explain them may have been rejected. The observation led Snider and Pickering to seek a cause, or an explanation for it. However, the cultural climate of their times strongly influenced their interpretations, and it is such influences that scientists try to avoid, by using the method of setting up and testing hypotheses. This is what the German meteorologist Alfred Wegener did in the 1910s and 1920s. In 1928, Wegener published the final edition of his book entitled *The Origin of Continents and Oceans*, in which he presented and discussed his hypothesis of the continents 'drifting' across the globe through time:

> The continents must have shifted. South America must have lain alongside Africa and formed a unified block which was split in two [which became] increasingly separated over a period of millions of years like pieces of a cracked ice floe in water.

He further proposed that all the continents had at one time been joined together as one large landmass (see Figure 11.1) — a supercontinent which he named Pangaea (pronounced 'pan-jee-ah', and meaning 'all land') — that had started to break apart about 165 Ma ago. Wegener was determined to substantiate his hypothesis of **continental drift** as far as possible with the evidence available at the time:

> It is only by combining the information furnished by all the Earth sciences that we can hope to determine 'truth' here, that is to say, to find the picture that sets out all the known facts in the best arrangement and that therefore has the highest degree of probability. Further, we have to be prepared always for the possibility that each new discovery, no matter which science furnishes it, may modify the conclusions we draw.

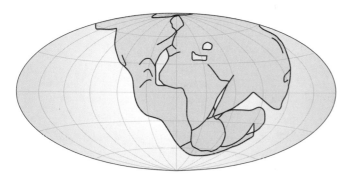

Figure 11.1   Wegener's map of the supercontinent Pangaea as he considered it to be about 300 Ma ago.

Drawing upon all the lines of evidence that the Earth sciences could offer, Wegener made a strong case for continental drift. But his hypothesis troubled many of his contemporary scientists, who subjected his evidence and arguments to intense scrutiny — the natural response of scientists to radical new ideas.

Just how good was the evidence for continental drift? This is a question you can answer, by examining three lines of evidence. The first two — fossils and ancient climates — were among the evidence presented by Wegener, whilst the third, palaeomagnetism[*] (from the Greek word *palaios* = 'old' plus magnetism), emerged later on. You will be asked to assess whether you think these lines of evidence support the hypothesis, and thereby start to draw your own scientific conclusions.

11.2   A first test of the hypothesis: fossils

Today, the plants and animals living on separate continents can be quite different. For instance, the marsupials such as kangaroos are almost exclusively restricted to Australia, and the armadillo is restricted to the Americas. This is because organisms are generally limited to colonizing the continents on which they originated because they cannot travel to distant landmasses across wide oceans. If a supercontinent such as Pangaea had existed, then animals and plant seeds would have been able to spread across vast areas of land. If these plants and animals were buried by sand or mud when they died, they would have been preserved as fossils where they fell. This means that, if the continents as we know them today really had been joined together in a supercontinent that then split apart, the fossils would be preserved on each continent. Therefore, one test of the continental drift hypothesis would be to look for fossils of similar types and ages on continents that are now far apart.

⬤ On which two continents that we have already mentioned would you expect to find similar fossils?

◯ Based on the outlines of Africa and South America, we proposed that these two continents were once joined together: this would make them ideal candidates for having similar fossils, and they are therefore the logical places to start looking.

So, let us look first at Africa and South America. Figure 11.2 shows the locations where fossils of a reptile called *Mesosaurus*[†] (pronounced 'Meezo-saurus') have been found in rocks about 260 Ma old. Fossils of this reptile occur in rocks of similar age in both Argentina and southern Africa. It is quite plausible, you might think, for the animal to have swum across the intervening ocean. Alternatively, it might have walked along a strip of land joining the two continents (like the land bridge joining the Americas today), that has since sunk below the sea. Such alternative hypotheses were among those put forward by Wegener's critics. However, *Mesosaurus* was only about 1 m long, and lived in brackish (slightly salty) water, so it is extremely unlikely to have been capable of crossing a large ocean such as the South Atlantic!

[*]The prefix *palaeo* is frequently used in the Earth sciences to indicate the study of an ancient part of a particular subject. You will encounter palaeoclimate, palaeolatitude, palaeontology (old life; i.e. the study of fossils), etc.

[†]Note that plants and animals are given scientific names in Latin. These are traditionally printed in text in *italics*, in order to distinguish them from informal names. When you are writing these names by hand, you should simply underline the name to make this distinction — e.g. <u>Mesosaurus</u> — rather than using italics.

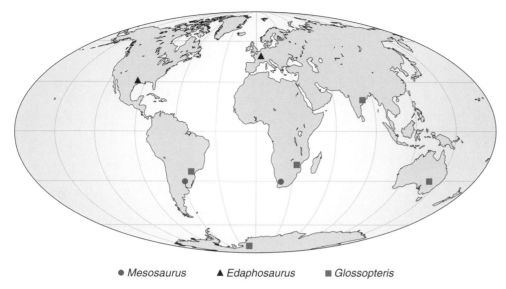

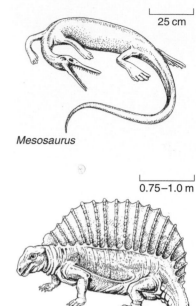

Mesosaurus

Edaphosaurus

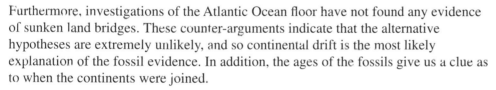

● *Mesosaurus*   ▲ *Edaphosaurus*   ■ *Glossopteris*

Figure 11.2   Present-day map of the world, showing the locations where three types of fossils have been found. The drawings in the margin indicate what the organisms are thought to have looked like. Although coloured in brown, the plant would have been green. The life colours of the two reptiles are unknown.

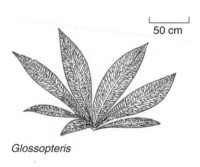

Glossopteris

Furthermore, investigations of the Atlantic Ocean floor have not found any evidence of sunken land bridges. These counter-arguments indicate that the alternative hypotheses are extremely unlikely, and so continental drift is the most likely explanation of the fossil evidence. In addition, the ages of the fossils give us a clue as to when the continents were joined.

Now consider some fossil finds on other continents. Looking again at Figure 11.2, you will see a second reptile called *Edaphosaurus* ('Edaffo-saurus') which had a characteristic tall fin or 'sail' on its back, and lived about 280 Ma ago. Fossils of this animal have been found on both sides of the Atlantic Ocean — except that this time they are much further north, on the continents of North America and Europe. Yet at the present day the plants and animals on these two continents are quite distinct. For instance, the closest relative of the European blackbird in America has a red breast and is called the American robin. The fossils of *Edaphosaurus* therefore suggest that Western Europe and North America were joined together around 280 Ma ago, in much the same way that Africa and South America were. So we now have evidence that suggests that South America and Africa, and North America and Europe were joined together 260 Ma and 280 Ma ago respectively.

Activity 11.1   Fossils and the continental jigsaw

This activity asks you to examine evidence from a third type of fossil to test the continental drift hypothesis. ◀

So, it would appear that we have good evidence that a number of continents, including Europe, North and South America, Antarctica, Australia and India were once joined, forming Wegener's supercontinent Pangaea. Because all these continents have since moved apart, we can also say that we have found good evidence in support of Wegener's continental drift hypothesis. Similar studies of other fossil occurrences have allowed Earth scientists to confirm these patterns but these details are beyond the scope of our study here.

11.3   A second test of the hypothesis: ancient climates

This section investigates the hypothesis that continents have drifted across the surface of the Earth by comparing the locations of different climates on the Earth today and in the past, using the geological record of ancient climates (or palaeoclimates). To see how this can be done, we will start by looking at where different climates are found on the modern Earth.

11.3.1   Modern climate belts and their sedimentary deposits

A wide range of climates exist on Earth today — such as hot and dry in the Sahara, or temperate and wet in Britain. Each climate is more or less restricted to a distinct range of latitudes. For instance, Figure 11.3 shows that regions with a hot dry desert climate are generally restricted to between 30° N and 30° S. Places with a hot and wet tropical climate are also found between these latitudes, but they are generally confined to a band between 20° N and 20° S. A third climate — that of the polar ice-caps — is found in the latitudes of 60° to 90° N and 60° to 90° S.

Each of the three climates identified in Figure 11.3 produces an environment that generates distinctive sedimentary deposits (Table 11.1). Arid desert environments can generate red sandstone from sand dunes like those in the Sahara desert. Tropical swamps, such as those found in the Amazon Basin, can eventually generate

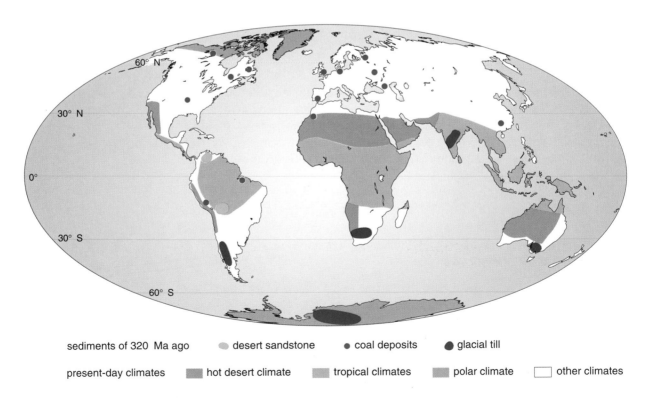

Figure 11.3   The distribution of three modern climate zones across the world, and the locations of desert sandstones, coal deposits and glacial tills that formed about 320 Ma ago.

accumulations of coal, as described in Block 2, Section 8.5.3. You are also familiar from Block 2, Section 3.1.1, with the third deposit — till — which is derived from erosion of surface rocks by ice sheets such as those found in the polar regions.

Table 11.1   Climates identified in Figure 11.3 and their corresponding environments, approximate latitude ranges, and the sediments they can produce.

Climate	Environment	Latitude range	Sediment
hot desert	hot and arid	30° N to 30° S	sandstone
tropical	hot and wet swamp	20° N to 20° S	coal
polar	cold ice sheets	60°–90° N and 60°–90° S	till

So, the climate of a region plays a crucial role in determining which type of sediment is formed there. Assuming that these sediments do not get eroded away, they form strata of sedimentary rock, which provide a geological record of the climate prevailing in a particular spot at a particular time. If the record of climate zones preserved in the sediments changes with time, it is logical to assume that either the global climate zones have changed or that each area under investigation has moved from one climate zone to another. It is hard to imagine how major changes in the pattern of global climate zones could happen, for example equatorial regions becoming very cold while polar regions become hot, so dramatic changes in climate, as indicated by particular types of sediments, could give evidence that continents have moved between different latitudes.

11.3.2   Patterns of past climates

Continental drift is proposed as a global process that occurs over long time-scales, and so we need to look at climate patterns over many millions of years. Let's consider what the distribution of climate-sensitive sediments that were deposited and preserved about 320 Ma ago can tell us. Figure 11.3 shows locations of desert sandstones, coals and till deposits of about this age from across the world.

⬤ After studying Figure 11.3 carefully, do you think that the climate-sensitive sediments of 320 Ma ago each occur in their appropriate present-day climate zone?

◯ Although a few do, most of the 320 Ma old sediments are not found in their appropriate present-day climate zones.

In fact, they appear to be distributed across the globe in quite a different pattern compared with the current climate patterns. The record of 320 Ma old glacial tills is not restricted to the normal latitude ranges of 60°–90° N and S; they also occur at lower latitudes in South America, Africa, India and Australia. This implies that these regions were, for some reason, subjected to much colder climates 320 Ma ago than they are today. The hot and humid conditions indicated by coal deposits mostly occur at much higher latitudes than one would expect from modern climate patterns. Most of the occurrences appear to be outside the tropics — in Europe, North Africa, North America and Russia. Only the desert deposits occur in their correct latitudinal range — between 30° N and 30° S — although in regions that have a tropical climate today. So, what has caused the patterns of climate to change radically since 320 Ma ago?

● Do you think this evidence can be explained by Wegener's continental drift hypothesis?

○ Yes. For instance, continental drift certainly could account for the evidence that some places that are now in tropical latitudes had a polar climate 320 Ma ago. The land where the 320 Ma old sediments accumulated has since moved to a location with a different climate.

Thus, South Africa must have moved northwards since 320 Ma ago. It had a starting position somewhere in the Antarctic polar region where the glacial tills were deposited around 320 Ma ago, and since then it has moved north to its current position, where desert sands are now being deposited on top of the 320 Ma old tills. Furthermore, the presence of numerous coalfields in Europe would suggest that Europe lay within about 20° of the Equator 320 Ma ago and has since moved to its present position in rather cooler latitudes. In order to make the visualization of these continental drift patterns easier we can re-arrange the continents into their 'pre-drift' configuration shown in Figure 11.4.

Figure 11.4 Locations of desert sandstone, coal and glacial till that formed 320 Ma ago shown on a map of the continents in their pre-drift configuration.

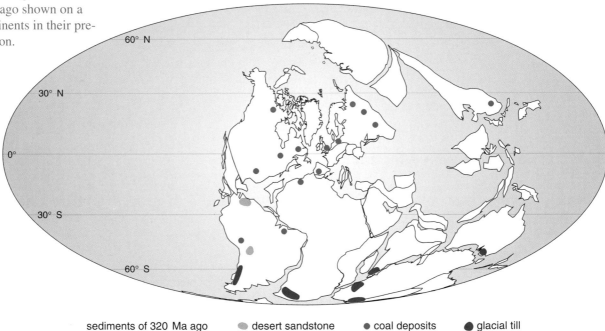

sediments of 320 Ma ago ● desert sandstone ● coal deposits ● glacial till

Question 11.1 Study Figure 11.4 carefully. Do the 320 Ma old climate-sensitive sediments fall into their correct climate zones? ◀

This re-arrangement into a pre-drift configuration has drawn many of the continents together into a large landmass. This is starting to look like Wegener's supercontinent, Pangaea. We are now getting some idea of when this supercontinent was in existence. We found fossil evidence for it at 260 Ma ago, and we now have climatological evidence to suggest that it was fairly well formed 60 Ma before that, by 320 Ma ago. In order to test the drift hypothesis further, and also to consider the break up of Pangaea, we turn, in the next section, to palaeomagnetism — a technique that was not available to Wegener.

11.4   A third test: the palaeomagnetic record

Wegener was keen to use every possible technique to test the continental drift hypothesis. Since his pioneering times, however, new technological and scientific discoveries have added to the range of tools that can be used to test continental drift. One such technique is **palaeomagnetism** — the study of the Earth's magnetism preserved in rocks at the time they were formed. This is particularly useful for studying continental drift because palaeomagnetic measurements of rocks can provide information about the latitude at which a particular rock formed. This relies on two key facts. First, the Earth's magnetism varies from place to place across the Earth, such that a compass needle that is free to move in any direction (both vertically and horizontally) comes to rest pointing into or away from the Earth at an angle that depends on latitude. Thus, a compass can actually be used to find not just the direction of North, but also the latitude. Second, many rocks contain magnetic, iron-rich minerals, like the aptly named magnetite, which behave as if they were miniature compasses that record the Earth's magnetism at the time and place the rock formed. These 'fossil compasses' can be read by going to a rock outcrop, collecting a sample, and making laboratory measurements of its magnetism to determine the latitude at which the rock formed; this is called its palaeolatitude. Unfortunately, the longitude at which the rock formed is not recorded by the magnetism in the rocks so an exact past position for that sample cannot be determined. Nevertheless, if the palaeolatitude of a rock in, say, Britain is different from the present latitude of the rock outcrop, then Britain must have moved over the Earth's surface since that rock formed. Let's use some real palaeomagnetic results to carry out another test of continental drift.

Activity 11.2   Fossil compasses in Africa and India

This activity uses palaeomagnetic results from Africa and India (Figure 11.5) to test the continental drift hypothesis. ◀

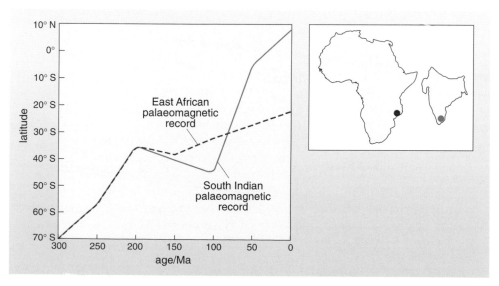

Figure 11.5   Graph showing palaeolatitudes of eastern Africa and the southern tip of India over the last 300 Ma. Note that time increases from left to right, along the horizontal axis, from 300 Ma ago to the present (an age of 0 Ma). The specific localities are indicated on the outlines of the two continents.

Although we now have three independent lines of evidence that support the continental drift hypothesis, we have not yet checked that they are consistent with each other. Let's examine the evidence from Africa. From the palaeoclimatic evidence we know that southern Africa was accumulating glacial tills around 320 Ma ago. This corresponds well with the palaeomagnetic evidence which indicates a very southerly palaeolatitude of 70° S around 300 Ma ago. From the fossil evidence we know that southern Africa and India had similar land plants at 260 Ma ago, suggesting that the two landmasses were once much closer together. This is also supported by their coincident 'travel paths', deduced from their palaeolatitudes, between 300 Ma and 200 Ma ago. Since the two continents were at the same latitudes they could feasibly have supported similar plants.

So, for the two time periods we have examined — 260–280 Ma ago and 320 Ma ago — there is evidence of continents having been in very different positions to those of today. All three strands of evidence, from fossils to ancient climates to palaeo-magnetism, suggest that some continents, such as Africa and India, were joined throughout this time. We also found that Antarctica, South America and Australia were probably joined to these two continents between 260 and 280 Ma ago. Thus, the evidence we have looked at indicates that Wegener's supercontinent Pangaea comprised all these continents. We know that the modern configuration of the continents is different, so movement — i.e. continental drift — must have occurred. The divergence of India's and Africa's palaeolatitude paths from approximately 170 Ma ago (Figure 11.5) hints at when the break-up of this supercontinent occurred and fits well with Wegener's proposed break-up age of 165 Ma.

11.5 From hypothesis to theory

We have reviewed three tests of the continental drift hypothesis and found that they support the hypothesis. They supplied evidence for the past existence of the supercontinent Pangaea and produced information and patterns that only made sense if some of the continents were arranged into groupings different from those of the present day. The inescapable conclusion is that all the continents have drifted across the planet through geological time. Still more tests of the hypothesis have been carried out by many Earth scientists, including Wegener himself, and his hypothesis remains unscathed.

So, although radical in his day, Wegener's hypothesis has stood the test of further observations and can be elevated to a theory. The scientific community now accepts that the continents 'drift' over the Earth, and that the familiar position of the continents shown on the poster map is just a snapshot from a continually-running movie of continents in motion. But, as many of Wegener's detractors were quick to point out, there is no immediately obvious driving mechanism for continental drift, and the theory says nothing about how the ocean basins and the ocean floor behave. Even Wegener admitted that these gaps in the continental drift theory were problematical, although he believed that one day they would be resolved. So, as a theory for the Earth (rather than just for the continents) continental drift is not completely convincing, although it would be churlish to deny Wegener's remarkable insight. The grander theory of plate tectonics was to emerge later in the 20th century, on the heels of another theory — that of sea-floor spreading, which is explained in Section 12.

11.6 Summary of Section 11

The theory of continental drift is based on evidence for the hypothesis, originally put forward by Alfred Wegener, that continental landmasses have moved across the surface of the Earth through time.

250 Ma ago, the continents as we know them today were arranged next to each other, constituting a super-continent called Pangaea. The subsequent break-up of Pangaea, and the drifting apart of the separated continental blocks, can be recognized from several lines of evidence, including the following:

- The coastlines of certain continents fit together. This can be accounted for by the break-up of a super-continent.

- Fossils of land animals and plants are found, in rocks of the same age, on continents that are now widely separated. This can be accounted for if the organisms lived on one large continent which split apart after the organisms had died and become fossilized.

- Certain sedimentary rocks, such as desert sandstone, coal and till, form only under particular climatic conditions and hence, by analogy with the global distribution of climate belts, in particular ranges of latitude. However, these rocks can be found in places outside the latitudinal ranges required for them to form. This can be accounted for if the rocks formed in the appropriate latitudes but have since drifted to other latitudes.

- Palaeomagnetic evidence of palaeolatitudes shows that continents have changed latitude over time. This is also accounted for by continental drift.

12 Sea-floor spreading

In Section 11 you investigated several lines of evidence that were best explained by the continents having 'drifted' across the surface of the Earth. We also noted that the continental drift theory ignores the ocean basins and, since the ocean basins account for the major part of the Earth's surface, it is fair to say that any theory for the Earth that ignores the oceans cannot be complete. In this section we address the origin of the ocean basins. This is easier said than done because the ocean floor is much less accessible than the continents, making it difficult to observe. For example, at the mean ocean depth of 3 700 m the pressure is 370 times as great as atmospheric pressure, and the temperature is around 0 to 3 °C. No light penetrates to this inhospitable place. It is a measure of this inaccessibility that it was only in the late 19th century that the Mid-Atlantic Ridge, one of the Earth's greatest mountain ranges and clearly visible on the poster map, was discovered by accident during the laying of trans-Atlantic telephone cables. Some of the mid-ocean ridges in the Pacific Ocean were not discovered until the 1950s. Yet, the mid-ocean ridges are arguably the most dramatic feature of the Earth's solid surface, so how did they form? One approach is to go there to see what they are like.

12.1 Exploring a mid-ocean ridge

In the mid-20th century, knowledge of the mid-ocean ridges accumulated very slowly; shallow earthquakes were found to occur beneath ridge crests (Section 7) and volcanic eruptions of basalt lava were observed on islands such as Iceland that lie on mid-ocean ridges (Section 8). To get a much fuller picture of mid-ocean ridges required specialized submersible craft, and these were first developed in the late 1960s. A submersible can descend much deeper than submarines, and can take a small crew of scientists, crammed into a space no bigger than the cabin of a small motor car, to the ocean floor. Submersibles provided the ability to carry out 'fieldwork' on the ocean floor for the first time. The views of this hidden world amazed the intrepid submariners and gave a host of new observations that begged to be explained.

Activity 12.1   Exploring the Mid-Atlantic Ridge

In this CD-ROM activity, you make a voyage of discovery to part of the Mid-Atlantic Ridge. This 'virtual dive' allows you to explore the features found there, and to learn about the processes that produce them. ◀

12.2 Sea-floor spreading and the origin of ocean basins

The mid-ocean ridges are as active as any continental mountain range, and often more so, given the range of volcanic, biological and geological activity seen on dives to the Mid-Atlantic Ridge and other mid-ocean ridges. The oceanic crust is being pulled apart at mid-ocean ridges, creating faults and fissures, and at the same time it is growing by the addition of lavas that are erupted along the length of the ridge. In contrast, the abyssal plains (Section 6.2.2) are remarkably inactive; furthermore, they are covered in a deep layer of sediment which must have taken time to accumulate, indicating that these parts of the ocean floor are older than those at mid-ocean ridges.

These observations are best accounted for by the theory of **sea-floor spreading** (Figure 12.1), which states that the ocean floor on either side of a mid-ocean ridge is moving away from the ridge, allowing hot magma to be injected at the ridge, where it solidifies to form new ocean floor. This in turn gets split apart, becoming moved aside and replaced by younger volcanic ocean-floor rocks. After many, many repetitions of this process, the lavas that were originally erupted at the ridge crest become more and more distant from their birthplace and an ocean basin grows.

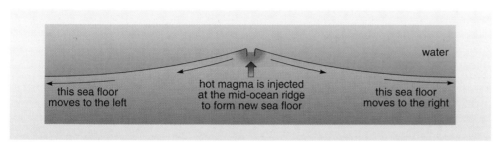

Figure 12.1 Sea-floor spreading accounts for the origin of the ocean floor.

Although the observations you made in Activity 12.1 are explained by the sea-floor spreading theory, the first convincing evidence for sea-floor spreading actually came from studies of the magnetic properties of the rocks making up the ocean floor. The convoluted tale of this discovery will be recounted later, but for now we can note that the magnetic results provided a great bonus — they allowed the speed, or rate, of sea-floor spreading to be measured relatively easily.

12.2.1 Rates of sea-floor spreading

In this section we investigate the rate, or speed, at which the Earth's surface is splitting apart by the action of sea-floor spreading, the so-called **sea-floor spreading rate**. The first step is to decide what to measure in order to work out the rate of spreading.

○ Which two variables should we measure in order to calculate the speed of something?

○ We need to measure the distance moved and the time taken (Section 3.3).

Let's consider an analogy of sea-floor spreading provided by two conveyor belts, arranged end to end but moving in opposite directions (Figure 12.2). In this analogy, two crates are placed onto the conveyors at the point where they diverge and are carried further and further apart as time goes on, just as the igneous rocks at a

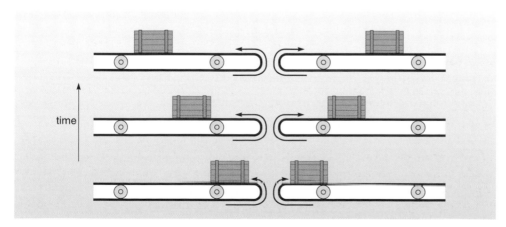

Figure 12.2 An analogy of sea-floor spreading given by two moving conveyor belts

mid-ocean ridge eventually become split apart and carried off in opposite directions by sea-floor spreading. The rate at which the two crates become separated is given by the distance separating them divided by the time elapsed since they were put onto the diverging conveyor belts. Thus, to find the rate at which the ocean floor spreads requires a way of labelling two points on the ocean floor that were once side by side at the ridge but are now some distance apart. We also need to know how long ago they were at the ridge. It turns out that these critical pieces of information are provided by invisible 'magnetic labels' on the ocean floor.

These invisible labels are held by the magnetic minerals within the rocks of the ocean floor, and they are read by a sensitive instrument known as a magnetometer, which is towed from a ship or plane. The magnetometer measures the Earth's magnetism, including a small contribution from the magnetism of the rocks beneath it. Small changes in the measurements distinguish between rocks that have different magnetic properties. For example, the results of a magnetic survey in the North Atlantic Ocean (Figure 12.3) show that there are areas where the magnetism is either stronger than usual (black areas) or weaker than usual (white areas). These **magnetic anomalies** are quite a surprise, given that the rocks on the ocean floor are monotonously composed of basalt with a thin covering of sediment. Equally impressive is the fact that the **marine magnetic anomalies** are arranged in bands, or stripes (albeit with ragged edges), several kilometres wide. These bands are sometimes known as magnetic stripes.

Figure 12.3 A map of magnetic anomalies southwest of Iceland shows a pattern of magnetic stripes. The Mid-Atlantic Ridge runs from northeast to southwest across the middle of the survey area.

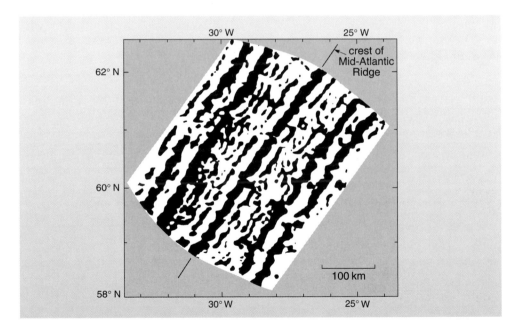

From Figure 12.3, can you see a relationship between the orientation of the magnetic stripes and the orientation of the crest of the mid-ocean ridge?

The magnetic stripes are parallel with the ridge crest.

What is the origin of these magnetic anomalies or stripes? To answer this question, we need to build on some of the information from previous sections about the Earth's magnetism and the magnetic properties of rocks. We saw in Sections 10 and 11 that the Earth has magnetism (generated by the liquid outer core) and that this varies with latitude. In fact the Earth has magnetic poles (rather like a bar magnet) that are in approximately the same positions as the geographic North and South Poles.

There is one further aspect of the Earth's magnetism about which you need to know. This concerns the Earth's magnetism in the distant past, and can be summed up by imagining that you embark on a voyage back in time holding a compass. Today, at the start of the voyage, the compass needle points roughly towards the North Pole. Travelling back through recorded history to 1 900 years ago, when the first compasses were invented in China, the same familiar condition applies. But, eight hundred thousand years ago, you'd find that the compass needle was pointing towards the South Pole! One million years ago the compass points to the North Pole again, and four million years ago to the South Pole. In fact, the palaeomagnetic record retained in rocks of different ages shows that the north and south magnetic poles have reversed at apparently random intervals of several million years or less throughout Earth history.

This means that the magnetism retained by a rock will have become established either at a time when the Earth's magnetism is as it is today, such that a compass needle points towards the North Pole (i.e. it will have **normal polarity**), or when the same compass would have pointed towards the South Pole (i.e. it will have **reversed polarity**). The switches between normal and reversed polarity are called **polarity reversals** and happen quickly. The polarity of the Earth's magnetism is recorded by the magnetic minerals in lava flows when they cool, so by measuring the polarity and age of a great many lava flows, mainly from the continents, it has been possible to establish the pattern of alternating periods of normal and reversed polarity over the last 600 Ma. This pattern and the dates of the polarity reversals define what is known as the **geomagnetic polarity time-scale**[*]; the most recent 4 Ma of the time-scale is shown in Figure 12.4.

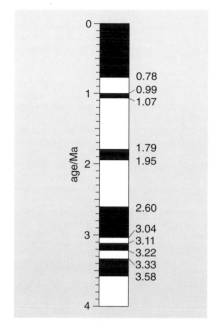

Figure 12.4 The geomagnetic polarity time-scale for the last 4 Ma. Black denotes normal polarity. White denotes reversed polarity.

Question 12.1 Use Figure 12.4 to answer the following questions:

(a) How many times in the last 4 Ma has the Earth's magnetic polarity reversed?

(b) What was the polarity of the Earth's magnetism 0.5, 1.5 and 2.5 Ma ago?

(c) When did the polarity last change from normal to reversed?

(d) A rock sample is known to have been formed sometime within the last 2 Ma and has normal polarity. Within what range of ages could it have been formed?

(e) What is the age of the most recent reversal? ◀

It is this division into normal and reversed polarity that accounts for the magnetic anomalies seen in Figure 12.3. Where the rocks beneath the magnetometer have reversed polarity, their magnetism slightly counteracts the normal polarity of the Earth's present-day magnetism, so the total magnetic signal is relatively weak. In contrast, rocks with normal polarity complement the Earth's magnetism, and the magnetometer detects a relatively strong total magnetic signal. Travelling outwards from the ridge, the rocks become older and the sequence of magnetic anomalies displays the sequence of polarity reversals. At the ridge itself, the rocks have been formed relatively recently, and retain normal polarity (shaded black on Figure 12.3). Further from the ridge crest a polarity reversal is detected and the rocks in the white stripe have reversed polarity. (Note that this coding of black stripes to label normal polarity and white stripes to label reversed polarity is a standard convention.) The

[*]The word geomagnetic means 'relating to the Earth's magnetism'; the prefix *geo*, as in geography, geology, and so on, means 'Earth'.

sequence of reversals to the southeast of the ridge is the same as the sequence to the northwest. The most obvious match between stripes on either side of the ridge crest involves the two broad black stripes and the intervening white stripe near the ends of the surveyed region. Each black (or white) stripe represents half of the ocean floor produced at the ridge during one of the periods when the Earth's magnetism had normal (or reversed) polarity. The two halves have been split apart by sea-floor spreading, analogous to the separation of the two crates on the diverging conveyor belts in Figure 12.2.

The symmetrical magnetic stripes are strong evidence in support of the sea-floor spreading theory. When the pattern of reversals revealed by marine magnetic surveys are compared with the pattern in the geomagnetic polarity time-scale, they are found to match (Figure 12.5).

Figure 12.5 The pattern of magnetic stripes on either side of an ocean ridge is the same as the pattern of reversals on the geomagnetic polarity time-scale.

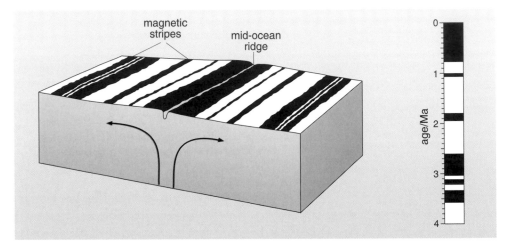

○ How can these polarity reversals help us to work out the spreading rate at the Mid-Atlantic Ridge?

○ If we can match an ocean floor polarity reversal with a reversal on the time-scale in Figure 12.4, then we know how long it took for the rocks associated with that polarity reversal to travel from their site of origin at the ridge crest to their present positions. We can therefore work out the spreading rate if we know the distance travelled.

Let's consider the most recent polarity reversal; it took place about 0.78 Ma ago (Figure 12.4). Rocks of this age on the ocean floor southwest of Iceland were originally erupted at the ridge but have since been split apart and moved aside, by the emplacement of younger rocks, and are now found about 8.5 km away from the ridge, i.e. some 17 km apart.

○ What was the speed of separation?

○ The speed v is the separation distance d divided by the time t elapsed:

$$v = \frac{d}{t}$$

Because the separation distance is $d = 17$ km and the time elapsed is $t = 0.78$ Ma, the speed is:

$$v = \frac{17\,\text{km}}{0.78\,\text{Ma}}$$

$$= 21.8\,\text{km}\,\text{Ma}^{-1}$$

$$= 22\,\text{km}\,\text{Ma}^{-1} \text{ to two significant figures.}$$

A speed measured in kilometres per million years is perhaps difficult to visualize and for this reason sea-floor spreading rates are conventionally reported in units of millimetres per year (mm y^{-1}, or mm a^{-1} in some books), or very often centimetres per year (cm y^{-1}).

⬤ What is 22 km Ma^{-1} in the unit of mm y^{-1}?

◯ 22 km is 22×10^3 m, which is $(22 \times 10^3) \times 10^3$ mm, in other words 2.2×10^7 mm. A million years is 10^6 y, so

$$22\,\text{km}\,\text{Ma}^{-1} = \frac{22\,\text{km}}{1\,\text{Ma}} = \frac{2.2 \times 10^7\,\text{mm}}{10^6\,\text{y}}$$

$$= 2.2 \times 10^{(7-6)}\,\text{mm}\,\text{y}^{-1}$$

$$= 2.2 \times 10^1\,\text{mm}\,\text{y}^{-1}$$

$$= 22\,\text{mm}\,\text{y}^{-1}.$$

Thus the numerical value of the spreading rate in km Ma^{-1} is the same as the value in mm y^{-1}. A rate of 22 mm y^{-1} is similar to the rate at which fingernails grow and is easier to imagine than is 22 km Ma^{-1}.

Information about all of the reversals near the Mid-Atlantic Ridge southwest of Iceland is given in Table 12.1 and is plotted as a graph in Figure 12.6.

Table 12.1   Positions of dated polarity reversals on the Mid-Atlantic Ridge southwest of Iceland.

Age of reversal/Ma	Separation distance/km
0.78	17
0.99	18
1.07	21
1.79	32
1.95	39
2.60	48
3.04	58
3.11	59
3.22	62
3.33	65
3.58	66

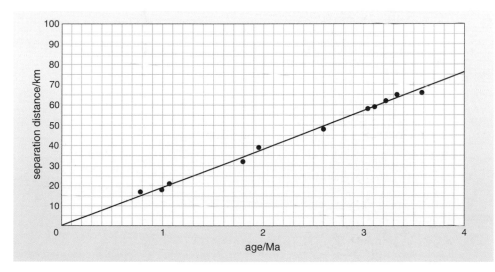

Figure 12.6   Graph of data in Table 12.1 and the straight line that best fits the data.

○ How would you describe the distribution of the points in Figure 12.6?

○ The points are scattered close to a straight line that passes through the origin of the graph.

The uncertainty in locating the exact positions of reversals on Figure 12.3, and uncertainties in assigning exact dates to each reversal in the geomagnetic polarity time-scale, mean that the value of each number in Table 12.1, and therefore the position of each point in Figure 12.6, carries some uncertainty. An average description of the somewhat scattered data is given by drawing a line through the array of points. This **best-fit line** is, as its name suggests, a line that gives the closest match to all the data points.

The fact that the line is straight and passes through the origin means that the separation after 2 Ma is twice the separation after 1 Ma, and the separation after 3 Ma is three times the separation after 1 Ma. This implies that the distance travelled is proportional to the time taken (see Box 12.1, *Proportionality in words, pictures and symbols*). In other words, the speed (= distance/time) has been constant.

Box 12.1 *Proportionality in words, pictures and symbols*

It is not uncommon for two quantities to be proportional to each other — the price you pay for some apples is proportional to the weight (or mass!) that you buy; the distance travelled at a constant speed is proportional to the time taken; the amount of electrical energy used to boil a kettle of cold water is proportional to the mass of water; and so on. Also, in Block 2 (Box 2.2) we noted that the change in length of the liquid in a thermometer is proportional to the change in temperature.

In every case, by definition of proportionality, one quantity is related to the other by a constant factor. Or, put another way, one quantity divided by the other has a constant value. If two quantities are proportional to each other, a graph of one quantity plotted against the other will be a straight line which passes through the origin (as in Figure 12.6).

So, if some quantity y is proportional to another quantity x, we can write:

y is proportional to x

or:

$\dfrac{y}{x}$ has a constant value

or we can draw a graph of y against x and it will be a line of constant gradient (i.e. a straight line) passing through the origin.

To express this more succinctly, a symbol is used for the words 'is proportional to'. This symbol is $\propto$. So we can write:

$y \propto x$

which is read as 'y is proportional to x'. This summarizes the facts that $\dfrac{y}{x}$ is constant, and that a graph of y against x is a straight line which passes through the origin, and has gradient $\dfrac{y}{x}$.

The general way of determining the gradient of a line was introduced in Box 10.1 and in *SGSG* Maths Help, Section 10.

The gradient of the best-fit line in Figure 12.6 gives the average speed of separation. So, to determine the average speed of sea-floor spreading at the Mid-Atlantic Ridge, the first step is to find the gradient of this line. In Figure 12.6 the straight line passes through the origin so the easiest way to work out the gradient is to use Equation 10.4:

$$\text{gradient} = \frac{y_2}{x_2} \qquad\qquad\qquad (10.4)$$

where in our case y_2 will be a distance coordinate read from the vertical axis, and x_2 the corresponding time coordinate read from the horizontal axis.

The x and y coordinates of any point on the best-fit line will do, but the choice is helped by using a point that is easily read — for example where one of the grid lines crosses the best-fit line. For instance, selecting 4.0 Ma for x_2 gives a value for y_2 of 76 km. Therefore:

$$\text{gradient} = y_2/x_2 = 76\,\text{km}/\,4.0\,\text{Ma} = 19\,\text{km}\,\text{Ma}^{-1}$$

○ Find the distance corresponding to an age of 2.0 Ma and calculate the gradient.

○ The distance is 38 km, giving a gradient of 38 km/ 2.0 Ma = 19 km Ma^{-1}.

So, as you would expect for a straight line, the gradient is the same at all points along it.

Question 12.2 Express 19 km Ma^{-1} in the unit of mm y^{-1}. ◀

Our earlier estimate of the spreading rate (22 mm y^{-1}) was based on just one piece of information whereas the estimate from the graph, which uses all the data, should be more representative of the spreading rate at the Mid-Atlantic Ridge. The spreading rate of 19 mm y^{-1} for the Mid-Atlantic Ridge is properly called the full spreading rate, defined as the rate at which points on opposite sides of the ridge move away from each other. This contrasts with the half spreading rate, defined as the rate at which a single point on one side of the ridge is carried away from the ridge crest.

Having discovered that the sea-floor spreading rate on the Mid-Atlantic Ridge is 19 mm y^{-1}, it might be tempting to assume that all of the Earth's mid-ocean ridges spread at this same rate. To see if this is the case, try the following activity.

Activity 12.2   Sea-floor spreading rates on the Southeast Indian Ridge

In this CD-ROM activity, you will use marine magnetic anomaly patterns for the ocean floor near the Southeast Indian Ridge, together with the geomagnetic polarity time-scale, to estimate sea-floor spreading rates in the Indian Ocean. As well as finding out more about sea-floor spreading rates, this will also let you practise your graph-plotting skills and gradient measurement. ◀

12.3   Continental drift and sea-floor spreading: examples of scientific discovery

Looking back at the evidence, there seems to be little doubt that the continents have drifted over the face of the Earth and that the ocean floor is created at mid-ocean ridges by the process of sea-floor spreading. In the past, however, many scientists could not accept these theories because the most compelling evidence had not been discovered or its true importance had not been realized. The way in which continental drift was established was very different from the discovery of sea-floor spreading. The stories of how these discoveries came about, which we will now tell, illustrate that scientific knowledge and theories only sometimes develop in an ordered, logical, progression. Sometimes their development involves the inspirational pulling together of what seemed previously to be unconnected facts. The conclusion is that science's exploration of the unknown is often an unpredictable voyage.

In the case of continental drift, it was the good jigsaw fit of continental coastlines that led Alfred Wegener to hypothesize that the continents had drifted apart at some distant time in the past. He then went on to consider what other types of evidence he might expect to find if continental drift really had happened. By doing this he tested the continental drift hypothesis and, as you saw in Section 11, there is compelling evidence preserved by fossils and rocks that the continents have drifted over the Earth's surface during the last few hundred million years. This systematic testing of a hypothesis is one way in which scientific theories become established.

The discovery of sea-floor spreading came about very differently. Unlike the observations of coastline fits that led Wegener and others to pursue ideas about continental drift, the observations that were to lead to the idea of sea-floor spreading were less visible and came from unlikely quarters. By the late 1950s, the superpowers had developed sophisticated military submarines, but the floor of the oceans in which submarine warfare might have to be waged was largely unknown. This drove the US Navy secretly to map the ocean floor and, unknown to the rest of the scientific world, to discover mid-ocean ridges in the Pacific. Independently, mid-ocean ridges in the Indian and Atlantic Oceans were being surveyed in curiosity-driven expeditions of discovery by scientists from the UK and USA.

While this was going on, other scientists were occupied in trying to discover as much as possible about the Earth's magnetism and the way in which rocks retained this magnetism. Although the possibility of magnetic polarity reversals had been proposed at the beginning of the 1900s, it took until the 1950s for this to become a popular topic of study. By the 1960s it was becoming possible to date precisely the eruption age of magnetized basalt lavas and this allowed the polarity reversals to be dated and the geomagnetic polarity time-scale to be defined. Meanwhile, other palaeomagnetists persuaded scientists studying the ocean to do magnetic surveys. This led, in 1958, to the discovery of marine magnetic anomaly patterns off the Pacific coast of North America. But no one at the time understood how these magnetic stripes were formed or what they meant.

Excited by the results from the explosion in ocean research, and influenced by contemporary ideas about continental drift, Harry Hess of Princeton University, USA, speculated, in 1960, that the ocean floors were formed at mid-ocean ridges by the intrusion and extrusion of basalt magma and grew by being carried away from the ridge by slow-moving currents flowing in the mantle. It was not until 1961 that Bob Dietz, a scientist at a US Navy laboratory, coined a term for this hypothetical process. He called it sea-floor spreading. But conclusive evidence that sea-floor spreading actually occurred seemed to be elusive and the hypothesis was regarded as controversial.

Unknown to everyone, all the pieces of the puzzle that were needed to support this hypothesis, and thus to substantiate the theory of sea-floor spreading, were available in the early 1960s. Then, the light dawned. At Cambridge University, a young research student, Fred Vine, and his supervisor Drummond Matthews realized that

The base of the lithosphere lies *within* the mantle (Figure 13.1) so the lithosphere incorporates not only the crust but also part of the mantle. The lithosphere is about 100 km thick, but this thickness is variable; oceanic lithosphere (lithosphere with oceanic crust) is thinner than continental lithosphere (lithosphere with continental crust).

But what determines the thickness of the lithosphere? The marked difference in strength between the lithosphere and the asthenosphere is caused by temperature increasing with increasing depth below the Earth's surface. At depths of about 100 km the temperature is close to the melting temperature of the mantle rock at this depth. Under these conditions the minerals in the mantle peridotite become soft, making the asthenosphere more easily deformed. The depth to the top of the asthenosphere (i.e. the thickness of the lithosphere) depends on the rate at which temperature increases with depth. At spreading mid-ocean ridges, temperatures are high close to the surface so the lithosphere is thin here. Beneath continents, temperatures increase only slowly with depth, so the lithosphere is thicker (Figure 13.1).

Question 13.1 Separate each of the following pairs of properties into the one that applies to the lithosphere, and the one that applies to the asthenosphere:

weaker/stronger

rigid/easily deformed

higher temperature/lower temperature

crust and top of mantle/within the mantle

earthquakes occur/no earthquakes occur ◀

Now we can return to considering the question 'What is a plate?'. We will start by going back to the global map of earthquake epicentres (Figure 7.7) to see what this can tell us about the lithosphere. This figure shows that most earthquakes occur in narrow seismic zones (Section 7.3), which are sites of faulting in the lithosphere. The seismic zones surround areas of lithosphere that have relatively little evidence of active deformation within them, but much faulting and deformation at their edges. These individual areas of lithosphere, separated by seismic zones, are called **lithospheric plates** (or more usually within Earth science, just **plates**). Plates are very thin in comparison with their horizontal dimensions; only about 100 km thick (the thickness of the lithosphere) but thousands of kilometres in width. There are seven major plates (the Pacific Plate is the largest) and numerous smaller plates (Figure 13.2, *overleaf*). The boundaries between the plates correspond with seismic zones, as you can see by comparing Figures 7.7 and 13.2.

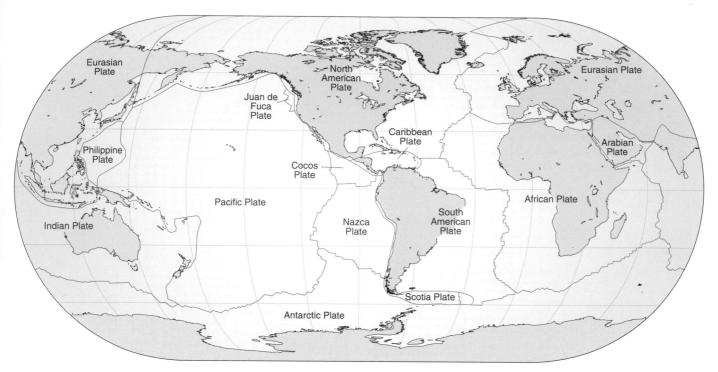

Figure 13.2 The Earth's lithospheric plates. The plate boundaries on continents are located less accurately than those in the oceans as seismic zones in continental lithosphere are wider than in oceanic lithosphere. Plate boundaries in the far north are uncertain.

○ Do plate boundaries coincide with the boundaries between continental and oceanic crust? (Remember that this boundary is around the position of the continental rise, not at the land–sea boundary; Section 6.3 and Section 10.2.2.)

○ In general no, except for the western edge of North, Central and South America.

○ Do all plates have both oceanic and continental lithosphere?

○ No, but most plates do. (Some plates have just oceanic lithosphere, e.g. the Cocos and Nazca Plates. There are no plates that have just continental lithosphere.)

Having dealt with the question 'What is a plate?', let us now consider what plates do. The lithospheric plates move around the Earth over the weaker asthenosphere and this is where the 'tectonics' comes into plate tectonics. The plates do not all move in the same direction; instead they move in different directions. The effect of continental drift is produced when a plate containing a continent moves relative to a plate containing another continent. For example, the North American continent is part of the North American Plate, whereas Europe is part of the Eurasian Plate. As the plates move relative to each other, so do the continents that are part of these plates. The observations of continental drift are therefore explained by plate tectonics.

Because the plates move in different directions they jostle each other at their edges. There the rocks of one plate are moving relative to the rocks of another plate, causing faulting and earthquakes, which is why plate boundaries are characterized by seismic zones. One way of visualizing this is to think of the analogy of a frozen pond, with a layer of ice at the surface and water below. Suppose the ice is cracked, and the pieces of ice are equivalent to plates. If you were to push an ice plate, the ice would move easily over the underlying water (equivalent to the asthenosphere) but would crash into the surrounding ice plates at its edge. The interior of the ice plate would not be deformed by such collisions, only the edges.

13.2 Plate boundaries

We now turn our attention to the edges, or boundaries of the plates.

○ Do plate boundaries (shown on Figure 13.2) coincide with any of the major topographic features of the Earth's surface (shown on the poster map and Figure 6.7)?

○ Yes. All mid-ocean ridges are plate boundaries. For example the plate boundary in the Atlantic Ocean is a mid-ocean ridge (the Mid-Atlantic Ridge). All ocean trenches are also plate boundaries; an example is the Peru–Chile Trench off the west coast of South America. Some mountain belts are plate boundaries, for example the Himalayas.

The most prominent topographic features on the Earth are associated with plate boundaries. However, the essence of plate tectonics concerns the relative movement of the plates, and it turns out that plate boundaries can be classified into three types, depending on the direction of relative motion between the plates on each side of the boundary.

At **divergent plate boundaries**, plates are moving away from each other (Figure 13.3a and 13.3d). The conventional symbol for a divergent plate boundary on a map is a double line. New lithosphere is added to the plates at the boundary. This is what happens during sea-floor spreading at mid-ocean ridges, so mid-ocean ridges are divergent plate boundaries. The direction of motion of the plates is usually perpendicular to the plate boundary, as in Figure 13.3a, but it does not have to be so; if it is not, then the ridge is said to be spreading *obliquely*.

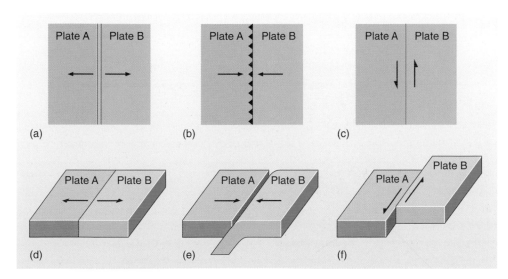

Figure 13.3 The three types of plate boundary, between plates A and B. The motion of each plate is shown by the arrows. (a), (b) and (c) are plan (map) views, and (d), (e) and (f) are block diagrams that give a three-dimensional view of the motion. (a) and (d) show a divergent plate boundary, indicated by the conventional double line symbol. (b) and (e) show a convergent plate boundary, with plates A and B moving towards each other. In this type of convergent boundary, plate B is descending beneath plate A, indicated by the barbs on plate A, the overriding plate. (c) and (f) show a transform fault plate boundary. The single line is the conventional symbol for a transform fault.

The theory of plate tectonics *incorporates* sea-floor spreading. But the creation of new lithosphere by sea-floor spreading must be balanced by the destruction of lithosphere elsewhere, otherwise the lithosphere would increase in area and the Earth would expand! Since the Earth is not expanding, lithosphere must be destroyed at the same rate as it is being created. This must occur at another type of plate boundary, a convergent plate boundary.

Along **convergent plate boundaries**, plates are moving towards each other. You may be able to predict what will happen in this case by thinking again about the plates of ice; if two ice plates are pushed towards each other, either one plate will move under the other, or the plates will crumple up. Similar situations occur with lithospheric plates. Figure 13.3b and 13.3e illustrates one form of convergent boundary, where plate B descends below plate A. The conventional symbol for a convergent plate boundary on a map is a barbed line, with the barbs on the side of the overriding plate.

Where one plate descends beneath another, an ocean trench is formed. A convergent plate boundary of this type may have an ocean trench and a volcanic island arc, or an ocean trench and a line of volcanoes along the edge of a continent. Alternatively the plates will crumple up and thicken into a mountain belt where they converge. As with divergent plate boundaries, the direction of motion does not have to be perpendicular to the plate boundary; oblique convergence is fairly common.

At **transform fault plate boundaries**, plates move past each other in opposite directions (Figure 13.3c and 13.3f). The conventional symbol for a transform fault boundary on a map is a single line.

Figure 13.4 shows where the different types of plate boundary are found.

Activity 13.1   Completing a table of plate boundary features

To help you distinguish between the different types of plate boundary, this activity requires you to summarize their important features in a table. ◀

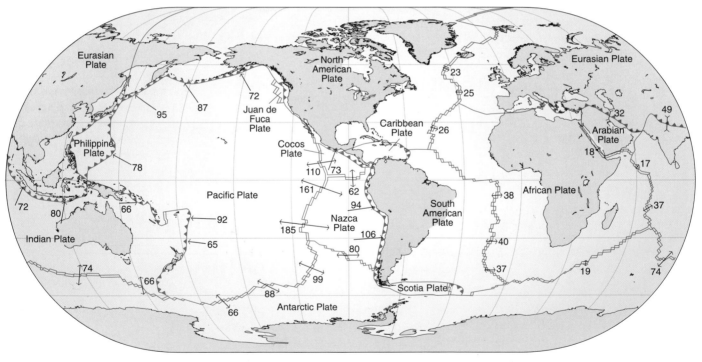

key   ⫽ divergent plate boundary   ⤸ convergent plate boundary   ╱ transform fault plate boundary

Figure 13.4   The Earth's lithospheric plates and plate boundaries. Plate boundaries in the far north are uncertain. Refer to Figure 6.7 for names of topographic features associated with plate boundaries. The black arrows and numbers give the direction and speed of relative motion between plates and are discussed in Section 13.4. Speeds of motion are given in mm y^{-1}, and for divergent plate boundaries these are full spreading rates. The length of each arrow is proportional to the speed of relative motion, so the longest arrows show the highest speeds of relative motion.

13.3   Plate motion

The motion of plates on the Earth involves motion over the surface of a sphere, which sounds fairly complex. However, we can still learn a lot about plate motion by considering something that is a little simpler — two plates moving on a horizontal surface (a 'flat Earth' model). This is a tactic used often in science; taking a potentially tricky situation and simplifying it to something more familiar or more manageable in order to start understanding the more complex situation.

13.3.1   Plate motion on a flat Earth

Consider the motion between two plates A and B on a horizontal surface, with plate B completely surrounding plate A (Figure 13.5a). The plate boundary between plates A and B is made up of four straight lines, and the relative motion between the plates is shown at the eastern boundary.

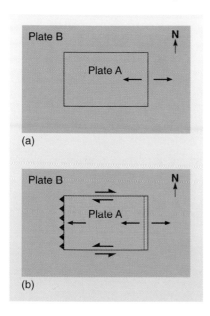

Figure 13.5   The relative motion between two plates on a flat Earth. These are plan views. Plate A is totally surrounded by plate B. The relative motion between the plates is shown by the arrows in (a), and the types of plate boundary deduced from this motion are shown in (b). Plate boundary symbols are as in Figure 13.3. The western boundary, showing plate A descending beneath plate B, is one of a number of possibilities for this convergent boundary; other possibilities are that plate B descends beneath plate A, or the plates crumple together.

⚪ Which type of plate boundary is the eastern boundary?

⚪ It is a divergent boundary as the relative motion between the two plates is away from each other.

How about the other boundaries? As plates are rigid, if plate A is moving west with respect to plate B at the eastern boundary, it must also be moving west at the other boundaries. At the western boundary this means that the plates are converging (plate A is moving west, towards plate B here) so this is a convergent boundary. At the northern and southern boundaries, which run east–west, the relative plate motion must be parallel to the boundaries, so they are transform faults. These plate boundaries are marked on Figure 13.5b using the standard symbols introduced in Figure 13.3.

Activity 13.2   Using a physical model to help understand plate motion

If you found the plate motion illustrated in Figure 13.5 difficult to understand, you should try this activity, which uses a physical model of plate motion. ◀

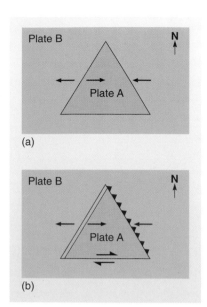

(a)

(b)

Figure 13.6 The relative motion between two plates on a flat Earth. Two of the plate boundaries are obliquely inclined to the motion. Plate boundary symbols are as in Figure 13.3.

Now we will investigate another plate-tectonic situation, where the motion between the plates is not perpendicular to the plate boundaries (Figure 13.6a). Plates A and B have plate boundaries in a triangular shape. What are the types of plate boundary in this situation? The southern boundary is the simplest to work out, as here the plate boundary is parallel to the relative plate motion, so the plates slip past each other at a transform fault. At the western boundary the plates are moving away from each other so this is a divergent plate boundary (this is an example of an obliquely-spreading divergent boundary of the type mentioned in Section 13.2). The plates are moving towards each other (obliquely) at the eastern boundary so this is a convergent plate boundary (Figure 13.6b). If this is not clear, try the paper-cutting technique in Activity 13.2!

Question 13.2 Work out which type of plate boundaries will be present between the two plates A and B in Figure 13.7 and draw them onto the figure using the conventional symbols (see Figures 13.3–13.6). ◄

Figure 13.7 For use with Question 13.2.

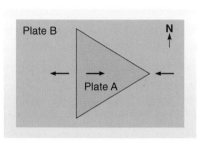

Question 13.3 The triangular plates in Figures 13.6 and 13.7 may seem unrealistic, but if you look at the Cocos Plate (Figure 13.4) you will see that it is approximately triangular. As a simplification, assume that the Cocos Plate is triangular in shape and that it is surrounded by only one other plate, then draw the Cocos Plate and the surrounding plate in the style of Figure 13.6b, showing the types of plate boundaries. ◄

13.3.2 Plate motion on a spherical Earth

The 'flat Earth' model of plate motion is useful, but has limitations; for example, it does not explain the observation that spreading rate varies along the length of a ridge (Activity 12.2) and, of course, we know that the Earth is not flat. Because of these limitations, you are now going to develop what you learnt in Section 13.3.1 about the motion and interaction of plates on a horizontal surface to consider what happens at plate boundaries on the spherical Earth.

Activity 13.3   Plate tectonics on a sphere

Plate motion on a sphere is three-dimensional (unlike the two-dimensional motion on a flat Earth) and this CD-ROM activity will help you to visualize this motion. ◄

13.4   The speed of relative plate motion

Activity 13.3 used the relative plate motion speeds at divergent plate boundaries, measured from sea-floor spreading rates. But how do we determine the speed of relative plate motion at convergent and transform fault boundaries? There are a number of methods for doing this, some involving plate movements over geological time periods (millions of years) and others involving present-day rates of motion. In Section 12.2.1 we calculated rates of sea-floor spreading, which were of the order of tens of millimetres per year. This is the long-term rate of relative movement between plates at divergent plate boundaries. Present-day ('instantaneous') rates of relative plate motion can be determined by methods that involve monitoring small changes in the distance between fixed points on two or more plates.

One of these methods uses the Global Positioning System (GPS). This is the system used in the navigation of ships and aircraft. Radio signals received from navigation satellites can be used to calculate the accurate location of any point on the Earth, and so can be used to determine changes in the distance between points on different plates. The results from this and other methods are shown in Figure 13.4, which you should look back at now.

Question 13.4   Using the information about relative plate speeds from Figure 13.4, and using Figure 6.7 to identify topographic features:

(a) Which neighbouring plates have the highest relative speeds of motion, and which type of plate boundary separates them?

(b) Where is the highest relative speed for a different type of boundary from that in (a)?

(c) Where is the lowest rate of sea-floor spreading?

(d) Give an example of a mid-ocean ridge where the sea-floor spreading rate varies along the ridge. Why does the spreading rate vary? ◄

We can use the directions of relative plate motion shown in Figure 13.4 to consider how common it is for plates to move obliquely at divergent and convergent plate boundaries, and how oblique the motion is. Consider first the motion at divergent plate boundaries.

○ Are there examples of obvious oblique motion, or is the motion mainly perpendicular to the diverging ridge segments? (Remember to look at the motion relative to individual ridge segments, denoted by the double lines, rather than the overall alignment of the mid-ocean ridge.)

○ In general, the motion is perpendicular or nearly perpendicular to the double lines identifying the position of divergent boundaries, with no very oblique motion.

At convergent boundaries, there are a number of places where the motion is distinctly oblique, such as the northwest edge of the Pacific Plate and the northern boundary between the Indian and Pacific Plates.

So transform faults are parallel to the plate motion, divergent plate boundaries are usually perpendicular or nearly perpendicular to the plate motion, but convergent plate boundaries are sometimes oblique to the plate motion.

○ Which of the Figures 13.5, 13.6 and 13.7 therefore represents a geologically unlikely situation?

○ Figure 13.6, which shows a ridge spreading very obliquely.

Before we leave this section, consider for a moment just how fast plates are travelling in everyday terms. The fastest sprinter can run 100 m in about 10 s, which is 10 m s^{-1}. A reasonable walking pace is about 5 km h^{-1}, which is about 1.4 m s^{-1}. In contrast, the fastest relative plate speed is 185 mm y^{-1}, which is around 6×10^{-9} m s^{-1}. So plates travel very slowly. To put their speeds into context, the fastest ones move at a relative rate similar to the rate at which hair grows. The slower ones move at only fingernail growth rates. However insignificant that seems, it is enough to release energy in the form of major earthquakes, and, over millions of years, to have separated Europe and North America by thousands of kilometres.

Question 13.5 How far will two plates have moved relative to each other in a million years if their relative speed is 185 mm y^{-1}? ◄

Question 13.6 Roughly how long will it take for the distance between London and New York to increase by 1 km at current sea-floor spreading rates? ◄

13.5 Summary of Section 13

The Earth's outer rigid layer, the lithosphere, is about 100 km thick. It overlies the weaker asthenosphere. The lithosphere is divided by seismic zones into fragments called plates. Plate tectonics is a theory that describes how plates interact and move. It incorporates the theory of sea-floor spreading and provides an explanation for continental drift.

There are three types of plate boundary, distinguished by the direction of relative motion between two plates. Divergent plate boundaries occur where plates are moving away from each other, and are found at mid-ocean ridges. Convergent plate boundaries occur where two plates are moving towards each other, and are characterized by an ocean trench and island arc, or an ocean trench and line of volcanoes along the edge of a continent, or a mountain belt. Transform fault plate boundaries occur where two plates move past each other in opposite directions.

The relative motion between two plates is a rotation of one plate relative to the other about an imaginary axis through the Earth's centre. This axis of rotation has an imaginary pole of rotation (and an anti-pole) at the Earth's surface. Non-oblique divergent and convergent plate boundaries lie along parts of great circles passing through the pole of rotation. Transform fault boundaries lie along parts of small circles centred on the axis of rotation.

The speeds of relative plate motion are about 10–200 mm y^{-1}.

Processes at plate boundaries

14

You saw in Section 13 that plate boundaries can be classified into three types, just by considering the relative motion of neighbouring plates. Two plates may diverge, converge or slide past each other. In this section we will investigate how each type of motion is related to the powerful earthquake or volcanic activity that characterizes plate boundaries.

14.1 Divergent plate boundaries

Divergent plate boundaries are sites of sea-floor spreading. It is here that new oceanic lithosphere is made, so divergent plate boundaries are sometimes referred to as constructive plate boundaries. Whatever term is used, the problem facing the scientist is to work out how new oceanic lithosphere is produced at divergent boundaries. The first step is to find out exactly what the oceanic lithosphere is made from.

14.1.1 The structure and composition of oceanic lithosphere

By exploring the ocean floor, scientists have discovered that the top of the oceanic lithosphere consists of a layer of fine-grained sediment overlying basaltic lava flows (as you too found in Activity 12.1). But what lies beneath the basalt lavas? To answer this question, and so gain a complete picture of the 100 km or so thick oceanic lithosphere, we draw on three lines of evidence.

Seismology

One of the conclusions about the interior structure of the Earth that comes from seismology is that the oceanic crust is a layer of rock about 7 km thick (Section 10). Seismology can be used to find out even more about this layer, and detailed seismic investigations have revealed that the oceanic crust is itself composed of layers, each with a different seismic wave speed. The uppermost seismic layer corresponds to the layer of sediment that covers the ocean floor, and the top of the next seismic layer corresponds to the lava flows of basalt. But identifying the deeper layers requires another approach.

Rock samples from the oceanic lithosphere

From Activity 12.1, you are already familiar with the lava flows, sediment and mineralized rocks that lie on the ocean floor. These surface rocks normally hide the deep interior of the oceanic crust, but sometimes erosion or the movement of rocks on either side of a transform fault exposes the deeper portions of oceanic crust (Figure 14.1a).

Figure 14.1 (a) Schematic block diagram of a mid-ocean ridge that has been cut by two transform faults, exposing the interior of oceanic lithosphere (the purple faces). (b) A cross-section showing nearly horizontal layers of rock near the Mid-Atlantic Ridge, as deduced from observations made on the undulating surface that slopes up from left to right (north to south).

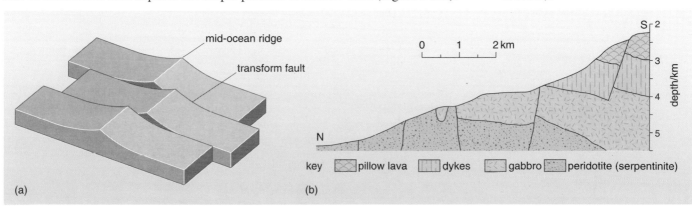

Figure 14.2 This cliff-face provides an end-on view of a dyke — a near-vertical sheet of igneous rock intruded into older rocks.

The faces of the transform faults shown in Figure 14.1a are vertical, but in real cases these rock faces collapse, resulting in an irregular sloping surface that exposes deep parts of the ocean crust at the foot, and rocks from the original ocean floor at the top. At the Vema transform fault, at 11° N on the Mid-Atlantic Ridge, French scientists used a submersible to traverse down one such slope. What they found there led them to draw Figure 14.1b, based on their observations of the different rocks encountered as they traversed down the slope and how they interpreted the rocks to continue as layers under the surface.

At the shallowest depth are basaltic pillow lavas, much as would be expected for the ocean floor. Below these are two layers which, although of the same chemical and mineral composition as the basaltic lavas, are very different in appearance. The shallower layer comprises near-vertical sheets of basaltic rock a metre or so wide. Each sheet of rock, known as a **dyke**, is the solidified contents of a vertical channel that carried magma along a crack in the crust. Dykes are common in the rocks around volcanoes, and an example of one is shown in Figure 14.2. The dykes seen in the Vema transform fault are packed very closely together, and this portion of oceanic crust consists of little else than parallel vertical sheets of dykes; it is called a **sheeted dyke complex**. The structure is analogous to a pack of playing cards standing vertically, each card representing a single dyke.

At greater depth, the rock is **gabbro** — a coarse-grained intrusive rock with the same mineral and chemical composition as basalt. This rock formed by the slow cooling of basaltic magma deep underground. The deepest rocks contain the mineral serpentine, which is formed when peridotite becomes chemically altered by reacting with heated seawater. This deepest rock, called serpentinite, is therefore interpreted to be the altered top of the mantle.

A complementary view of the oceanic lithosphere has been obtained by the Ocean Drilling Programme, the international scientific endeavour to investigate the ocean floor by drilling into it from a ship. The deepest penetration into oceanic crust (up to 1997) was achieved in 1993 by drilling 2.1 km into the Nazca Plate, some 200 km south of the divergent plate boundary with the Cocos Plate in the eastern Pacific Ocean (see Figure 13.2 for the locations of plates). After drilling through 275 m of sediment, the drill passed through about 600 m of pillow lavas before entering slightly coarser-grained basalt, which was interpreted as a sheeted dyke complex.

Ophiolites — stranded oceanic lithosphere

The continents are probably the last place you would think of looking if you were interested in studying the oceanic lithosphere. So when geologists found that the mountains of Oman (in the Middle East), and the Troodos Mountains of Cyprus are composed of the same types of rock as those of the oceanic lithosphere (Figure 14.3), and are arranged in the same vertical sequence, a dramatic explanation was called for. The most logical explanation is that these mountains are parts of the oceanic lithosphere that became 'stranded' on shore and incorporated into continents by plate-tectonic movements, particularly during plate collisions. These associations of basaltic pillow lavas, sheeted dykes, gabbros and peridotites (or serpentinites) on land are known as **ophiolites** (pronounced 'oaf-ee-o-lights'; the word is derived from the Greek words *ophis* for 'snake' and *lithos* for 'rock', an allusion to the green scaly appearance of serpentinite, a word that itself reflects its snaky appearance). Small-scale examples of the association between basaltic pillow lavas, sheeted dykes, gabbro and peridotites can be found in Britain (for example the Lizard Peninsula in Cornwall, in the Lleyn Peninsula and Anglesey in North Wales, and at Ballantrae in southwest Scotland).

(a)

(b)

Figure 14.3 Parts of ancient oceanic lithosphere within the 500 km long Oman ophiolite: (a) basaltic pillow lavas; (b) sheeted dykes; (c) The green rocks in the foreground and middle distance are peridotite.

(c)

Putting the evidence of a seismically-layered oceanic crust together with observations of rocks from drilling and submarine exposures, and with ophiolites, a consistent picture emerges of the simplicity and uniformity of the Earth's oceanic lithosphere. It consists of a crustal layer some 7 km thick overlying peridotite, which is part of the mantle. The crustal part is layered and comprises sediment overlying basaltic lavas overlying basaltic sheeted dykes overlying gabbro.

14.1.2 The formation of oceanic lithosphere

Section 14.1.1 outlined observations about the structure and composition of the oceanic lithosphere. How can we use these observations to explain how oceanic lithosphere is formed? Let's start by considering the major crustal layers.

Question 14.1   Each of the processes A–C accounts for one of the components (1–3) of the oceanic crust. Which process is responsible for each component?

A   Transport of basalt magma along vertical cracks in the crust

B   Slow crystallization of basalt magma

C   Volcanic eruption on to the ocean floor

1   Gabbro

2   Pillow lavas of basalt

3   Sheeted dykes of basalt ◄

Piecing together the origins of the separate components of oceanic crust, the first conclusion we can reach is that, apart from the relatively thin covering layer of sediment, the rocks of the oceanic crust have an igneous origin. This means that they were ultimately derived from a magma — but where did this magma come from? By carrying out experiments in which different types of rock are heated at high pressure and temperature, to simulate conditions within the Earth, it has been found that basalt magma is produced by melting peridotite in the mantle. So, considering the whole of the oceanic lithosphere, we can think of it as being the product of a 'factory' that produces, stores, transports and delivers basaltic magma from the mantle to the crust at mid-ocean ridges (Figure 14.4). Once basalt magma has been formed by melting of mantle peridotite, it embarks on an upward journey, but it also starts to cool and crystallize. The basalt may stop rising, and accumulate in a magma chamber within the crust where it slowly crystallizes to produce gabbro. Some magma escapes into fissures above the magma chamber and flows to the surface where it erupts as lava on the ocean floor. The magma left in the fissure cools and solidifies, forming a dyke. At a later date another fissure opens up and another dyke is intruded between its predecessors, much as an extra playing card might be forced into the end-on pack of playing cards we imagined earlier. As more and more dykes are intruded, the crustal 'pack of cards' is widened, perpetuating the process of sea-floor spreading.

When the lavas and dykes cool, they become magnetized, providing a record of the polarity of the Earth's magnetism. The resulting magnetic stripes (Figure 12.5) allow the rate of sea-floor spreading, that is the speed at which two plates are diverging from each other, to be estimated, as described in Section 12.2.1.

So sea-floor spreading produces two diverging plates of oceanic lithosphere by removing basalt from the mantle and adding it to the crust. These igneous processes are accompanied by shallow earthquakes, indicating that rocks are being broken and faulted. The faults and fractures contribute to another feature of mid-ocean ridges which you met in Activity 12.1. Seawater flows into the fissured crust, where it becomes heated by shallow magma and the underlying hot mantle. This sustains a circulation system, in which cold seawater is drawn into the flanks of the ridge and

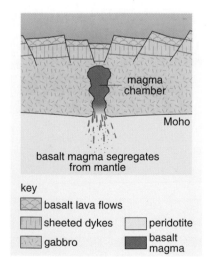

Figure 14.4 The magmatic processes occurring at a mid-ocean ridge account for the structure and composition of oceanic lithosphere.

becomes heated as it descends (Figure 14.5). The hot water dissolves metals out of the rocks in the crust, and hot metal-rich water is eventually expelled near the ridge crest, forming black smokers. The dissolved metals combine with sulfur to form metalliferous mineral deposits in and around black smoker chimneys. Ancient examples of these deposits are to be found in ophiolites, such as the Troodos ophiolite on Cyprus. Here, deposits of copper ore associated with sedimentary rocks and lavas formed at a mid-ocean ridge have been mined since ancient times. Indeed the name Cyprus comes from the Greek word for copper — *cupros*.

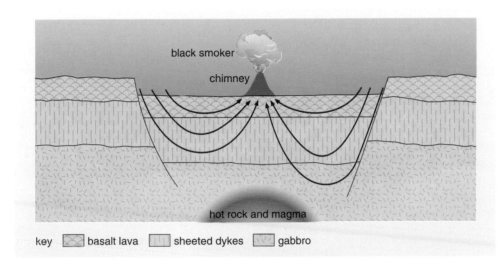

Figure 14.5   Sketch of a hydrothermal system at a mid-ocean ridge, not drawn to scale. The arrows depict the path of seawater as it flows into the fractured crust, is heated and reacts chemically with the oceanic crust, and is expelled as hot water, producing black smokers.

In summary, sea-floor spreading accounts for the origin of oceanic lithosphere at divergent plate boundaries. It explains the layered structure of oceanic lithosphere, the basaltic composition and rock types of the oceanic crust, striped marine magnetic anomaly patterns, and the shallow earthquakes, volcanic eruptions and metal-rich hot springs at mid-ocean ridges.

14.2   Convergent plate boundaries

Divergent plate boundaries are sites of volcanic eruptions and shallow earthquakes, but the catastrophic volcanic eruptions and devastating earthquakes that are reported on the news usually occur at convergent plate boundaries, where two plates are moving towards each other. That these differences exist suggests that the processes that occur at convergent plate boundaries are very different from those at divergent plate boundaries. To find out about the processes occurring at convergent plate boundaries, we need to consider some specific examples.

- The edge of a plate may be made of continental or oceanic lithosphere, so what combinations of lithosphere types might be present at convergent boundaries?

- There are potentially three types of convergent plate boundary: where both edges are oceanic lithosphere, where both edges are continental lithosphere, and where one edge is oceanic and the other continental lithosphere.

Question 14.2   According to Figure 13.4, there are convergent plate boundaries along the western side of South America, along the Izu–Bonin Trench in the western Pacific (see Figure 6.7), and in the Himalayas. In each case, identify the two plates involved and decide whether continental, oceanic or both types of lithosphere are involved. ◀

Having identified these three types of convergent plate boundaries, we shall now have a look at what processes are going on there, and see whether these processes depend on the types of convergent boundary. Because earthquakes are caused by movement within the Earth, one way to find out more about the motion of the plates is to locate where the earthquakes occur. The earthquake foci at each of the plate boundaries we considered in Question 14.2 are shown in Figure 14.6. This diagram is similar in style to the diagram showing activity on the San Andreas Fault associated with the Loma Prieta earthquake (Figure 7.5c), only here a much larger region is being considered.

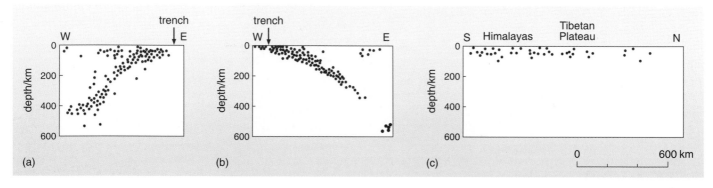

Figure 14.6   Cross-sections perpendicular to convergent plate boundaries showing the distribution of earthquake foci near (a) the Izu–Bonin Trench in the western Pacific, (b) the northern Chilean Andes (20° S) on the western side of South America, and (c) Tibet (85° E).

⬤ What is the depth of the deepest earthquake in each region shown in Figure 14.6?

◯ The deepest earthquakes in the region of the Izu–Bonin Trench and the Peru–Chile Trench are at about 600 km, whereas below Tibet the deepest is at about 100 km.

The Tibetan example is different from the other two in having mostly shallow-focus earthquakes (i.e. less than 70 km; Section 7.3), whereas the others have many intermediate and some deep-focus (more than 300 km) earthquakes.

⬤ How are the earthquake foci in Figure 14.6 distributed?

◯ In Tibet, the earthquakes are distributed fairly evenly across the plate boundary. Near the Izu–Bonin Trench and Chile the earthquakes are mostly confined to an inclined zone, about 100 km thick, which reaches depths of several hundred kilometres.

Inclined zones of earthquakes such as those near the Izu–Bonin Trench and Chile were first discovered beneath Japan by Kiyoo Wadati in 1934, but their origin was a puzzle. Twenty years later, an American, Hugo Benioff, found similar inclined earthquake zones elsewhere around the Pacific rim and he realized that each one defined an enormous inclined fault zone that reached far into the Earth. Then, when the theory of plate tectonics was put forward in the 1960s, it suddenly became obvious that these earthquakes occurred where one plate was descending into the mantle beneath another plate, as in Figure 14.7. The intermediate and deep-focus earthquakes occur within and at the edges of the descending plate. The inclined zone of earthquakes is now known as a **Wadati–Benioff zone** (or sometimes just as a Benioff zone). If you refer back to Figure 7.7, you can identify some of the larger Wadati–Benioff zones around the Pacific because they are the only regions where deep-focus earthquakes occur. The descending plate is said to be subducting, and the general area of the Earth where this happens is called a **subduction zone**. Subduction zones may also be referred to as destructive plate boundaries because here one of the plates is being removed from the Earth's surface by descending into the mantle.

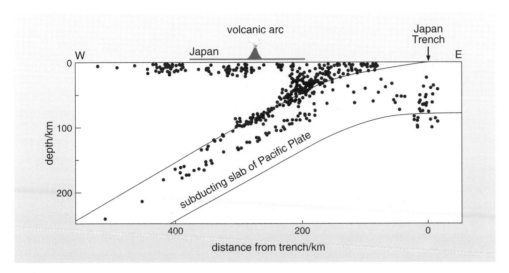

Figure 14.7 The distribution of earthquakes defining the Wadati–Benioff zone beneath Japan marks the position of the Pacific Plate as it descends beneath the Eurasian Plate.

⬤ What major features are present on the Earth's surface in the vicinity of subduction zones? (Use the plate boundary map, Figure 13.2, in conjunction with Figure 6.7 and the poster map to answer this question.)

⬤ Volcanic arcs are found on the crust that overlies the Wadati–Benioff zone, and deep ocean trenches occur parallel to the arc. If two oceanic plates are converging, then a volcanic island arc forms on the over-riding oceanic plate (e.g. the Izu–Bonin arc); if an oceanic plate is subducting beneath continental lithosphere, then the volcanoes form near the edge of the continent (e.g. the volcanoes of the Andes).

The association of volcanic arcs and ocean trenches, which we noted in Section 8.2, is a characteristic feature of subduction zones, but how are they explained by the subduction process? The trench can be thought of as a deep notch running along the length of a plate boundary where oceanic lithosphere bends beneath the edge of another lithospheric plate (either oceanic or continental). As the oceanic plate passes under the leading edge of the overriding plate, the layer of oceanic sediment may be scraped off. So, instead of descending into the mantle with the rest of the oceanic plate, this sediment is forced to pile up on the edge of the overriding plate, as illustrated in Figure 14.8 (*overleaf*). In extreme cases, the trench may become completely filled and the accumulated sediment reaches sea-level. This is what has happened at the subduction zone in the Caribbean, with the islands of Barbados being the tip of a wedge of sediment several kilometres thick.

Figure 14.8 The components of a typical subduction zone illustrated in a block diagram. Although not drawn to scale, the diagram represents a region about 150 km high, 500 km long and 100 km wide.

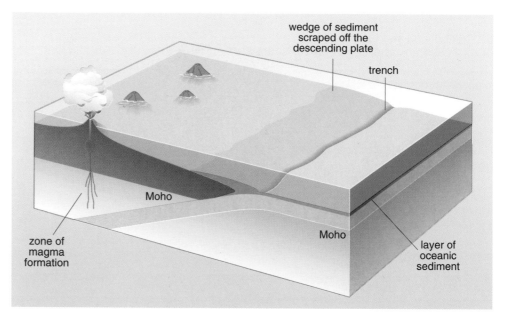

The reasons why volcanoes are found at subduction zones, and are arranged along an arc parallel with the plate boundary, have been debated for several decades. Competing hypotheses involving melting of subducted oceanic lithosphere or melting of the mantle above the subducted lithosphere turned out to be difficult to distinguish with any degree of certainty. Only after careful laboratory experiments to reproduce the melting of different rock types did a convincing resolution emerge. Most Earth scientists now agree that melting takes place in the mantle above the subducted lithosphere and that the melting zone, and hence the magmas produced there, contains some water released from the descending oceanic lithosphere. The implications of this are interesting, because it helps to explain one of our earlier observations — the observation that explosive volcanoes tend to be associated with ocean trenches rather than mid-ocean ridges (Section 8.2). The relatively high water content of the magma is critical here, because it is the escaping water (as steam) that makes the eruptions explosive. The magmas can also solidify as intrusive igneous rocks within the crust, and may release metal-rich fluids into cracks, fissures and veins underground, to form ore deposits. Many of the large copper, tin and gold deposits in the Andes were formed in this way.

Let's now broaden our view of subduction zones and consider what happens when continental lithosphere is attached to oceanic lithosphere that is subducting under another continent. This is the situation shown in Figure 14.9a. As subduction proceeds, the ocean that lies between the continents must become narrower (Figure 14.9b). Eventually all the oceanic lithosphere is consumed (Figure 14.9c) and the two continents collide (Figure 14.9d). This produces our third type of convergent boundary — the type where two plates of continental lithosphere are on opposite sides of the boundary.

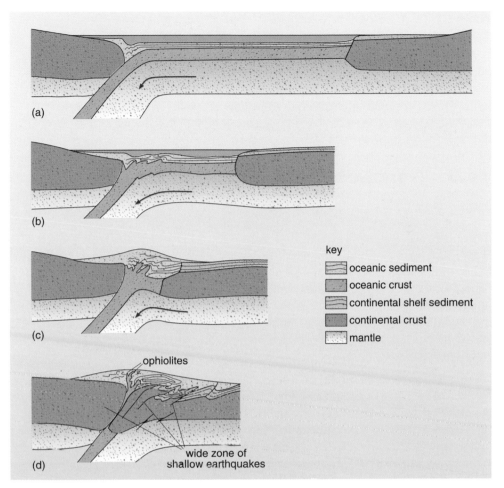

Figure 14.9 The sequence of events, seen in cross-section, that starts with subduction of oceanic lithosphere (a) and ends with the collision of two blocks of continental lithosphere, forming a continent/continent convergent plate boundary. Note that the sedimentary layers are part of the crust.

The continents crumple together and subduction stops because the continents have a sufficiently low density to remain buoyant; they remain 'floating' at the surface rather than sinking into the mantle. Fragments of oceanic lithosphere can be trapped in the collision (ophiolites), and the colliding continents become buckled into a major mountain belt (Figure 14.9d) with oceanic sedimentary rock elevated to the tops of mountains. The faulting that accompanies the collision generates earthquakes, but not volcanoes. This is just the series of events that have led to the Himalayan Mountains and the broad region of shallow- and intermediate-focus earthquakes across Tibet shown in Figure 14.6c. The crumpled and thickened crust provides the deep burial and heating required to recrystallize the rocks, so metamorphism occurs in the deep roots of mountain belts formed by continental collision.

○ Look at the map of plate boundaries (Figure 13.4) and the poster map to see if you can identify one other convergent plate boundary where colliding continents have produced a mountain belt along the plate boundary.

○ Collision of the Arabian plate with the Eurasian plate is associated with the mountain belt running NW–SE from Turkey to the Gulf of Oman (the Zagros Mountains). This plate boundary is characterized by shallow seismicity and volcanoes are absent.

Activity 14.1   Compare and contrast different types of convergent plate boundary

We started this section by noting that there are three types of convergent plate boundary, depending on the types of lithosphere at the plate boundary. This activity asks you to compare and contrast these three types of convergent plate boundary. It will consolidate your understanding of this topic, as well as providing practice in producing a short account in which you make comparisons and contrasts between different things. ◀

14.3   Transform fault plate boundaries

Transform fault plate boundaries occur when plates slide past each other in opposite directions, causing shallow earthquakes, but without creating or destroying lithosphere and without generating volcanoes. The San Andreas Fault, illustrated in Figures 7.3 and 7.5, is one example. It involves part of California (on the Pacific Plate) sliding northwest along the fault past the rest of North America (on the North American Plate). Transform faults connect the end of one plate boundary to the end of another plate boundary, so there are potentially three types of transform faults: those that link two divergent boundaries, those that link two convergent boundaries, and those that link a convergent boundary with a divergent boundary. Figure 14.10 shows an example of each type.

Can we find real-life examples of these plate boundaries? Transform faults linking two divergent boundaries, as in Figure 14.10a, are the most common, and account for the displacements between adjacent segments of mid-ocean ridges seen on the poster (Section 6.2.2). They lie on small circles about the pole of relative rotation between the two plates (Activity 13.3 and Section 13.3.2). For example, the Cocos–Nazca Ridge (also known as the Galapagos Spreading Center) is a divergent plate boundary that is split into several segments by transform faults (Figure 14.11). Transform faults associated with subduction zones are much less common, but a real example of the situation sketched in Figure 14.10b occurs at the eastern end of the Cocos–Nazca Ridge. Here, a heavily-faulted seismic zone delineates a transform fault (the Panama Fracture Zone) connecting a divergent boundary (the eastern end of the Costa Rica Rift, which is the easternmost part of the Cocos–Nazca Ridge) with the eastern end of a convergent boundary (the Middle America Trench).

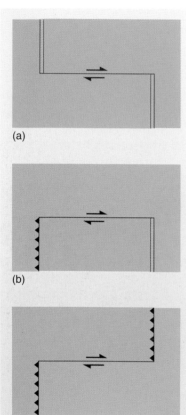

Figure 14.10   Sketches of three types of transform plate boundary. The single-headed arrows give the relative sense of movement on either side of the transform fault; other symbols used are the conventional ones for a divergent boundary (double lines) and convergent boundary (barbs). (a) Transform linking two divergent boundaries. (b) Transform linking convergent and divergent boundaries. (c) Transform linking two convergent boundaries.

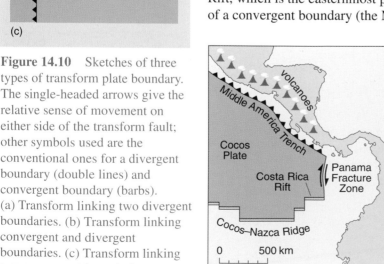

Figure 14.11   Map of plate boundaries around the eastern parts of the Cocos Plate, in the eastern Pacific Ocean near central America. For simplicity, plate boundaries east of the Panama Fracture Zone (see Figure 13.4) have been omitted.

14.4 Using plate tectonics to explain (nearly) everything

We have frequently stated that plate tectonics provides a comprehensive explanation of many diverse aspects of the Earth, such as its surface features, earthquakes, volcanism and certain mineral deposits. To illustrate the success of plate tectonics in accounting for several aspects of the active Earth, this section, and in particular Activity 14.2, considers how a great many of the features associated with the Pacific coast of western North America can be explained by plate tectonics. As our starting point, consider the plate boundaries in Figure 14.12a. This shows a transform fault linking a subduction zone with a divergent boundary, which is in turn linked to a second divergent boundary by another transform fault.

Figure 14.12 (a) Sketch of a plate boundary system. (b) Sketch of a plate boundary system similar to (a), which corresponds to the plate tectonics of western North America summarized in (c). The red triangles in (c) are active volcanoes.

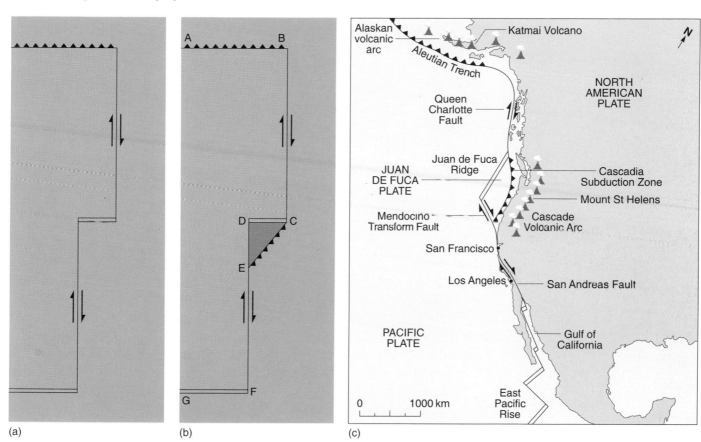

(a) (b) (c)

⬤ How many plates are present in Figure 14.12a?

◯ Two. Relative to the green plate, the brown plate is moving towards the top of the page. (One way of visualizing this is to cut a sheet of paper into the 'P' shape defined by the plate boundaries, and to slide the left-hand plate past the right-hand plate. Spaces will open up in the positions of the divergent boundaries, and subduction will occur along the convergent boundary.)

With the addition of a small subduction zone (Figure 14.12b), this sketch contains all the essential elements of the plate-tectonic situation in western North America (Figure 14.12c). Complete your study of Section 14 by doing the following activity in order to review many of the processes occurring at plate boundaries.

Activity 14.2   Using plate tectonics to explain the active Earth

Western North America and the adjoining Pacific Ocean floor is a region that is subject to volcanic and earthquake activity, both on land and on the ocean floor. In this activity you will discover how the simple system of plate boundaries in Figure 14.12b can account for the features shown in Figure 14.12c. ◄

14.5   Summary of Section 14

Divergent plate boundaries are also known as constructive plate boundaries because new oceanic lithosphere is constructed here by the process of sea-floor spreading. The composition and structure of oceanic lithosphere can be discovered from several lines of evidence. These include seismological evidence for a layered lithosphere, including a crust of about 7 km thickness which is itself layered. Rock samples obtained by dredging and drilling, and studies of ophiolites, indicate that oceanic crust comprises a thin layer of sediment overlying a layer of basaltic lavas overlying a sheeted dyke complex overlying gabbro.

The composition of all the igneous rocks in oceanic crust is basaltic; they differ only in their grain size, reflecting differences in the rate of magma cooling. Basaltic magma is generated in the mantle beneath mid-ocean ridges (divergent plate boundaries) and rises into the crust. Within the crust it may cool slowly to form gabbro or may be transported in dykes to the ocean floor where it erupts to form lava. Sea-floor spreading generates new oceanic lithosphere by the injection of basaltic magmas into existing oceanic lithosphere at mid-ocean ridges.

Oceanic lithosphere is destroyed by subduction at a convergent plate boundary, also known as a destructive plate boundary. Subduction produces a deep ocean trench, a Wadati–Benioff zone of earthquake foci dipping beneath the over-riding plate, and a volcanic arc above the Wadati–Benioff zone which generates explosive eruptions and metal-rich ore deposits. Subduction occurs when dense oceanic lithosphere sinks into the mantle. Continental lithosphere is not subducted because it is too buoyant to sink into the mantle.

Where two pieces of continental lithosphere collide at a convergent plate boundary, they produce a mountain belt. This is associated with shallow earthquakes but no volcanism; an example is the Himalayas.

Plates slide past each other at transform fault boundaries, producing shallow earthquakes but no volcanic activity. Transform faults are commonly associated with mid-ocean ridges, where they cut the ridge at right angles. Transform faults also occur on land; for example, the North American Plate slides southeast past the Pacific Plate along the San Andreas Fault in California.

Why do plates move?

15

Having found out that the plates *are* moving, in this section we aim to find out *why* the plates are moving — what drives their motion? Important clues that will lead us to an answer to this question come from the speeds at which different plates move over the Earth's interior, and from certain volcanoes that are found in the middle of plates, for example those on Hawaii.

15.1   The Hawaiian hot spot

Situated in the middle of the Pacific Plate, the Hawaiian Islands are a popular tourist destination and home to some of the world's most intensively studied volcanoes. (Some of their eruptions appear in the video associated with Activity 8.1.) On the poster map, the Hawaiian Islands are a cluster of barely discernable dots in the middle of the Pacific Ocean, but they are no mere specks of volcanic rock. The highest point on the largest island (the Big Island) is 4.2 km above sea-level, making it higher above the ocean floor (9–10 km) than Mt Everest is above sea-level. The volume of the Big Island is a staggering 10^5 km^3, enough volcanic rock to cover the entire British Isles to a depth of 300 m. All of the Hawaiian Islands have been produced by basaltic volcanism but only the Big Island is still active and growing in size.

What are we to make of this volcanism, situated in a plate interior, some 4 000 km from the nearest plate boundary? After all, plate tectonics seems to do such a good job of explaining why volcanoes are common at plate boundaries. Does this mean that the plate-tectonics theory has failed, and that Earth scientists need to start again and come up with something better? The good news is that plate tectonics still stands, but to explain the volcanoes of Hawaii requires something extra: that the mantle under Hawaii must be unusually hot in order to cause the melting needed to supply the volcanoes with basaltic magma. An anomalously hot zone such as this is called a **hot spot**. Hot spots are attributed to plumes of hot material upwelling from great depths in the Earth, probably from the bottom of the mantle. Other hot-spot volcanoes are dotted around the world (Figure 15.1); most of them

Figure 15.1   The global distribution of hot spots. Names are given for reference only; don't attempt to remember them all.

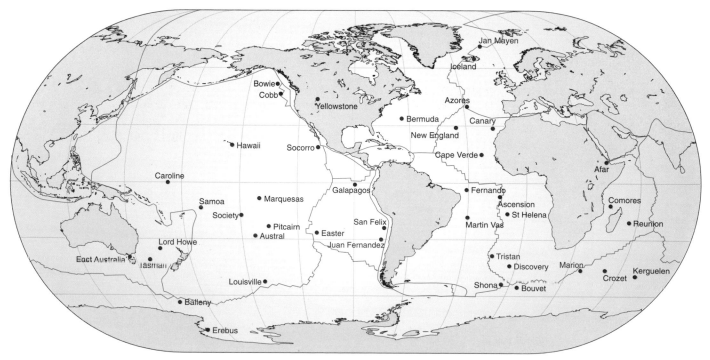

are found far from plate boundaries but some, such as Iceland, coincide with divergent plate boundaries. This is probably coincidence since plumes are derived from the deep mantle whereas plate boundaries are surface features; as plates move, some boundaries inevitably find themselves in the path of ascending plumes.

Hawaii is part of a chain of islands and submarine mountain peaks (called seamounts) stretching almost 6 000 km across the northwest Pacific, making the prominent 'L'-shaped feature we noted on the poster map in Section 6.2.3. Like Hawaii itself, these islands and seamounts are constructed from basaltic volcanic rocks. But unlike Hawaii's Big Island, they are extinct volcanoes. In fact the ages of the islands change systematically along the chain (Figure 15.2).

Figure 15.2 (a) The Hawaii–Emperor chain extends from Hawaii to the Meiji Seamount off Kamchatka. The ages of selected islands and seamounts are indicated in millions of years. (b) Graph of age versus distance from Hawaii measured along the Hawaii–Emperor chain, and the best-fit straight line through the data.

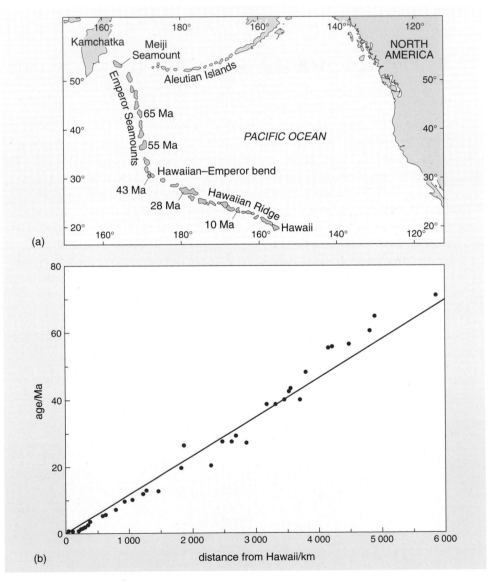

Moving away from Hawaii, how long ago were the basaltic lavas erupted at the volcanoes (a) one-third, and (b) two-thirds of the way along the chain?

(a) about 20 to 25 Ma ago and (b) about 45 Ma ago.

It appears that age is proportional to distance, suggesting that the site of volcanic activity has migrated at a constant speed.

Question 15.1   (a) Use the graph of age versus distance in Figure 15.2b to estimate the average rate at which volcanic activity has appeared to move along the Hawaiian–Emperor seamount chain. Express your answer in mm y^{-1} to two significant figures.

(b) In what direction has this movement been? ◄

Your answers to Question 15.1 should lead you to expect that future volcanic islands will be built up to the southeast of Hawaii. Indeed, the foundations of the next island in the Hawaiian chain are already in place. About 30 km south of Hawaii lies a conical submarine mountain (Loihi), with volcanic craters and hot-water vents at its summit.

But, fascinating as these volcanoes are, how do they relate to plate movements?

15.2   Hot-spot trails and absolute plate motion

Is the trail of volcanoes along the Hawaiian Ridge caused by a hot spot moving beneath a stationary Pacific Plate, or is the plate moving over a static hot spot? This is a tricky question to answer because it is not immediately obvious how these two possibilities can be distinguished. However, there are other hot spots beneath the Pacific Plate, and the chains of extinct volcanoes that they have produced are similar in shape and age progression to the Hawaiian chain. The simplest explanation of this is that all the hot spots are more or less fixed in place and the Pacific Plate moves over them. If each hot spot was moving independently, we would expect to find that each volcanic chain had a different shape or age progression. Thus, hot spots can be considered as fixed markers in the interior of the Earth. This is a very useful result because it allows the rates of plate motion relative to the interior to be found from the age progression along hot-spot trails.

One way of visualizing the movement of the Pacific Plate over the Hawaiian hot spot is to imagine a sheet of paper moving over a candle flame (Figure 15.3). The candle flame singes the moving paper, leaving a trail of scorch marks that records the past positions of the hot flame. The marks furthest from the flame are the oldest and the paper has moved in the direction from the youngest to the oldest scorch mark.

Figure 15.3   A sheet of paper moving over a flame (a) is analogous to the movement of a lithospheric plate over a hot spot (b).

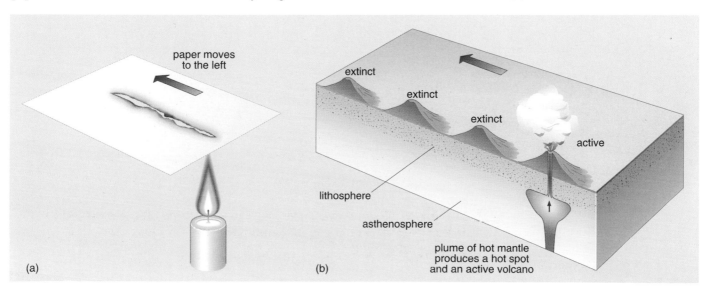

(a)

paper moves to the left

(b)

extinct

extinct

extinct

active

lithosphere

asthenosphere

plume of hot mantle produces a hot spot and an active volcano

○ If the Hawaiian hot spot is stationary and the Pacific Plate moves over it, then which one of the following two statements is correct?

(a) The Pacific Plate is moving northwest at 86 mm y^{-1} with respect to the Hawaiian hot spot.

(b) The Pacific Plate is moving southeast at 86 mm y^{-1} with respect to the Hawaiian hot spot.

○ Statement (a) is the correct one, as can be verified by considering the candle-and-paper analogy.

○ The Hawaii–Emperor chain has a bend, or kink, in it (Figure 15.2 and poster map). What do you think has caused this?

○ Because the hot-spot trail records the direction of plate movement, a change in the direction of the trail signifies a change in the direction of plate motion.

Thus, the Pacific Plate must have changed from moving north to moving northwest at the time of the bend, about 43 Ma ago. Other seamount chains on the Pacific Plate show the same shape (see the poster map).

When the age progressions along other hot-spot trails are worked out, the speeds and directions of plate motion relative to the fixed frame of reference given by hot spots are found to be as given in Figure 15.4. So we now have two ways of considering the rates at which the plates are moving. In Figure 13.4 we showed how one plate moves relative to its neighbour, whereas Figure 15.4 shows how each plate moves relative to the interior of the Earth. The latter motions are called **absolute plate motions** because they do not rely on describing how a plate moves relative to something (another plate) that is itself moving. To appreciate the confusion that can arise from considering relative plate motions, look at the relative plate motion on the southern Mid-Atlantic Ridge on Figure 13.4. The sea-floor spreading rates indicate that Africa is moving eastwards; but if you were standing on the Central Indian Ridge, Africa would appear to be moving to the

Figure 15.4 Present-day motion of lithospheric plates relative to hot spots (absolute plate motion) are shown by the arrows. These indicate the amount of movement that would occur in 50 Ma.

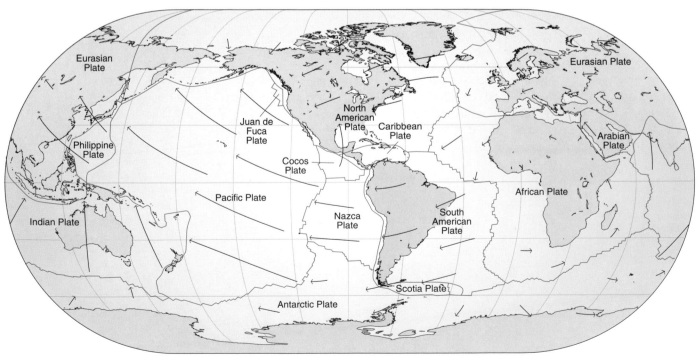

west! This confusion is avoided if we take the static interior of the Earth as our viewing point, allowing us to define an absolute speed for each plate. It is these absolute speeds that can give us clues as to what determines how fast a plate moves.

Question 15.2   Which plate has the fastest absolute speeds, and which plate has the slowest absolute speeds? ◀

15.3   Speed limits for plates

Why don't all plates have the same absolute speeds? There are a number of factors that cause plates to move and other factors that retard motion, with different speeds arising because the relative importance of these factors varies from plate to plate. To decide what these factors might be, let's start by considering why oceanic lithosphere subducts.

Normally the lithosphere lies on top of the asthenosphere — in fact it floats on the asthenosphere because its mean density is less than that of the asthenosphere. This is because the crust contains many rock types that are less dense than the peridotite in the asthenosphere. However, the density of oceanic lithosphere also depends on how cold it is, and this depends on how old it is. Because oceanic lithosphere is produced by igneous activity at mid-ocean ridges, it is relatively hot when formed. But it cools gradually over many millions of years as sea-floor spreading carries it far from the mid-ocean ridge. As it cools it becomes denser, and scientists are agreed that the subducting portion of oceanic lithosphere is slightly denser than the asthenosphere. (The problem of why subduction starts in the first place has not yet been resolved. What is more certain is that once subduction has started it will keep going.) Thus at least one factor contributing to plate motion could be the sinking of the subducting slab into the mantle, which pulls the rest of the plate with it — an effect called the **slab-pull force**.

○ Can the slab-pull force be the only force causing plates to move? (*Hint*: are all moving plates attached to subducting slabs of lithosphere?)

○ Plates such as the Antarctic and North American Plates have no subducting parts (see Figure 13.4), yet they are moving, so some additional force must be acting.

A driving force associated with divergent, rather than convergent, plate boundaries is provided by the lithosphere sliding off the raised ridge — this is the **ridge-slide force**. Counteracting these driving forces is the frictional **drag force** acting on the underside of the plate (Figure 15.5). You can model these three effects by using a sheet of paper, as shown in Box 15.1, *Forces on a plate*.

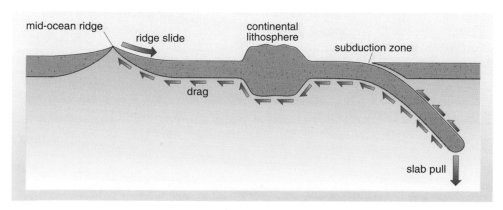

Figure 15.5   A schematic cross-section of a lithospheric plate, labelled with the forces that cause the lithospheric plate to move over the asthenosphere and the drag force that retards motion.

Box 15.1 Forces on a plate

A sheet of paper on a smooth table top provides a model of a lithospheric plate on the asthenosphere.

If the paper is nudged gently along the table (Figure 15.6a), the paper will slow down and come to a halt because of the frictional drag between the table and the paper. As in the case of a glass being pushed across a table (Section 4.1.1 and Figure 4.4), the frictional drag is an unbalanced force that leads to deceleration. This is analogous to the drag that acts to slow down the motion of lithospheric plates as they slide over the asthenosphere. Newton's first law of motion applies to lithospheric plates as well as to glasses, so, to keep the plate moving, a driving force must be maintained.

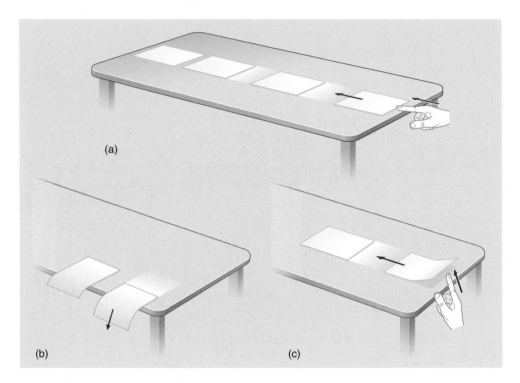

Figure 15.6 A sheet of paper moving over a table illustrates the forces involved when a lithospheric plate moves over the asthenosphere. (a) Drag on the base of the plate. (b) Slab-pull force. (c) Ridge-slide force.

If the paper is allowed to hang over the edge of the table, analogous to a lithospheric plate subducting, then the weight of the 'slab' will pull the rest of the paper with it when there is insufficient paper in contact with the table for the drag to stop the motion (Figure 15.6b). This is a model of the slab-pull force.

Ridge-slide can be modelled by raising one end of the paper above the table to simulate the elevation of the oceanic lithosphere at a mid-ocean ridge. Given sufficient elevation, the paper slides over the table, just as a lithospheric plate might slide over the asthenosphere (Figure 15.6c).

To test whether these factors account for the motion of plates, we can ask ourselves how they might be expected to influence the absolute speeds of plates and then check those expectations against the available evidence from Figure 15.4. For example, if the slab-pull force is important in causing a plate to move quickly, then we would expect to find that fast-moving plates would have a large proportion of their outer edge attached to a subducting slab. Similarly, if ridge-slide is important, then plates with a divergent plate boundary along one side should move rapidly.

Question 15.3   By comparing Figures 15.4 and 13.4, decide which of the following attributes describe (a) the plate with the fastest absolute speeds, and (b) the plate with the slowest absolute speeds:

1   The plate contains a large area of continental lithosphere.

2   The margins of the plate are attached to a subducting slab.

3   There is a divergent plate boundary on one side of the plate. ◀

From the evidence, it appears that plates attached to subducting slabs do indeed move relatively rapidly, and plates with divergent boundaries also move rapidly, confirming slab-pull and ridge-slide as important driving forces. On the other hand, plates with large areas of continental lithosphere tend to move slowly, suggesting that these plates are associated with large forces that inhibit their motion. In particular, the low speeds of plates carrying continental lithosphere suggests that these exert a large drag force, perhaps because the continental lithosphere is especially thick (as indicated in Figure 15.5) and this slows the plate's movement over the asthenosphere.

Although slab-pull, ridge-slide and continental drag account for the main features of plate motion, this is not the whole story. There are additional forces at work such as the resistance where plates grind past each other at transform fault boundaries and where plates collide. There are also suggestions that the rocks in the mantle are sufficiently hot to be constantly flowing as a result of convection and that this gradual movement drags on the base of plates, contributing to their motion.

15.4   Summary of Section 15

Certain volcanoes, such as those on Hawaii, are not associated with plate-boundary processes; instead they are formed from a rising plume of deep-mantle material – – a hot spot. These plumes remain stationary, while plates move over them, creating a line of volcanoes that become older in the direction of absolute plate motion. The age of each volcano gives the time it was over the mantle plume, and allows us to calculate the plate's absolute rate of movement over the asthenosphere. Kinks in hot-spot island chains are evidence for past changes in the direction of absolute plate motion.

A world map of absolute plate motions reveals the slowly-moving plates (Eurasian, African) and the fast-moving ones (Pacific, Indian).

The main plate driving forces are slab-pull and ridge-slide, and the main force resisting plate motion is the drag on the base of the plate, particularly beneath thick continental lithosphere.

16 Plate tectonics and Earth history

The theory of plate tectonics helps us to understand the Earth as it is today and, because it describes how the Earth's oceans and continents slowly change over time, it can also be used to interpret the Earth in the past. In the first part of this section we will consider how the Earth's oceans and continents grow and are destroyed, and look at how plate tectonics has determined the history of the Earth's crust. In the second part we will look at plate motion in the past, and reconstruct the oceans and continents that have existed during the last 400 Ma. We will also make predictions for future changes to the present plates, continents and oceans.

Although geologists have long understood that there are two fundamentally different areas of the crust — oceanic and continental (see Section 6.3) — up to the beginning of the 1960s the oceanic crust was thought to be older than the less dense continental crust. The theory of sea-floor spreading, and data on the age of oceanic crust from ocean drilling, have shown us that the oceanic crust is relatively young (all less than about 180 Ma old; see Figure 16.1) in comparison with the 4 600 Ma age of the Earth.

The continents are on average much older than the oceans, and include rocks up to 4 000 Ma old. The difference in ages between continental crust and the younger oceanic crust is due to differences in how they form, and in the case of oceanic crust, how it is destroyed. As you saw in Section 14, new oceanic crust is formed from mantle rocks at mid-ocean ridges (divergent plate boundaries), then spreads away from the ridge, before finally being subducted back into the mantle at subduction zones. Any piece of oceanic crust exists only for a (geologically) short time before being recycled back into the mantle. This means that there is no old oceanic crust around (with the exception of small pieces preserved on the continents in ophiolites).

Figure 16.1 The ages of the oceanic and continental crust. The white areas are where data are too poor for accurate ages to be determined.

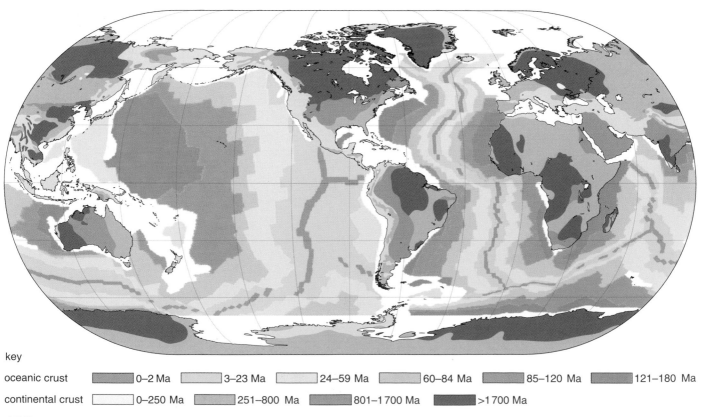

key

oceanic crust   0–2 Ma   3–23 Ma   24–59 Ma   60–84 Ma   85–120 Ma   121–180 Ma

continental crust   0–250 Ma   251–800 Ma   801–1 700 Ma   >1 700 Ma

Continents are different — 4 000 Ma old continental rocks are still around today. Continents can be eroded, and may change their shape by splitting or colliding, but they do not vanish totally. This is fortunate for Earth scientists, as it allows the study of the Earth back to an early stage in its history. We will consider the continental crust, and how it has developed, later in this section, but first we will look in more detail at the oceans.

16.1   The cycle of oceanic lithosphere creation and destruction

Although there is no oceanic lithosphere older than 180 Ma, individual oceans may be older. The Pacific Ocean, for example, first came into existence about 300 Ma ago. The oldest parts of the Pacific oceanic lithosphere have now been subducted, but we know the ocean existed 300 Ma ago through various geological clues that have been left. For example, the tiny Juan de Fuca Plate in the northeast Pacific (Figures 13.2 and 14.12) is the final remnant of a much larger and older oceanic plate that has been (and is still being) subducted beneath North America. At present, the Pacific Ocean is closing (reducing in size), but it will probably take another 200 Ma or so to vanish completely, so the lifetime of the Pacific Ocean could be about 500 Ma. If this is a fairly typical age for a large ocean, then there has been time in the Earth's history for many cycles of ocean creation and destruction.

The relationship between plate tectonics and the ocean cycle can be explored by considering a very much simplified model of the Earth, such as Figure 16.2. Figure 16.2a is a cross-section through this model with two oceans, separated by two continents. Ocean AD (i.e. the ocean between points A and D) has a spreading mid-ocean ridge, and is expanding. Ocean BC has subduction zones at both edges as well

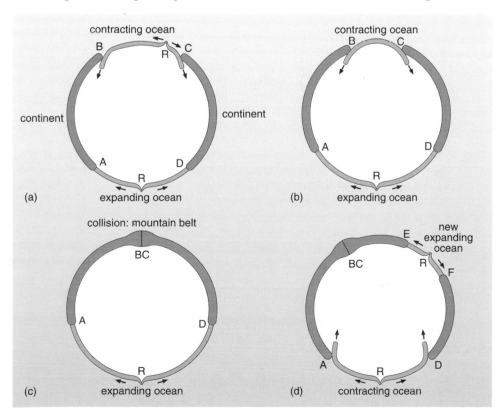

Figure 16.2   The ocean cycle. (a) Initially, both oceans have spreading mid-ocean ridges, R, and ocean BC has subduction zones at B and C. Ocean AD is expanding and ocean BC is contracting. (b) At a later time, the ridge in ocean BC has been subducted. (c) Later, the ocean BC has closed completely. (d) Later still, subduction has started in ocean AD and a new ocean EF has opened, splitting the continent.

as a spreading ridge. Overall, because ocean AD is expanding, and because the model Earth must stay the same size, it follows that ocean BC must be contracting. At a later time (Figure 16.2b) the spreading ridge in ocean BC has been subducted and if the rates of subduction have not changed, the ocean BC is now contracting faster than in Figure 16.2a.

⬤ . Will the spreading rate of the ridge in ocean AD have changed (if the subduction rates do not change) between Figure 16.2a and Figure 16.2b?

◯ Yes; as ocean BC is contracting faster in Figure 16.2b, ocean AD must expand faster, so the ridge will have a higher spreading rate.

Figure 16.2c shows the situation at a later stage. Ocean BC has closed completely, and the continents have collided, forming a mountain belt. There is now only one large continent (a 'supercontinent') and one large ocean.

⬤ What will happen to the spreading rate of ocean AD at this stage?

◯ The collision of the two continents will probably reduce their speed of convergence, and so the spreading rate of ocean AD will reduce to match.

There are a number of different scenarios that could happen after this; one of them is shown in Figure 16.2d. The ocean AD, which had very old, cold and therefore dense lithosphere at its edges, has developed subduction zones at each edge, and is contracting. It will eventually close up completely, like ocean BC. Because this ocean is contracting, spreading must start somewhere else to maintain the size of the model Earth. This is happening where the supercontinent has split, forming two new continents, AE and FD, separated by a new expanding ocean, EF.

Question 16.1 Draw, in the style of Figure 16.2, an alternative stage (d), where the supercontinent AD has not split apart. ◀

The ocean cycle shown in Figure 16.2 is an illustration of one of the fundamental deductions from plate-tectonic theory, that geological processes on one part of the Earth can affect processes a long distance away, on, or at the margins of, other plates. For example, the closure of ocean BC can cause a different ocean, AD, to stop expanding, develop subduction zones and begin to contract.

Question 16.2 Figure 16.3 is a simplified cross-section of the Earth at the present day, approximately through the Tropic of Capricorn (23.5° S), showing the continents and oceans, drawn in the same style as Figure 16.2 but without the mid-ocean ridges and subduction zones marked. Draw ridges and subduction zones on the cross-section, using information from this section and Figures 6.7 and 13.4, mark each ocean as 'expanding' or 'contracting', and name each ocean, mid-ocean ridge and trench. ◀

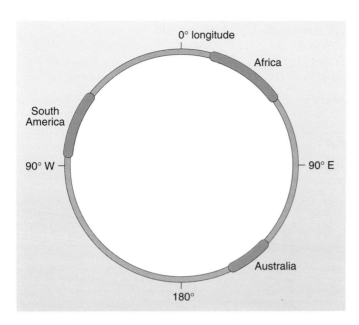

Figure 16.3   For use with Question 16.2.

16.2   Plate tectonics and the growth of continental crust

We have seen that plate tectonics, and in particular sea-floor spreading, is responsible for the origin and growth of oceanic lithosphere (Section 14.1). And plate tectonics is responsible for the destruction of oceanic lithosphere through subduction, resulting in a relatively 'young' ocean floor and the operation of a cycle of ocean formation and destruction.

Plate tectonics also plays a role in the growth of continental crust but, as we shall see, the history of the continents is different from that of the oceans. The first evidence of this is the much greater age of the continents (see Figure 16.1). A second indication is that a wide range of igneous, sedimentary and metamorphic rocks are present on the continents, in contrast to the essentially igneous oceanic crust. Together these indicate that the processes that form and destroy continental crust must be very different from those that influence oceanic crust.

Continents can be considered to grow in two ways — by addition of *new* material from a different part of the Earth such as the mantle or the oceanic lithosphere, and by re-arrangement of *existing* continental material.

New material can be added in two ways:

1   Igneous activity at subduction zones (Section 14.2). South America, for example, with volcanoes and intrusive igneous rocks along its western side, has the volume of its continental crust increasing, because magma is being removed from the mantle and added to the overlying crust.

2   Oceanic lithosphere that has been uplifted onto continents as ophiolites (Section 14.1.1 and Figure 14.3). Although ophiolites are composed of oceanic rocks, they have become locked into continental crust.

The processes in which existing continental material gets redistributed and re-arranged are many and sometimes complex. For example, two continents can collide, forming a larger continent, as when India collided with Eurasia (as you may recall from Activity 11.2). Continents can also grow not just by the collision of two substantial continents to give a larger continent, but by processes that add smaller areas onto continents. One of these processes is illustrated in Figure 16.4. Consider what will happen to a plate with both oceanic and continental lithosphere, with the oceanic part being subducted beneath an island arc. When the continent reaches the island arc, the arc and continent collide, and subduction stops, as the continent will not subduct beneath the arc because of its low density. The island arc is added to the edge of the continent so the continent increases in size (Figure 16.4b). This process is called **island-arc accretion**. Western North America, for example, was partly formed when a number of island arcs that originally existed in an ancient Pacific Ocean collided with the continent along convergent plate boundaries.

Figure 16.4 Island-arc accretion. (a) Oceanic lithosphere is being subducted at an island arc. The plate with this oceanic lithosphere also has continental lithosphere. (b) When the continent reaches the subduction zone, the arc and continent collide forming a larger continent.

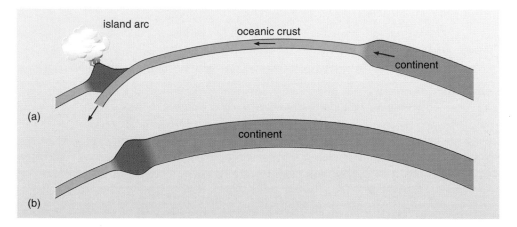

So continental crust can be re-organized by plate tectonics, but continental material can also be redistributed by sedimentary processes. Consider what happens to continents when they are eroded by the action of wind, water or ice. Erosion of continents produces rock and mineral fragments and dissolved material that may end up either as new sedimentary rock on land or on the ocean floor. The new rock on land is still part of the continent, so it doesn't *add* material to the continental crust. How about the ocean-floor sediments, which are now part of the oceanic crust? The igneous oceanic crust is recycled into the mantle at subduction zones, but some of the sediment is scraped off the descending oceanic plate, onto the upper continental plate, a process called **subduction-zone accretion** (Section 14.2 and Figure 14.8). This process adds oceanic sediment to the margin of an island arc or continent. Although this creates 'new' continental crust at a particular locality, the materials involved are not new but were derived from existing continental crust — so subduction-zone accretion *recycles* continental crust but does not create new material.

Are there any processes that can remove continental crust, similar to the subduction of oceanic crust back into the mantle?

Unlike the oceanic lithosphere, very little continental crust is recycled into the mantle.

○ Why is continental crust prevented from being subducted when it reaches a subduction zone?

○ Continental crust is less dense than the mantle (Section 14.2), so it is too buoyant to be subducted.

Despite this, some of the ocean-floor sediment at a subduction zone is sometimes carried down with the igneous oceanic crust subducted into the mantle. So it *is* possible to destroy at least some of the continental crust (after its erosion and re-formation as oceanic sediment).

Now consider the balance between the rate of creation of new continental crust by volcanic activity at subduction zones and by ophiolite formation, and the rate of destruction by subduction of sediment. If those rates were equal, the total amount of continental crust would not change. Most Earth scientists believe that more continental crust is being created than destroyed, so the amount of continental crust is *increasing* with time.

This does not necessarily imply that *individual continents* are growing. Some are, by the processes we have just described, but others are in the process of splitting into smaller continents.

Question 16.3   Use Figure 13.4 to identify where one continent has relatively recently split into two continents separated by oceanic lithosphere. (A recently-formed ocean will be very narrow because not much oceanic lithosphere will have been generated in the short period of sea-floor spreading.) ◄

It is worth remembering that all types of continental growth — from the joining of two large continents, to subduction-zone volcanism, ophiolites, subduction-zone accretion and island-arc accretion — and continental destruction are caused by plate tectonics. An Earth without plate tectonics would be very different indeed.

16.3   Plate motion in the past and future

Having studied the cycle of ocean creation and destruction (Section 16.1) and the growth and recycling of continental crust (Section 16.2) we can now apply this knowledge to investigate the plate-tectonic history of the Earth, with its past continents and oceans. We can also make predictions of what will happen to our present plates in the future.

The recognition of present-day plate boundaries, and measurement of the rates of absolute and relative present plate motion, are relatively straightforward, using earthquakes, volcanoes, hot spots and the Earth's major surface features. But how can we find out about plates in the past? The main evidence of a present-day plate boundary — earthquakes — does not generally produce features that are preserved in older rocks. How can we find out about past plate motion?

Question 16.4   What four types of evidence can be used to determine the position of continents or plates in the past? (You may need to refer back to Sections 11 and 12.) ◄

As well as determining the position of plates in the past (such data are called plate reconstructions), it is also possible to predict what will happen to plates in the future — at least for the (geologically) near future of a hundred million years or so. The starting point for these predictions is present plate motion, which we know fairly accurately (Figure 13.4). Predictions for too far in the future, or in too great detail, are subject to greater uncertainty. Because the movement of any one plate is severely constrained by the movements of all the others, a major change in the direction or rate of motion of one plate (caused, for example, by a continental collision) usually causes the pattern of motion of plates to be rearranged globally (as in Figure 16.2, for example) into one of a number of different possibilities (Question 16.1). Several such rearrangements have occurred in the past. An exact prediction of what will happen cannot be made — we can only suggest *possibilities*. Predictions for the future are not certain: they are just best estimates based on the data we have at present.

Activity 16.1   Plate motion in the past and future

In this CD-ROM activity you will investigate plate reconstructions for the past 400 Ma and predictions for the future 100 Ma. ◀

Question 16.5   Los Angeles, on the western side of the San Andreas Fault, is part of the Pacific Plate, and San Francisco, on the eastern side, is part of the North American Plate (Figure 14.12). The cities are about 560 km apart at present but are moving together as the plates slide past each other. The relative speed of movement of the two plates along the fault is about 20 mm y^{-1}. At this present rate, how long will it take for Los Angeles to become a suburb of San Francisco? ◀

16.4   Summary of Section 16

All of the oceanic crust is less than 180 Ma old. There is no older oceanic crust still in existence (except in ophiolites) as it has been recycled into the mantle by subduction.

Continental crust is up to 4 000 Ma old. It originates by volcanic activity at subduction zones and by ophiolite formation. Continental crust has a low density, so whole continents do not subduct, but some eroded continental rock can be subducted in the form of oceanic sediment. The amount of continental crust on the Earth is increasing with time. Individual continents can increase in size by subduction-zone accretion and island-arc accretion, as well as by continental collision. Continents can also split into smaller continents.

Past plate reconstructions can be made from data on continental fit, occurrence of fossils, ancient climates and palaeomagnetism (for continents as well as marine magnetic anomalies). Marine magnetic anomalies are the most useful data, but only for the last 140 Ma or so.

Plate movement has created and destroyed oceans, and created supercontinents and also split them. Some countries or continents have moved large distances, changing latitude and climate.

Future predictions of plate motion use present plate motion as a starting point. Exact predictions cannot be made: Earth scientists can only suggest possibilities.

The rock cycle

17

You saw in Section 16 how material from continental crust can be eroded, deposited as sediment on the ocean floor, then scraped off and accreted to form new continental rocks. This process, and other aspects of continental and oceanic growth that result from plate tectonics, are examples of how rocks are formed and destroyed on the Earth. As you are reading this, rocks are being heated and squashed in mountain belts at convergent plate boundaries to form new metamorphic rocks (Section 14.2); other rocks at mid-ocean ridges and subduction zones are melting to form magmas that eventually cool as new igneous rocks; and the erosion of rocks is forming new sediments. For example, each grain of sand or mud in a river estuary was derived from weathering and erosion of rocks further upstream. The liberated particles were transported by the river and eventually deposited (as in Figure 17.1). Over many centuries these sediments may become deeply buried under more sedimentary material, becoming compacted and cemented to form a sedimentary rock (Section 9.3). Thus, the rocks of the mountains can be remade as new sedimentary rocks. But what is the origin of the rocks that were eroded to produce the new sediments?

Figure 17.1 The mountains of North Wales, in the distant background, are the source of the mud deposits of the Mawddach Estuary, seen in the foreground.

Any sedimentary rock must have been formed by a sequence of weathering, erosion, transport and deposition not too dissimilar to that forming new sediments today. Here is the germ of a startling conclusion: the continual action of rock-forming processes means that the rocks of the Earth's crust become transformed *and retransformed* into new types of rock. The rocks making up the cliffs at the shore, or high mountain crags, are made from materials that were once parts of some other rocks. And, given time, these same cliffs and crags will themselves be transformed, a fact that will be only too familiar if you live in an area subject to the effects of coastal erosion. We have here the indications of a cycle, analogous to the carbon or water cycles that you met in Block 2, in which any rock may become converted into other rock types. This is the **rock cycle**.

17.1 Moving around the rock cycle

Figure 17.2 illustrates the simplicity of the rock cycle: the three classes of rock are linked by arrows indicating that any type of rock can be converted into any other type of rock.

Figure 17.2 A schematic diagram of the rock cycle. The blue arrows represent formation of sedimentary rocks, red arrows formation of igneous rocks, and yellow arrows formation of metamorphic rocks.

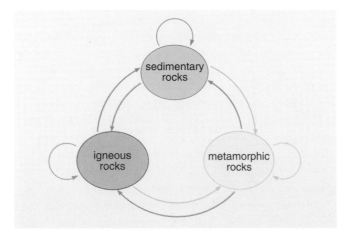

○ How many arrows lead to each class of rock?

○ Three. One arrow comes from each of the other rock classes, and one is a loop within the class.

Each set of three coloured arrows is associated with one general type of rock-forming process. Thus, the blue arrows in Figure 17.2 represent the sedimentary processes by which sedimentary rocks form from pre-existing rocks of any type. Yellow arrows represent the formation of metamorphic rocks from any other rock, be it sedimentary, igneous or metamorphic, by recrystallization as a result of deep burial and/or heating. Igneous rocks form (red arrows) when magmas cool, and most magmas are produced by the melting of mantle peridotite; some magmas form when existing metamorphic, sedimentary or igneous rocks become so hot that they melt.

Figure 17.2 is a purely schematic representation of the important idea that all types of rock can be derived from, or lead to, another type of rock. An alternative way of illustrating the possible ways of moving material around the rock cycle is with a diagram that places the processes into their geological contexts. Since the rock cycle involves processes occurring on the Earth's surface and also within its interior, we use a cross-section through the Earth, as shown in Figure 17.3. In this diagram we have concentrated on the most prominent processes within the rock cycle. Less significant processes like the melting of igneous or sedimentary rocks to form new magmas, and the recrystallization of metamorphic rocks to form new metamorphic rocks, do not appear on Figure 17.3.

At the start of Section 17 we noted how one sedimentary rock may be turned into sediment, redeposited and potentially turned into a new sedimentary rock. However, the new sediment is not just the old sedimentary rock stuck back together again after having been broken apart and transported. Some of the original mineral grains will have been dissolved and some get transported further than others, becoming deposited alongside grains from other rocks. If you examine some grains of sand from a beach, you'll generally find some broken fragments of sea-shells; these

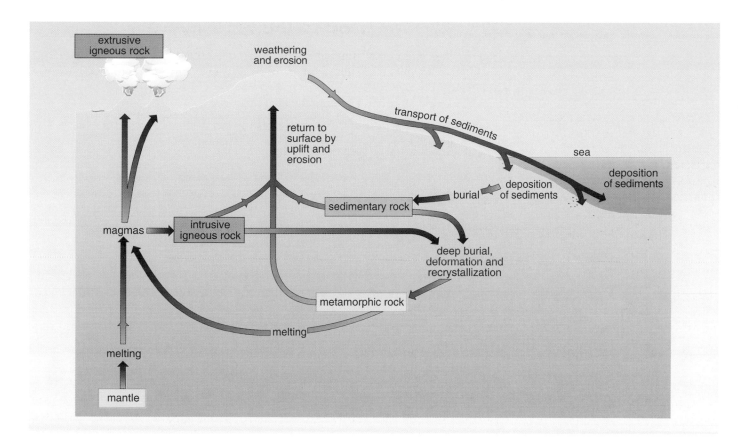

certainly weren't part of the rocks supplying the mineral grains. Likewise, magmas are formed by *partial* melting of pre-existing rocks, so the original rock does not get entirely converted to magma. Of the processes that move material round the rock cycle, only metamorphism involves the conversion of one rock type to another without it gaining or losing any material.

Figure 17.3 The rock cycle. The arrows show the paths and processes taken in transforming one type of rock (contained in a box) to another type.

Activity 17.1   Using a diagram of the rock cycle

In this activity you will draw together information in Figure 17.3 and your knowledge of rocks from earlier sections to summarize several aspects of the rock cycle. ◀

17.2   The rock cycle and plate tectonics

The rock cycle operates because the sedimentary, metamorphic and igneous processes you first met in Section 9 are maintained by the dynamic nature of the Earth. On the grand scale of the Earth, it is plate tectonics that drives many of the rock-cycle processes, with activity being concentrated at plate boundaries rather than distributed evenly over the Earth.

◯ Suggest a plate-tectonic setting where metamorphic processes take place.

◯ The increases in pressure and temperature needed to cause metamorphism in the crust occur in continental collision zones. Metamorphism also occurs in the crust within subduction zones where rocks get dragged down to great depths and hence experience great pressure.

● In which plate-tectonic settings do igneous processes take place?

○ Melting takes place in the mantle beneath divergent plate boundaries, above the subducting plate at convergent plate boundaries, and far from plate boundaries at hot spots. (Occasionally, crustal rocks will melt to form magmas where metamorphism is particularly intense at continental collision zones.)

Sedimentary rocks form under a great variety of circumstances such as glacial environments, deserts and the coral reefs on continental shelves. Some great rivers, such as the Nile and Mississippi, transport sedimentary material many thousands of kilometres across plate interiors, laying down fertile muddy sediments and modifying the coastline by forming deltas. Other great rivers, such as the Ganges, Indus and Brahmaputra, rise in the high mountain belts where plates are colliding. In these collision zones, plate convergence thrusts mountains into the sky, but the steep mountain slopes and high rainfall encourage weathering and erosion, with the surprising net result that sites of mountain building are actually prodigious suppliers of sediment, which gets washed away to be deposited elsewhere. The Bay of Bengal contains several million km^3 of sediment that has been removed from the Himalayan Mountains by erosion and transported to the sea.

Plate tectonics thus maintains the rock cycle, not only by producing metamorphic and igneous rocks at plate boundaries, but also through its influence on sedimentary processes. Although the rock cycle moulds the geology of the crust, it does not operate independently of other parts of the Earth. For one thing, the rock cycle crucially involves the mantle, which is the source of most magma. Neither is the rock cycle isolated from other processes taking place in the Earth. For instance, consider the following question.

Question 17.1   Which parts of the rock cycle involve the Earth's atmosphere? You might find it helpful to look at Figure 17.3, as well as recalling information from Block 2. ◄

The rock cycle also interacts with the water and carbon cycles, which themselves interact with each other and with the rock cycle. In the carbon cycle, volcanoes are a source of atmospheric carbon dioxide, and carbonate rocks and fossil fuels are enormous stores of carbon. Through the carbon cycle, rocks are intimately linked into life on the Earth. This last interaction may not seem so obvious at first, but think again about fossil fuels — the carbon in a lump of coal, barrel of crude oil or petrol tank, was once part of a living organism. This is why we turn to life on the Earth in the next section.

17.3   Summary of Section 17

Rocks are formed by geological processes acting on pre-existing rocks, so that new rocks are produced from the materials within older rocks. Because plate tectonics and motions in the atmosphere and oceans make the Earth a dynamic planet, these rock-forming processes are continually maintained. The result is that sedimentary, metamorphic and igneous rocks are produced within a cycle — the rock cycle — which is the path taken by Earth materials in response to chemical, biological and physical changes acting upon rocks.

Those parts of the rock cycle that produce many new sedimentary rocks involve the weathering and erosion of pre-existing rocks, followed by transport and deposition of eroded mineral grains and rock fragments. Other new sedimentary rocks are formed by biological processes, such as the accumulation of shells. In both cases these processes occur on the surface of the Earth.

Most igneous and metamorphic rocks are produced near the boundaries between lithospheric plates, so these parts of the rock cycle are 'activated' by plate tectonics, and they take place within the interior of the Earth.

18 The biosphere

We ended Section 17 with a discussion of how processes within the rock cycle influence other components of the Earth system, like the atmosphere, the water cycle and the carbon cycle. In addition to these interactions, it is also apparent that geological processes in the rock cycle affect living things. For example, the weathering products of rocks become the soils and sediments that organisms require for nutrients, physical anchors, water storage and many other functions. Many plants, for instance, prefer or require certain soil types — beech trees thrive on limestone soils, while many species of heather and peat moss are killed by too much limestone; the loose-structured sand that dune grass thrives in would not support large trees. Most animals, because they ultimately depend for their food on the plants that are rooted in soil, are just as tied to processes occurring within the rock cycle.

Life is not only dependent on rocks as such, but also on the environments generated by the geological evolution of the Earth — volcanic islands, mountains, coasts, and so on. Animals often use geological structures for protection; cliff-nesting seagulls or cave-dwelling bats come to mind. The energy and nutrients from deep-ocean vents, as you saw in Activity 12.1, support a diverse community of organisms that are not dependent on photosynthesis. Sometimes organisms are tied to the rock cycle in ways that might seem bizarre to us — for instance, the megapode, a bird in Papua New Guinea, incubates its eggs using the heat from the ground around volcanoes!

Plate tectonics also influences life on our planet, and not just by causing hazardous volcanic eruptions and earthquakes. Continental drift can slowly carry the native species of a continent to a different climate zone, requiring them to migrate or adapt to the new climatic conditions. New species may evolve as a result, and some of the original species may become extinct. Also, the collision of two continents may bring together plants and animals that had previously been separated. For some species, the introduction of more efficient organisms or new predators may spell extinction, whereas for others the new habitat may allow them to expand their range. Mountain building also provides new habitats for organisms.

Life is influenced by the land, oceans, freshwater, and atmosphere of the Earth in many ways, both direct and indirect. What is perhaps less obvious is the converse — that all of these components of the physical environment of Earth are irrevocably affected by living organisms. The profound effect of life on the Earth is the subject of this final section in this block.

18.1 The business of life

Life can be found nearly everywhere on the surface of the Earth — from the deepest ocean floor to the peaks of the highest mountains and into the atmosphere. Anywhere, it seems, where there are water and nutrients, and where temperatures are not too extreme, life is possible. The part of the planet that is capable of supporting life is known as the **biosphere**. The biosphere extends from the bottom of deep ocean trenches to a few thousand metres of altitude in the atmosphere, in an encircling shell around the Earth with an average thickness of about 14 km. As far as we know, this thin skin is the only place in the Solar System that today supports life.

The effects of life on non-living parts of the Earth are the result of a vast number of individual organisms going about the 'business of life' for the last four billion years or so. The business is simple: they must survive and maintain themselves, and produce the next generation. As you will see in later blocks, all living organisms, even the simplest bacteria, are highly ordered systems of specialist molecules. Building and maintaining any ordered system, whether a house, a bicycle, or a living organism, requires raw materials and energy.

○ Which element is the fundamental raw material for the construction of living things?

○ Carbon (Block 2, Section 8).

All living organisms, from penicillin to penguins, are composed of chains of carbon atoms linked with other atoms, primarily hydrogen, oxygen, nitrogen and sulfur. Organisms acquire carbon from either carbon dioxide in the atmosphere, carbon dissolved in water (oceans, lakes, rivers), or carbon in other organisms. Nearly all living organisms *ultimately* depend on the process of photosynthesis to make the Earth's carbon and the Sun's energy available to them.

○ Photosynthesis should be a familiar term to you. Write down a word equation for the process.

○ Carbon dioxide and water and energy from the Sun *react to form* organic matter and oxygen (Block 2, Section 8).

Green plants use the energy in sunlight to convert carbon dioxide and water into simple carbon-based organic compounds, or sugars. These sugars can be broken down to release stored energy, or built up into more complex compounds to form plant tissue. In Block 2, Section 8, we noted that the plant material formed as a result of photosynthesis does not keep building up on the Earth's surface — it decomposes. Decomposers break down plant material and release the carbon through respiration. Today, since the amount of plant material produced globally through photosynthesis each year is approximately matched by the amount of plant material consumed through respiration, the amount of vegetation on the Earth's surface is approximately in a steady state, with our 'green planet' as the obvious product.

But something else, less visible, is another result of photosynthesis.

○ Which gas is released from plants during photosynthesis?

○ Oxygen.

Let's explore some consequences of that.

18.2 Life and the atmosphere

At first glance, Earth is not very different from its neighbour planets Venus and Mars. As we saw in Section 5, they are roughly the same size, they were formed in similar ways and they are composed of similar types of rocky materials. However, with a closer look, the Earth reveals itself to be a strikingly different place. Its surface is largely covered by an ocean of water, for instance. The Earth also has a very different atmosphere from those of its neighbours.

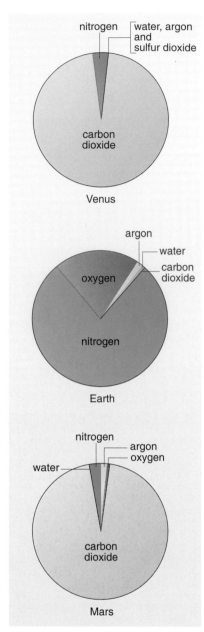

Figure 18.1 Pie charts of the main constituents of the atmospheres of Venus, the Earth and Mars. (Pie charts were first described in the Study File for Block 2.)

According to Figure 18.1, what are the major differences between the composition of the atmosphere of the Earth and those of her two nearest neighbours?

The atmospheres of Venus and Mars are dominated by carbon dioxide with small proportions of nitrogen and small to negligible amounts of oxygen. The main atmospheric gases on Earth, on the other hand, are nitrogen and oxygen, with small amounts of carbon dioxide.

Now, a visitor from outer space who knew nothing more about these three planets would immediately single out the Earth as very strange. Particularly startling is the high level of oxygen gas in the atmosphere of the Earth. Oxygen is a highly reactive gas — it combines readily (sometimes explosively) with many other elements and compounds (a common example is when oxygen and water combine with iron to form rust). Once combined with other elements, oxygen tends to stay combined because it takes a lot of energy to get the oxygen back out. Any oxygen that found its way into the atmosphere of a planet, then, would be fairly quickly removed by chemical reactions.

The high level of oxygen in the atmosphere of the Earth can only mean one thing — some continuous supply of oxygen keeps replacing the oxygen that chemically combines with other elements. Without a continuous supply, all the oxygen on the Earth would eventually be locked up in rocks, in carbon dioxide, or combined with other elements. Furthermore, the near-absence from the Earth of the very stable gas carbon dioxide (which, unlike oxygen, does not readily react with other elements and compounds) is also a puzzle. Without continuous removal, carbon dioxide would accumulate in the atmosphere. It looks, in fact, as if something is tinkering with the atmosphere of this special planet.

Which process continuously supplies oxygen to the atmosphere and continuously removes carbon dioxide from the atmosphere?

Photosynthesis by green plants.

Plants have indeed dramatically changed the composition of the Earth's atmosphere by acting as a living filter, removing carbon dioxide from the atmosphere and releasing oxygen. A large amount of atmospheric carbon dioxide has also been removed and stored in the calcium carbonate shells of marine organisms, mainly plankton (Block 2, Section 8).

Without ever setting foot on the Earth's surface, our alien scientist would come to a startling and inescapable conclusion:

> The high level of oxygen and low level of carbon dioxide in the Earth's atmosphere are due to the presence of life.

Indeed, any scientist who discovers another planet with such an atmosphere would come to the conclusion that it too harbours life.

The oxygen-rich atmosphere produced by plants has a major indirect effect on life. Some of the oxygen in the stratosphere (Block 2, Section 6.2) absorbs ultraviolet radiation, and is converted into ozone. This has created a 'band' of high ozone levels encircling the Earth at about 30 km above the surface — the 'ozone layer'. The ozone absorbs ultraviolet (UV) light from the Sun, and this protects the Earth's surface from receiving high levels of this radiation, which is extremely damaging to living organisms. (You have probably heard about an alarming 'hole' that appears in the ozone layer at high latitudes during summer, and the implications this has for possible increased rates of skin cancer in humans.) Without plants to produce the oxygen that is converted to ozone, the Earth's land surface would be sterilized by intense UV radiation from the Sun.

Water can absorb UV radiation, so aquatic organisms could survive in a world without an ozone layer, but land plants and animals could not. Indeed, this is one of the main arguments for the suggestion that aquatic plants such as phytoplankton and seaweeds existed for many billions of years before land plants — the land plants could not exist until aquatic plants had generated enough atmospheric oxygen to produce the ozone shield.

Question 18.1   In Block 2 we discussed another aspect of the Earth that is indirectly affected by life — global mean surface temperature (GMST). Given what you know about the effect of life on atmospheric carbon dioxide, do you think the Earth's GMST would be higher, lower, or about the same as today in the absence of life? Why? ◄

The profound effect of life on the balance between oxygen and carbon dioxide in Earth's atmosphere is due to the actions of organisms respiring and photosynthesizing. These organisms directly affect the cycles of carbon and oxygen on Earth. But organisms use and recycle not only carbon and oxygen but also nitrogen, sulfur, calcium, magnesium, iron and many other elements. In fact, there are few chemical reactions on the surface of the Earth that are *not* affected by life.

The interactions between living organisms and chemical cycles make up the biogeochemical cycles of elements that were first discussed in Block 2, Section 8.2.2. Recall that the effect of humans on the carbon cycle is most noticeable in the carbon dioxide level of the atmosphere, because it is a small reservoir with direct links to many other reservoirs and processes in the cycle. For the same reason, the effects of all life on the global cycling of elements are reflected primarily in the chemical compositions of the atmosphere, freshwater and oceans, since air and water are the main media through which organisms exchange material and energy. But life also affects the *physical* cycling of water around the Earth, as we shall explore next.

18.3 Life and the water cycle

Life affects the water cycle in both direct and indirect ways. Plants transport water from the soil into roots and leaves, then release much of that water through tiny pores called stomata on the undersides of their leaves in the process of transpiration (Block 2, Section 7.2.2). Plants, then, serve as a kind of 'green pump' — moving water from soils into the atmosphere.

○ What would be one eventual consequence of more water moving into the atmosphere?

○ More water in the atmosphere eventually means more precipitation (rain, snow, etc.).

By pumping water into the atmosphere, plants can change the pattern of rainfall over a region. Conversely, when land is cleared of vegetation, the rainfall over that area may decrease — or, depending on complex weather patterns, may decrease elsewhere. Local and regional changes in patterns of precipitation due to changes in the vegetation can affect regional temperature and wind patterns, and these in turn can affect large-scale atmospheric circulation patterns.

If the precipitation rate in a cleared region were to stay constant, however, then the removal of plants means that more water would run off in streams and rivers rather than being used by the plants and moving into the atmosphere through transpiration. Now, humans have been clearing forests for wood production and agriculture at ever-increasing rates. Over the last hundred years there has been an increase of roughly 3% in the global runoff of water from rivers into the sea. It is quite possible that this is a case of humans changing the global water cycle through the massive clearing of formerly forested land (it is also possible, however, that it is due to some other factor, such as a change in global climate). In addition, removal of plants, which bind soil together with their roots, increases the erosion rate — an effect on the rock cycle.

There are numerous indirect effects of life on the water cycle. We have already discussed the importance of life on the balance of carbon dioxide and oxygen in the atmosphere. It is likely that without living organisms removing carbon dioxide through photosynthesis and carbonate secretion, the Earth would be a much warmer planet. Since a warmer planet evaporates more water than a cooler planet, a high-carbon dioxide, warm Earth would probably have much more water in its atmosphere. More water vapour (another greenhouse gas) in the atmosphere could cause the surface temperature to increase yet more, thus evaporating more water.

○ This is an example of what effect?

○ It is positive feedback (Block 2, Section 7.5).

And what would be the outcome of this? Because of the many other feedback processes that come into play, like cloud formation or weathering, the effect of changes in the quantity of atmospheric carbon dioxide on the Earth's water cycle is a matter of continuing debate. Although it is clear that the action of living organisms in removing large amounts of carbon dioxide from the atmosphere has greatly influenced the cycling of water around the Earth, exactly how is not so certain!

18.4 Life and the rock cycle

Even the rock cycle is greatly influenced by life. An obvious example is the formation of limestones. For example, chalk is formed from sediments composed of the remains of countless microscopic organisms which secreted protective shells made of calcium carbonate (Section 9.3). Other limestones are formed from the calcium carbonate shells of larger organisms. Similarly, modern coral reefs are built of communities of coral organisms, which also form calcium carbonate structures for protection and defence. Some of these coral reefs cover areas large enough to be seen from space (Figure 18.2).

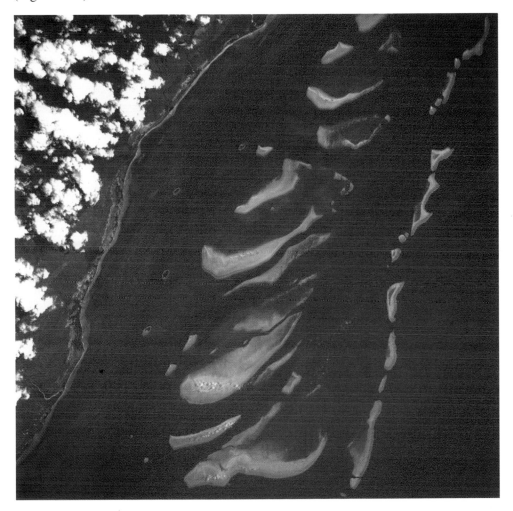

Figure 18.2 Part of the 2 000 km long Great Barrier Reef from space. The reef lies off the northeast coast of Australia, seen on the left of the picture, at distances of between 15 and 50 km. This picture, taken from the Space Shuttle 230 km above the Earth, shows several coral islands and reefs; the largest is about 20 km long.

Another way in which the organisms in the biosphere affect the rock cycle is through weathering (Figure 18.3). Rocks are partly broken down by the physical action of wind, rain, ice, and extremes in temperature, but this is greatly accelerated by plant roots, micro-organisms, and other living organisms in the soil. The action is partly physical — think of grass growing through a pavement, or saplings wedged in the cracks in a boulder — but the most important process is chemical.

The process works like this. All living things respire and, through respiration, most release carbon dioxide. Plants release some carbon dioxide directly into the soil water through their roots. Carbon dioxide, as you should recall (Block 2, Section 8.4.4), dissolves readily in water, and the dissolved carbon dioxide makes the soil water slightly acid. The acid is quite weak; in fact, it has about the same acidity as a fizzy drink (which also contains dissolved carbon dioxide). However, prolonged contact with this slightly acid soil water slowly breaks down the minerals in rocks — they weather faster. (Many plants also release other acids of their own to hasten the process, since some of the materials released from rocks by weathering are nutrients.) A lichen slowly crumbling a stone wall is doing so through chemical weathering, and is forming soil for other plants to follow and continue the process.

(a)

(b)

Figure 18.3 Physical and chemical weathering of rocks can be greatly enhanced by vegetation. (a) Vegetation breaking apart pavement, showing physical weathering. (b) Lichen break down the rock they grow on to obtain nutrients.

The contribution to weathering by organisms has resulted in soil formation (soil is a mixture of weathered rock and organic material) and an increased amount of sedimentary material in the rock cycle. We can thus safely say that a significant amount of the Earth's sediments and sedimentary rock (that derived from carbonate sediments formed by organisms and that derived from sediments due to plant-enhanced weathering of rock), and all of its soil, are products of biological processes. We can also safely say that not only does life require the environment generated by the rock cycle, but that some of that very environment is the product of life!

So life has profoundly affected the carbon and oxygen cycles, other biogeochemical cycles, the water cycle, the rock cycle, and the Earth's climate. Indeed, almost everything we know of as 'normal' in our world is in some way modified by life. In Block 4 we shall turn to this phenomenon 'life' and examine it in more detail.

Question 18.2   Describe one way in which life influences each of: (a) the atmosphere; (b) the lithosphere; (c) the water cycle. ◀

Question 18.3   In semi-arid regions in northern Africa and the Middle East, where grazing of marginal land has greatly reduced the vegetation cover, deserts are expanding at an alarming rate. What could be an explanation for this phenomenon? ◀

18.5   Summary of Section 18

The biosphere is the thin zone around the Earth's surface that is capable of supporting life.

The connections between the biosphere, hydrosphere, atmosphere and lithosphere form continuous and intertwined cycles within cycles.

Photosynthesis is responsible for the Earth's unique oxygen-rich atmosphere, and the two processes of photosynthesis and calcium carbonate secretion by marine organisms are responsible for the Earth's relatively low amounts of atmospheric carbon dioxide. These processes in turn have allowed the evolution of oxygen-breathing living organisms, the formation of an ozone layer that gives protection from harmful ultraviolet radiation, and the maintenance of a climate that allows life to persist.

Organisms use and recycle not only carbon and oxygen but also nitrogen, sulfur, calcium, magnesium, iron and many other elements. There are few chemical reactions on the surface of the Earth that are *not* affected by the biosphere.

Life affects the water cycle through its modification of global climate, and the rock cycle through enhanced rock weathering, soil formation, and the formation of many sedimentary rocks, particularly limestones.

Activity 18.1   Reviewing your study of Block 3: learning from different resources

In this block you have studied a large amount of material presented in diagrams, graphs and tables, and on video and CD-ROM. This activity will help you to review your use of this wide range of resources. ◀

Questions: answers and comments

Question 2.1 (a) If the Sun's surface temperature fell, then its luminosity (total radiated power) would decrease. {See Block 2, Section 5.2.2.}

(b) If its radius increased, then its luminosity would increase. {The power radiated by a given area is fixed by the temperature (part (a)), so if the area increases and the temperature stays the same, the total radiated power will increase.}

Question 2.2 The distance from the Earth to the Sun is small compared with the vast distances to other stars. The difference between measuring from the Earth or from the Sun is therefore such a small fraction of the total distance involved that it does not matter whether we measure from the Earth, or from the Sun.

Question 2.3 If two stars have the same surface temperature then the power radiated *per unit area* will be the same. Therefore, if the two stars are at the same distance, the star that appears brighter must be bigger. If they have the same surface temperatures, the stars must have the same colour tint.

Question 3.1 (a) The distance to the Sun from the viewpoint in Figure 3.5a is 10^{21} m, and the distance from the viewpoint in Figure 3.4 is 10^{16} m. The factor by which the larger distance exceeds the smaller is $\frac{10^{21}\,\text{m}}{10^{16}\,\text{m}}$, which is $10^{(21-16)}$, i.e. 10^5.

(b) 10^{22} m is ten times 10^{21} m, so we would have gone ten times further. It is misleading, therefore, to consider 10^{22} m to be not very different from 10^{21} m. A point which is 10^{22} m away lies 9×10^{21} m beyond a point which is 1×10^{21} m away. {This is a common error in comparing large powers of ten: even $10^{1\,001}$ is ten times larger than $10^{1\,000}$.}

Question 3.2 (a) In 60 Ma star C has travelled about a third of the way around its orbit, so its orbital period is about 180 Ma.

(b) In 60 Ma, a star (like A) at the outer edge of the disc has travelled about one-eighth of its way around its orbit, so its orbital period is about 480 Ma.

Question 3.3 To reach the viewpoint in Figure 3.5a we have travelled a distance of 10^{21} m at $3 \times 10^7\,\text{m s}^{-1}$. To obtain the time interval we use Equation 3.2:

$$\text{time interval} = \frac{\text{distance travelled}}{\text{speed}}$$

$$= \frac{10^{21}\,\text{m}}{3 \times 10^7\,\text{m s}^{-1}}$$

$$= 3 \times 10^{13}\,\text{s}$$

There are 3.16×10^7 seconds in a year. Therefore:

$$\text{time interval} = \frac{3 \times 10^{13}}{3.16 \times 10^7}\ \text{years}$$

$$= 1 \times 10^6\ \text{years}$$

{The speed was quoted to one significant figure, and so the answer should be quoted to this precision. Thus the time interval is 1×10^6 years, to one significant figure, i.e. about a million years.}

{Note that even light, which travels at $3.00 \times 10^8\,\text{m s}^{-1}$ (ten times faster than the spacecraft), would take 100 000 years to travel from the Sun to the end point of our journey. Therefore, from this distant viewpoint, we would see the Sun and its neighbourhood as it was 100 000 years earlier.}

Question 3.4 (a) {Note that this is the same sort of rearrangement that applied to:

$$\text{speed} = \frac{\text{distance travelled}}{\text{time interval}}$$

to get:

$$\text{distance travelled} = \text{time interval} \times \text{speed} \qquad (3.3a)$$

To make this rearrangement, we multiplied both sides of the equation by the time interval. Similarly, to rearrange:

$$\text{density} = \frac{\text{mass}}{\text{volume}}$$

so that mass is the subject, we multiply both sides by the volume.}

Multiplying both sides of the equation by the volume:

$$\text{volume} \times \text{density} = \text{volume} \times \frac{\text{mass}}{\text{volume}}$$

which leads to:

mass = volume × density

(b) {Note that this is the same sort of rearrangement that we applied to:

distance travelled = time interval × speed   (3.3a)

to get:

$$\text{time interval} = \frac{\text{distance travelled}}{\text{speed}} \qquad (3.2)$$

To make this rearrangement, we divided both sides of the equation by the speed. Similarly, to rearrange:

mass = volume × density

so that volume is the subject, we divide both sides by the density.}

Dividing both sides of the equation by the density:

$$\frac{\text{mass}}{\text{density}} = \frac{\text{volume} \times \text{density}}{\text{density}}$$

which leads to:

$$\text{volume} = \frac{\text{mass}}{\text{density}}$$

Question 3.5   The starting equation is:

area = length × width

We want to have (width) on its own, so we must get rid of (length) from the right-hand side of the equation. This can be done by dividing both sides of the equation by (length):

$$\frac{\text{area}}{\text{length}} = \frac{\text{length} \times \text{width}}{\text{length}}$$

$$\frac{\text{area}}{\text{length}} = \frac{\text{length}}{\text{length}} \times \text{width}$$

On the right-hand side we are dividing (length) by itself, and this has a value of 1:

$$\frac{\text{area}}{\text{length}} = 1 \times \text{width}$$

We need not retain the 1, and so:

$$\frac{\text{area}}{\text{length}} = \text{width}$$

It does not matter in which order we write this equation, so the desired equation is:

$$\text{width} = \frac{\text{area}}{\text{length}}$$

Question 3.6   (a) From near the centre of a nearly spherical elliptical galaxy the stars will be equally distributed in all directions rather than being concentrated in a broad band across the night sky. There will therefore be no equivalent of the Milky Way. {More careful observations would reveal no nuclear bulge, and no spiral arms.}

(b) Spiral arms seem to be major sites of star formation in the Galaxy, and the stars form in open clusters. Without spiral arms there will be little star formation, and open clusters will be few, or perhaps completely absent.

Question 4.1   (a) Two of the forces are the underwater thrust arising from the propellers (screws), and the friction of air and water. We know these forces are balanced because the tanker is moving in a straight line at constant speed. There are two other forces: the downward force of gravity, and the upward force of the water. As the tanker is not sinking, nor rising into the air, these forces are also balanced.

(b) If a head wind springs up the forces are no longer balanced. The tanker will slow down but the original speed can be restored if the thrust of the propellers is increased.

Question 4.2   (a) If the rope is at rest then the force on the rope exerted by one team is balanced by that exerted by the other team.

(b) If the speed of the rope is increasing in the direction of the blue team then the blue team are pulling with a greater force than the red team. The forces on the rope are unbalanced.

(c) The red team have now increased the force of their pull to be equal in value to that of the blue team. This halts the increase of speed and so the rope moves at a constant speed in a straight line, the forces now being balanced.

Question 4.3   The wind exerts a sideways force that will cause a change of direction. Therefore, the velocity of the tanker changes.

Question 4.4 In cases (a), (b), and (c), there is a change in velocity. Therefore, by definition, there is an acceleration. Also, by Newton's first law of motion, since there is a change in velocity then an unbalanced force is acting.

(a) A train slows down on a straight track: there is no change in direction but there is a change in speed, so there is a change in velocity.

(b) A car goes around a bend at constant speed: there is no change in speed but there is a change in direction, so there is a change in velocity.

(c) A shark turns to chase its unfortunate prey and increases its speed as it does so: there is a change in speed and a change in direction, so there is a change in velocity on both counts.

(d) A plane descends along a straight flight path at constant speed: this is motion in a straight line at constant speed so there is no change in velocity, and consequently no acceleration and no unbalanced force.

Question 4.5 The acceleration (Equation 4.1) is:

$$\frac{26.8\,\text{m s}^{-1}}{10.0\,\text{s}}\text{ , which is }2.68\,\text{m s}^{-2}$$

Thus, from Newton's second law of motion (Equation 4.2):

magnitude of the unbalanced force on the car =
$(1\,100\,\text{kg}) \times (2.68\,\text{m s}^{-2})$

$= 2\,948\,\text{kg m s}^{-2}$

$= 2\,950\,\text{N to three significant figures}$

{Note that the final answer has been given to three significant figures — the same as in the data.}

The direction of the unbalanced force is the direction of the acceleration: along the straight road.

Question 4.6 We need to rearrange Equation 4.2 for Newton's second law of motion to make the acceleration the subject. We do that by dividing both sides of the equation by the mass, and this leads to the equation:

magnitude of acceleration of tanker

$= \dfrac{\text{magnitude of the unbalanced force on the tanker}}{\text{mass of tanker}}$

The unbalanced force due to the following wind is given in the question as $4.0 \times 10^6\,\text{N}$. Thus:

$$\text{magnitude of acceleration of tanker} = \frac{4.0 \times 10^6\,\text{N}}{2.0 \times 10^8\,\text{kg}}$$

$= 0.020\,\text{N kg}^{-1}$

The newton (N) is shorthand for kg m s^{-2}, so:

magnitude of acceleration of tanker $= 0.020\,\text{kg m s}^{-2}\,\text{kg}^{-1}$

$= 0.020\,\dfrac{\text{kg}}{\text{kg}}\,\text{m s}^{-2}$

$= 0.020\,\text{m s}^{-2}$

The direction of the acceleration is the direction of the unbalanced force: the forward direction. {So the tanker gains speed in the direction in which it was travelling before the wind sprang up.}

Question 4.7 Suitable symbols would seem to be s for speed, d for distance travelled, t for time interval. Equation 3.1 would then be:

$$s = \frac{d}{t}$$

{In fact, speed is usually given the symbol v, on the basis that speed is the magnitude of velocity. Special speeds are given special symbols. For example, the speed of light is usually given the symbol c.}

To make t the subject of the equation, the procedures in Box 3.1 can be used. We start with the equation above, rewritten using the more usual symbol for speed:

$$v = \frac{d}{t}$$

and multiply both sides of the equation by t:

$$t \times v = t \times \frac{d}{t}$$

The ts cancel out on the right, so:

$$t \times v = d$$

We now divide both sides of the equation by v:

$$\frac{t \times v}{v} = \frac{d}{v}$$

which is:

$$t = \frac{d}{v}$$

{A quicker method is to multiply both sides of the original equation by $\frac{t}{v}$:

$$\frac{t}{v} \times v = \frac{t}{v} \times \frac{d}{t}$$

The vs cancel out on the left, and the ts cancel out on the right, to give:

$$t = \frac{1}{v} \times \frac{d}{1}$$

which is:

$$t = \frac{d}{v}, \text{ the same answer as above.}$$

Question 4.8 (a) The gravitational force would decrease because the mass of the Earth decreased. The distance to the Earth's centre would not change so this is not a factor.

(b) The astronaut is further from the Earth's centre when in the space shuttle, so the gravitational force is less that it is on the same astronaut on the ground. {Note that the gravitational force on the astronaut is not zero. This might seem difficult to reconcile with the so-called weightlessness of the astronaut. This 'weightlessness' arises because the astronaut is in orbit around the Earth, and so the astronaut is always falling towards the Earth, but the sideways motion in the orbit means that the astronaut is always 'falling over the horizon'. Indeed 'weightlessness' is a misnomer: the proper term is 'free fall', and it is quite descriptive. To the astronaut free fall is just like the experience you get in mid flight when you jump off a chair, or off a diving board, but for the astronaut the feeling goes on, and on, and on …}

Question 4.9 The Galaxy acts gravitationally on the Sun rather as though there were a large mass at the Galactic centre. This is rather like the way the Sun acts gravitationally on the planets. Thus, just as the planets are in nearly circular orbits around the Sun, so the Sun is in a roughly circular orbit around the Galactic centre.

Question 5.1 The density of the Sun increases gradually from about 1 kg m^{-3} in the photosphere, to about 1.5×10^5 kg m^{-3} at the centre. Therefore, at some depth it must have a density of 1 000 kg m^{-3}, the density of tap water. The temperature also increases gradually with depth, but only reaches 1.5×10^7 °C in the centre. This is well short of 10^8 °C, so there is no depth at which the temperature is this high.

Question 5.2 (a) The interior of Jupiter is too cool for the fusion of hydrogen: its internal temperatures do not exceed 2×10^4 °C, far short of the 10^7 °C needed for hydrogen fusion. {You will see later that there is plenty of hydrogen in the interior of Jupiter — it's the low temperature that's the problem, not the lack of fuel.}

(b) The Sun's photosphere, at about 5 500 °C, is far too cool for the fusion of hydrogen.

Question 5.3 From Equation 5.1 and Table 5.1, the density of the Earth is:

$$\rho_E = \frac{59\,740 \times 10^{20} \text{ kg}}{1.082 \times 10^{21} \text{ m}^3}$$

$$= \frac{5.974 \times 10^{24} \text{ kg}}{1.082 \times 10^{21} \text{ m}^3}$$

$$= 5\,521 \text{ kg m}^{-3}$$

to the appropriate number (four) of significant figures. Likewise, for Pluto:

$$\rho_P = \frac{150 \times 10^{20} \text{ kg}}{6.4 \times 10^{18} \text{ m}^3}$$

$$= \frac{1.5 \times 10^{22} \text{ kg}}{6.4 \times 10^{18} \text{ m}^3}$$

$$= 2\,300 \text{ kg m}^{-3}$$

to two significant figures.

{Note that we converted the data in Table 5.1 to scientific notation. This allows you to check more readily that the answer from your calculator is reasonable, by letting you manipulate the powers of ten separately from the now small numbers that multiply them. Thus, we have $\rho_P = \left(\frac{1.5}{6.4}\right) \times 10^{(22-18)}$ kg m^{-3}, which is about 0.2×10^4 kg m^{-3}, or 2×10^3 kg m^{-3}. Note also that we used the subscripts E and P to distinguish between the symbols for the densities of the Earth and Pluto. You will meet other examples of subscripts being used in similar ways in the course.}

Question 5.4 From Figure 5.2 we see that Uranus and Neptune are substantially smaller in size and mass than Jupiter and Saturn. Figure 5.2 also shows that hydrogen and helium are significant components but not so dominant as in Jupiter and Saturn: indeed, Jupiter and Saturn resemble each other, and Uranus and Neptune resemble each other. Thus the creation of a subdivision is justified, and *sub*-giant is a good name for a subdivision containing objects that are smaller than the others.

185

Question 5.5 (a) The Earth resembles the other terrestrial planets in:

- its density and composition: Table 5.1 shows that they have similar densities and Figure 5.2 shows that they all have rocky compositions;

- size {though the Earth is the biggest and most massive of the terrestrial planets (Table 5.1), it is merely at the upper end of a modest range of mass and diameter rather than in a class of its own.}

(b) It differs from the other terrestrial planets in:

- having an oxygen-rich atmosphere;

- having oceans of liquid water;

- perhaps having some unique geological processes;

- supporting living organisms.

{You were only asked for two differences.}

Question 6.1 Winds are currents of moving air. The air moves because of unequal heating of the atmosphere above adjacent landmasses or between land and sea. The warmer the air, the lower its density and, if the density of warm air near the Earth's surface is sufficiently less than that of the overlying air, the warm air will rise. Cool air is displaced outwards and downwards, replacing the warm air. It is this movement of warm and cool air which we feel as wind. {Block 2, Section 6.2.1.}

Question 6.2 (a) The temperature at the surface is about 20 °C, whereas at 2 km depth it is about 3 °C.

(b) Near the surface, the temperature does not change appreciably down to a depth of one or two hundred metres, and below about 1 000 m the temperature decreases only gradually. Between these two zones is a zone within which the temperature decreases much more dramatically with increasing depth, with the most rapid change between about 250 m and 500 m.

Question 6.3 As you leave the British Isles, you cross the pale blue of the continental shelf. The water then deepens over a small distance. Continuing westwards the depth remains fairly constant (uniform shade of deep blue) before becoming irregular (several shades giving a speckled appearance) and shallower (pale blue) about half-way across the North Atlantic. Further westward, the depth to the ocean floor increases irregularly before reaching moderately constant depth again, and then decreasing over a small distance onto the continental shelf of the North American continent.

Question 6.4 (a) The ridge is about 3.5 cm wide in Figure 6.6, and since 1 cm is equivalent to 500 km, the actual width is 3.5×500 km, or about 1 750 km.

(b) The ridge crest is below about 7 mm (equivalent to 3.5 km) of water, and the abyssal plain is about 11 mm (equivalent to 5.5 km) deep.

(c) The height of the ridge can be measured directly or calculated from the answers to part (b): it is about 5.5 km − 3.5 km = about 2 km high.

Question 6.5 Following the Mid-Atlantic Ridge south, it splits into two branches. The shorter, westward branch (not labelled in Figure 6.7 but called the South American–Antarctic Ridge) is less distinct than the eastern branch, which is the Southwest Indian Ridge. The latter ridge is followed to the northeast before it splits into the Central Indian Ridge, which connects with the Carlsberg Ridge (which then intersects Arabia), and the Southeast Indian Ridge. The Southeast Indian Ridge can be followed between Australia and Antarctica, before changing its name and becoming the Pacific–Antarctic Ridge. This in turn branches into the East Pacific Rise and the Chile Rise. Figure 6.7, and the poster, show the Juan de Fuca Ridge, off the western coast of North America, is not connected with the rest of the mid-ocean ridge system.

Question 7.1 (a) The rivers and some of the roads have been displaced across the fault, which is the linear feature running from the top to the bottom of the photograph.

(b) The block on the left (southwest) has moved northwest along the fault, and the block on the right (northeast) has moved in the opposite direction, to the southeast. This is deduced from the sense of displacement of the rivers and roads across the fault.

Question 7.2 This is an increase of $(8.1 - 6.1) = 2$ units on the Richter scale, which is an increase of:

(a) $10^2 = 10 \times 10 = 100$ times in ground motion;

(b) about $40 \times 40 = 1\ 600$ times in energy released.

Question 8.1 All of the eruptions that produced tall eruption columns or pyroclastic flows were from volcanoes in volcanic arcs (compare the locations given in Activity 8.1 with Figure 6.7). The effusive eruptions were from Hawaii in the Pacific Ocean and Etna, Sicily.

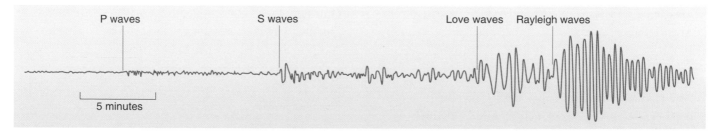

Figure 10.17   Answer to Question 10.1.

Question 10.1   See Figure 10.17. {Remember that body waves travel faster than surface waves, so arrive earlier. Of the surface waves, Love waves usually travel faster than Rayleigh waves. Surface waves produce more ground motion than body waves, with Rayleigh waves producing more ground motion than Love waves.}

Question 10.2   (a) Seismic (only). This boundary was identified and located using seismic data alone. You may have considered Figure 10.15 and included density in your answer (the boundary is very clear on the density–depth curve), but the position of the boundary was deduced from seismic data, then the density–depth curve was adjusted to fit in with this.

(b) Seismic and magnetic. (S waves do not travel through the outer core, which supports the interpretation that it is liquid. The Earth's magnetism is probably produced by a metallic liquid layer.)

Question 11.1   Yes, the climate-sensitive sediments fall more or less into their correct climate zones on the pre-drift reconstruction. The sandstones and the coal deposits appear to be more or less restricted to the latitude ranges for desert and tropical climates of today. Similarly, the glacial till deposits also fall much closer to their appropriate climate zone near the South Pole. This reconstruction supports a continental drift interpretation of these sediments. {The distribution of climate-sensitive sediments only fits their expected latitudinal range if the continents are re-arranged in such a way as to bring together many landmasses that are separate today.}

Question 12.1   (a) The number of switches from black to white and white to black is 11. There have been 11 polarity reversals in the last 4 Ma.

(b) Normal, reversed, reversed.

(c) The most recent change from normal (black) to reversed (white) took place 0.99 Ma ago.

(d) It could have formed any time between 1.95 and 1.79 Ma ago, or between 1.07 and 0.99 Ma ago, or after 0.78 Ma ago.

(e) 0.78 Ma.

Question 12.2 $19\,mm\,y^{-1}$. This is because 19 km $= 19 \times 10^3$ m $= (19 \times 10^3) \times 10^3$ mm. And 1 Ma $= 10^6$ y. So 19 km/1 Ma $= 1.9 \times 10^7$ mm/ 10^6 y $= 1.9 \times 10$ mm y^{-1} $= 19\,mm\,y^{-1}$. {A shortcut is to remember that the value of the speed in km Ma^{-1} is the same as the value in mm y^{-1}, as we showed earlier in Section 12.2.1.}

Question 13.1   Lithosphere: stronger, rigid, lower temperature, crust and top of the mantle, earthquakes.

Asthenosphere: weaker, deformable, higher temperature, within mantle, no earthquakes.

Question 13.2   See Figure 13.8. The western boundary will be a divergent plate boundary, as plate A is moving away from plate B here. Both the eastern boundaries are convergent, although obliquely. Figure 13.8 shows plate A descending beneath plate B, but you could instead have shown plate B descending beneath plate A, if you drew the barbs on plate A instead of plate B.

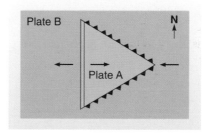

Figure 13.8   Answer to Question 13.2.

Question 13.3 See Figure 13.9. The Cocos Plate is shown moving away from the other plate at the western and southern divergent boundaries and towards the convergent northeastern boundary, so the relative movement must be in the direction of the arrow (you could have drawn this equally validly at a slightly different angle to that shown here). Remember, however, that this simplified situation of just two plates is unreal; the Cocos Plate is actually surrounded by three different plates.

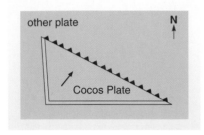

Figure 13.9 Answer to Question 13.3.

Question 13.4 (a) The highest relative speeds are where the Pacific and Nazca Plates are moving away from each other at a speed of up to 185 mm y^{-1}. The boundary between them is a divergent plate boundary. This is the East Pacific Rise (see Figure 6.7).

(b) The highest relative speed for a different type of plate boundary is at the west coast of South America, a convergent boundary between the Nazca and South American Plates, with a speed of 106 mm y^{-1}. This boundary is along the Peru–Chile Trench.

(c) The lowest rate of sea-floor spreading (17 mm y^{-1}) is in the northern Indian Ocean, between the African and Indian Plates, on a mid-ocean ridge called the Carlsberg Ridge. {By the way, the ridge *is* named after the brewery, who sponsored the oceanographic expedition that discovered it. If you study a detailed map of ocean floor features you will find other familiar names.}

(d) Like the Southeast Indian Ridge, which was the subject of Activity 12.2, *all* mid-ocean ridges have variable spreading rates. On Figure 13.4 this is obvious for the Mid-Atlantic Ridge, East Pacific Rise, Southeast Indian Ridge and Pacific–Antarctic Ridges. The spreading rate varies because the plates are moving on a sphere (Activity 13.3).

Question 13.5 From Equation 3.3, distance travelled = speed × time interval, or

$$d = vt$$

So:

$$d = 185 \text{ mm y}^{-1} \times 10^6 \text{ y}$$

$$= 185 \times 10^6 \text{ mm}$$

$$= 185 \text{ km, since } 10^6 \text{ mm} = 1 \text{ km}$$

Question 13.6 From Equation 3.2, time = distance travelled/speed, or:

$$t = d/v$$

London is on the Eurasian Plate, and New York on the North American Plate. In Figure 13.4 these plates are separating at a rate of 25 mm y^{-1}, or 25×10^{-3} m y^{-1}. So:

$$t = \frac{10^3 \text{ m}}{25 \times 10^{-3} \text{ m y}^{-1}}$$

$$= 4 \times 10^4 \text{ y, or } 40\,000 \text{ years}$$

{However, the plate motion is not parallel to a line between London and New York, so the London–New York separation rate will be lower than 25 mm y^{-1}, and therefore the time will be somewhat more than 40 000 years.}

Question 14.1 Basaltic pillow lavas (2) are produced by volcanic eruptions on to the ocean floor (C).

Sheeted dykes (3) are an array of dykes which transported basalt magma along vertical cracks in the crust (A).

Gabbro (1) is produced by slow crystallization of basalt magma (B). {Gabbro is a coarse-grained intrusive rock, which indicates it cooled slowly underground.}

Question 14.2 Along the western side of South America, the oceanic Nazca Plate is converging with the continental part of the South American Plate. At the Izu–Bonin Trench, the oceanic Pacific Plate is converging with the oceanic Philippine Plate. In the region of the Himalayan mountains, a continental part of the Indian Plate is converging with the continental part of the Eurasian Plate.

Question 15.1 (a) Just as on the travel time versus distance graphs for seismic waves (e.g. Figure 10.9), the speed at which volcanic activity moves is the inverse of the gradient of the best-fit straight line. To calculate the gradient, and hence the speed, choose two points on the best-fit straight line which are some distance apart and find their coordinates in order to find the 'rise' and 'run'. For example, at a distance of 5 500 km the age is 65 Ma, and at a distance of 1 000 km the age is 11 Ma. The gradient of the line is:

$$\frac{(65-11)\,\text{Ma}}{(5\,500-1000)\,\text{km}}$$

$$= \frac{54\,\text{Ma}}{4\,500\,\text{km}}$$

$$= 0.012\,\text{Ma}\,\text{km}^{-1}$$

The speed is therefore $1/0.012\,\text{Ma}\,\text{km}^{-1} = 83\,\text{km}\,\text{Ma}^{-1}$. This is equivalent to $83\,\text{mm}\,\text{y}^{-1}$. {A more accurately determined value is $86\,\text{mm}\,\text{y}^{-1}$.}

(b) Towards the southeast overall. {However, it started moving south before changing to moving southeast.}

Question 15.2 The fastest plate is the Pacific Plate. The slowest is the African, although the Eurasian and Antarctic Plates move only slightly faster.

Question 15.3 (a) The fast-moving Pacific Plate has a subducting slab on one side (2) and a divergent plate boundary on the opposite side (3). The Pacific Plate contains very little continental lithosphere (the South Island of New Zealand).

(b) The slow-moving African Plate is partly bounded by a divergent boundary (3) but also contains a large area of continental lithosphere (1). {Similar attributes are held by the slow-moving Eurasian and Antarctic Plates. None of the slow-moving plates are attached to significant lengths of subducting slabs.}

Question 16.1 The crumpling and convergence of continental lithosphere at BC will eventually cease, because of the resistance of the rock to further crumpling, so the supercontinent will not change in width. This means the ocean will also have to keep the same size, which it could do in two ways. The first is illustrated in Figure 16.5, where the ocean has developed subduction zones at its edges, with the rate of spreading balanced by the rate of subduction. (You may have drawn a diagram with only one subduction zone, which would also be a valid answer.) The second way involves the ocean stopping spreading and not developing subduction zones.

This is unlikely, as it would mean that plate-tectonic driving forces had ceased. There are no oceans on the Earth at the moment, for example, without spreading ridges or trenches.

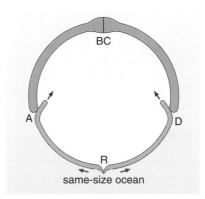

Figure 16.5 Answer to Question 16.1.

Question 16.2 See Figure 16.6. The Atlantic and Indian Oceans are expanding; the Pacific Ocean is contracting.

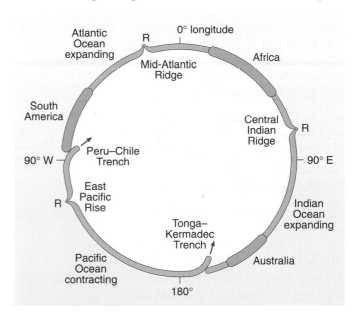

Figure 16.6 Answer to Question 16.2.

Question 16.3 You need to look for a mid-ocean ridge in a narrow ocean separating two continents or parts of continents to find areas where sea-floor spreading has recently started. The best example is the split between Africa and Arabia, occupied by the Red Sea. Another is the split of Baja California from the rest of Mexico (southwest North America) — recall your investigation of western North American plate motions in Activity 14.2.

Question 16.4 The four types of evidence are the global distribution of fossils; the global distribution of ancient climatic features in rocks; palaeomagnetism of rocks on land (Sections 11.1–11.4); and marine magnetic anomalies (Section 12.2).

Question 16.5 The time can be calculated as follows:

$$t = \frac{d}{v} \text{ (from Equation 3.2)}$$

Now $d = 560$ km, $v = 20$ mm y^{-1} = 20 km Ma^{-1}. (Remember that we showed in Section 12.2.1 that the numerical values of speed were the same whether we use units of mm y^{-1} or km Ma^{-1}.) Therefore:

$$t = \frac{560 \, \text{km}}{20 \, \text{km Ma}^{-1}}$$

$$= 28 \, \text{Ma}$$

Question 17.1 The following list summarizes processes within the rock cycle that influence the atmosphere, as well as aspects of the atmosphere that influence the rock cycle.

• Gases are added to the atmosphere from volcanoes.

• Winds, rain and ice cause weathering and/or transport sedimentary material.

• Desert sediments are mostly transported in and deposited from air.

• Rock-forming organisms such as corals (forming certain limestones) and plants (forming coal and chalk) influence the atmosphere's composition through photosynthesis and respiration.

Question 18.1 Plants, molluscs, corals and calcium carbonate-secreting plankton in the ocean effectively remove carbon dioxide, a potent greenhouse gas, from the atmosphere. In the absence of life, atmospheric carbon dioxide would surely be much higher, and therefore GMST would be higher. {You may remember the greenhouse effect on the GMST of Venus from Section 5.2.2.}

Question 18.2 (a) The relatively high levels of oxygen and low levels of carbon dioxide in the atmosphere are partly the result of photosynthesis by green plants.

(b) Much of the Earth's limestone rock was formed by the action of organisms, especially marine plankton. Many soils and sediments are formed from physical and chemical weathering due to plants.

(c) Transpiration by plants pumps water into the atmosphere and reduces the amount of precipitation that runs off in streams and rivers.

Question 18.3 One explanation could be that the removal of vegetation has reduced the regional rainfall, since there are many fewer plants to pump water from soil to air through transpiration. {In fact, precipitation has indeed decreased in this region over the last 40 years, but scientists cannot be sure whether this is due to lowered transpiration rates or to other, more indirect factors.}

Acknowledgements

Grateful acknowledgement is made to the following sources for permission to reproduce material in this block:

Title page: NASA; *Figure 2.1*: Celestron International; *Figures 2.4, 2.5b, 5.7*: Akira Fujii; *Figure 2.5a*: Dennis di Cicco; *Figure 3.1*: Lund Observatory, Sweden; *Figures 3.2, 3.4*: From *Powers of Ten*: *About the Relative Size of Things in the Universe* by P. Morrison © 1982 by Scientific American Library. Used by permission of W. H. Freeman and Company; *Figure 3.5a*: The Regents, University of Hawaii; *Figure 3.5b*: Royal Astronomical Society; *Figures 3.8, 3.11b*: US Naval Observatory, Washington DC; *Figures 3.10, 3.11d*: Anglo-Australian Telescope Board; *Figures 3.11a, c, e*: National Optical Astronomy Observatories; *Figure 4.14*: Engraved by W. T. Fry from the original by Godfrey Kneller /Mansell Collection; *Figure 5.3*: NASA/JPL; *Figure 5.4*: NASA/Space Telescope Science Institute; *Figure 5.5*: NASA/National Space Science Data Center/Bruce C. Murray, teamleader; *Figure 5.6*: NASA; *Figure 5.8*: Julian Baum; *Figure 6.3*: Adapted from Canters, F. and Decleir, H. (1989) *The World in Perspective*: *A Directory of World Map Projections,* John Wiley and Sons Ltd. Reprinted by permission of John Wiley and Sons Ltd; *Figures 6.7 and 13.2*: Adapted from Fowler, C. M. R. (1990) *The Solid Earth*: *An Introduction to Global Geophysics*, Cambridge University Press; *Figure 7.1*: US Army Corps of Engineers; *Figure 7.3*: John S. Shelton; *Figure 7.5*: Plafker, G. and Galloway, J. P. (1989) 'Lessons learned from the Loma Prieta, California, earthquake of October 17th, 1989', USGS Circular 1045, United States Geological Survey; *Figure 7.6*: Adapted from Mestel, R. (1995) 'Minor fault, major disaster', *New Scientist,* 28 January 1995, IPC Magazines Ltd; *Figure 7.7*: Adapted from The British Geological Survey World Seismicity Database. Global Seismology and Geomagnetism Group, Edinburgh; *Figure 8.1*: John Murray; *Figure 8.3*: Adapted from Johnson, R. W. (1993) *AGSO Issues Paper No. 1, Volcanic Eruptions and Atmospheric Change*, Australian Geological Survey Organisation, © Commonwealth of Australia 1993; *Figures 9.1, 9.2, 9.4, 9.5 and 10.1*: Andy Tindle; *Figure 10.3*: Adapted from Smith, D. G. *The Cambridge Encyclopedia of Earth Sciences*, Cambridge University Press, © Trewin Copplestone Books Limited, 1981; Adapted from *Inside the Earth*: *Evidence from Earthquakes* by B. A. Bolt © 1982 by W. H. Freeman and Company. Used with permission; *Figures 10.4, 10.15 and 10.17*: Adapted from *Inside the Earth*: *Evidence from Earthquakes* by B. A. Bolt © 1982 by W. H. Freeman and Company. Used with permission; *Figure 10.10*: Adapted from Plummer, C. C. and McGeary, D. (1996) *Physical Geology with Interactive Plate Tectonics CD-ROM*, 7th edn, Wm. C. Brown Publishers. Copyright © 1996 by Times Mirror Higher Education Group, Inc; *Figure 11.1*: Adapted from Wegener, A. (1966) in Biram, J. (trans.) *The Origin of Continents and Oceans*, Methuen and Co, © 1966 Dover Publications. Originally published in *Die Entstehung der Kontinente und Ozeane*, 4th edn, (1929) Friedrich Vieweg & Sohn, Braunschweig; *Figure 11.2 (top right)*: Marvin, U. B. (1973) *Continental Drift – Evolution of a Continent*, Smithsonian Institution Press; *Figure 11.2 (centre right)*: Colbert, E. H. (1973) *Wandering Lands and Animals*, Hutchinson; *Figure 11.2 (bottom right)*: Smith, P. (1985) *Encyclopedia of the Earth*, Hutchinson; *Figure 11.4*: Smith, A. (1996) *CD-ROM of Plate Reconstructions*, Cambridge Palaeomap Services Ltd; *Figure 12.3*: Reprinted from *Deep Sea Research*, **13**, Hiertzler, J. R. *et al.* 'Magnetic anomalies over the Reykjanes Ridge', 1966, pp. 427–443, with permission from Elsevier Science Ltd, The Boulevard, Langford Lane, Kidlington, OX5 1GB, UK; *Figure 13.4*: Adapted from Bott, M. H. P. (1982) *The Interior of the Earth, Its Structure, Constitution and Evolution*, Edward Arnold; *Figure 14.1b*: Adapted with permission from *Nature*, **337**, p. 728, Auzende, J. M. *et al.*, 'Direct observation of a section through slow-spreading oceanic crust'. Copyright 1989 Macmillan Magazines Ltd; *Figures 14.2, 17.1, 18.3*: Tony Waltham; *Figure 14.3*: Nigel Harris; *Figure 14.6*: Adapted from Nur, A. and Ben-Avraham, Z. (1982) 'Oceanic plateaus, the fragmentation of continents and mountain building', *Journal of Geophys. Res.*, **87**, American Geophysical Union; *Figure 14.7*: Adapted from Hasegawa, A., Umino, N. and Takagi, A. (1978) 'Double-planed deep seismic zone and upper-mantle structure in northeastern Japan Arc', *Geophys. J. R. Astr. Soc.*, **54**, Blackwell Science Ltd; *Figure 15.2*: Adapted from Clague, D. and Dalrymple, G. B. (1987) *USGS Professional Paper* **1350**, United States Geological Survey; *Figure 16.1*: Adapted from Scotese, C. R., Gahagan, L. M. and Larson, R. L. (1988) 'Plate tectonic reconstructions of the Cretaceous and Cenozoic ocean basins', *Tectonophysics*, **155**, Elsevier Science Publishers BV and Fowler, C. M. R. (1990) *The Solid Earth*: *An Introduction to Global Geophysics*, Cambridge University Press; *Figure 18.2*: NASA/Johnson Space Center.

Index

Entries and page numbers in **bold type** refer to key words which are printed in **bold** in the text and which are defined in the Glossary. These are terms that we expect you to be able to explain the meaning of, and use correctly, both during and at the end of the course. An entry followed by ^G indicates a term which is defined in the Glossary but which is not bold in the text. Where the page number is given in *italics*, the indexed information is carried mainly or wholly in an illustration or table. Section summaries and answers to questions are not indexed.